Computer Peripherals

Second edition

Barry Wilkinson

Principal Lecturer
Brighton Polytechnic

and

David Horrocks

Senior Lecturer
University College, Cardiff

Edward Arnold
A division of Hodder & Stoughton
LONDON   MELBOURNE   AUCKLAND

To Chris and Jim, Wendy and Johanna

First published in Great Britain 1980
Second edition 1987
Reprinted 1989, 1992

ISBN 0 340 41479 0

Typeset by Macmillan India Ltd, Bangalore
Printed and bound in Great Britain for Edward Arnold,
a division of Hodder and Stoughton Limited,
Mill Road, Dunton Green, Sevenoaks, Kent TN13 2YA
by Athenaeum Press Ltd, Newcastle upon Tyne

Preface to the first edition

Anyone coming into contact with computers, even if only superficially, cannot fail to become aware of the importance of peripherals. Developments in peripheral devices have been many and varied in recent years and a wide range of devices with differing capabilities is now manufactured.

However, the current interest in this topic is not generally reflected in the many books on computers. Most of these books devote no more than a chapter to peripheral devices and are unable therefore to describe more than a few of them.

This book attempts to meet the need for a wide-ranging and straightforward account of how present-day peripheral devices work and what they are capable of doing. Emphasis is placed on the underlying principles of operation of the devices, rather than on providing a product description of manufacturers' wares. The aim is to include all the main types of perpheral device which may be encountered.

To maintain the relevance of the material, and keep the page count within reasonable limits, devices that are still at the development stage and not yet fully available are not included. One or two exceptions to this have been made where it can be foreseen, with some confidence, that a device is to be marketed in the near future.

No special academic or technical background is required of the reader, although some interest in, and knowledge of basic computer operation is assumed. Also, familiarity with simple concepts and ideas of electronics would be helpful in some parts of the book.

This text should be of value to students studying engineering and computer technology at polytechnics, technical colleges and universities, especially when used in conjunction with one of the many books on computers. This book will also be of interest to those dealing with computers, in and out of the computing industry, who would like an account of the subject which is informative but not over-technical.

The first chapter discusses the role of peripherals and is followed by a chapter which presents the ways that peripherals connect to a computer and how information and data are passed between them.

Chapters 3–9 deal with the various peripheral devices, mechanisms and techniques under major headings and form the main part of the book. These chapters need not be read in order, and the reader can safely turn first to those chapters of greatest interest.

The final chapter, on data communications, which can be considered as an extension of Chapter 2, gives an account of the communication equipment and techniques used when peripherals, perhaps large in number, are remote from the processor.

The writing of this book has been an enlightening experience, and a co-operative venture for its authors, neither of whom would claim to have made the larger contribution.

DHH and ABW

Preface to the second edition

Encouraged by the success of the first edition we have extensively revised the text both to broaden the coverage in some areas (for example, transducers are now dealt with) and to describe the many new and important devices that are now available.

Changes have occurred among all types of peripheral devices: In display devices large panel displays are now common, some of which use the new super-twist liquid crystal display technology; low cost laser printers now enable desk top publishing to be done; small computers with high quality graphics now display 'icons' and 'windows' under the control of a 'mouse'; for backing stores, Winchester disc technology has resulted in devices with the virtues of low cost, high storage capacity, and small size. Other developments have occurred with voice input and output systems, badge readers, 'smart carts', optical storage, etc., etc.

The interconnection of computers and peripheral devices using data communication has also seen significant changes; both wide area and local area networking are now prevalent.

We have endeavoured to include all these significant developments in this second edition.

DHH and ABW

Contents

1

The role of computer peripherals

1.1 Preamble

A digital computer system comprises a central processor unit (with memory) which performs arithmetic operations and controls the operation of the computer system, and peripheral devices connected to the central processor. These devices input information, output information and store information for future use. For a medium-sized computer system, say, costing £50 000, about 15% of this cost will typically be due to the central processor and 85% due to the peripheral devices connected to the central processor. This book is concerned with that 85% – the construction, operation and control of the peripherals.

Before entering into the subject in the following chapters let us look, by way of introduction to the peripherals of a computer system, at some of the present-day applications (and the roles the peripherals play). These applications have expanded and diversified in the last 30 years to cover all aspects of life from business and commerce to social activities and leisure. As a name of a peripheral or keyword is introduced in this text, it will be italicized.

1.2 Payroll and accounts

Whenever one receives an invoice for payment of a gas or electricity or rates bill, or for other services or goods, there is every likelihood that the amount on the invoice will have been calculated using a computer, and the invoice printed under control of the computer by a computer peripheral, in this case a *printer*.

Similarly employees of all but the smallest concerns are likely to receive their wage slips printed and calculated by computer. Computer systems that handle such items as wages and accounts come within the sphere of 'data processing', where often large amounts of data are processed. These data can be entered into the computer using a variety of input devices.

Punched cards have in the past been widely associated with data-processing applications where maybe the same calculation is performed on different data. Each punched card measures about 18.7 cm by 8.2 cm and has holes punched in rows through the card in selected positions to represent alpha-numeric characters. This is done by skilled operators using a keyboard punch. The information on the cards can be entered into the computer using a *card reader*, a stack of cards at a time. In a wages calculation, for example, each card might hold the information concerning one employee, with the computer instructed to read the cards in the stack sequentially and calculate the wages, PAYE, etc. of each employee.

Nowadays the most common means of input to a computer is via a 'typewriter' type of keyboard. The information is entered and results can be viewed on a 'television' type display, with the keyboard and display built as a composite unit, the *visual display unit* or VDU as it is called.

The data, whilst being immediately processed, are kept with the computer proper, but otherwise are often relegated to a *backing store*. In a data-processing system, the amount of data to be stored may be vast, and this can be stored on *magnetic tape* wound on 'open reels' measuring $10\frac{1}{2}$ in (26.7 cm) in diameter (for example).

Payroll and accounts may be separate functions or there may be some form of cross coupling. In a manufacturing company, for example, the cost of the product is directly related to the cost of the labour. This costing operation can utilize the payroll information in a composite system.

The size of the computer system depends upon the complexity of the problem and size of the organization, and can range from a large mainframe computer having a multitude of peripherals (card readers, VDUs, magnetic-tape units, printers, etc.) through the smaller mini-computers, down to the recent micro-computer systems. This last variety has been given the name 'small-business system' when applied to business applications and is suited to the small concern.

Figure 1.1 shows a computer system suitable for payroll and other commercial applications.

Figure 1.1 Computer system suitable for commercial applications (IBM 3084 system: Courtesy of IBM United Kingdom Ltd).

1.3 Retail stock control and distribution

This is one area where the person shopping is likely to notice a change to 'computerization' in the coming years. The retail trade encompasses all the high-street shops and the larger cash-and-carry warehouses and hypermarkets located away from the high streets. Most of the larger high-street organizations have or are in the process of installing a computer system for store inventory and collection of data at the checkouts. All have computer systems for general stock-control functions (in addition to payroll).

However, it is in the large volume sales of supermarkets, hypermarkets and cash-and-carry warehouses that the more radical changes can be made. At the checkout (point of sale), the function of the cashier can be automated as follows (Fig. 1.2). As the customer's goods are handled (say physically moved from one trolley to another), sensors detect special labels on the goods which provide information such as the price (excluding value-added tax), value-added tax rate, quantity, and an identifying product code. This information is entered into the system together with information entered manually – for example, a customer

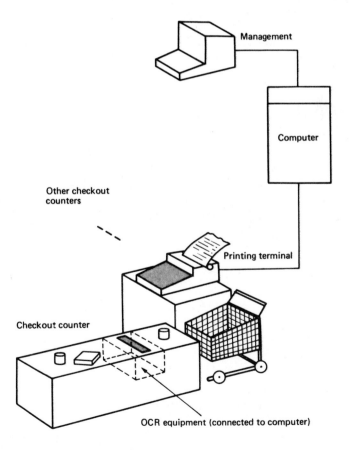

Figure 1.2 Supermarket check-out sytem.

code (the customer might have an account with the concern). The appropriate printout is produced, giving details of all the goods bought and the grand total. Such systems may be based upon small or medium-sized computers.

The input peripheral in these systems comes under the heading of 'special purpose' direct entry. The labels may be sensed optically (using *optical character recognition*) or by other means. Another perhaps more familiar application of automatic data entry is the handling of bank cheques. These cheques have magnetic markings which enable direct reading of the cheque number, branch and bank.

1.4   Transaction processing

The principal peripheral in a computer transaction-processing system is the visual display unit. An example of transaction processing is a business order system (Fig. 1.3). Orders are received by telephone or letter and entered into the system and stored on *magnetic discs*. Invoices, despatch notes and other documents are produced on a printer. For telephone orders, the customer can be informed immediately whether the goods required are in stock.

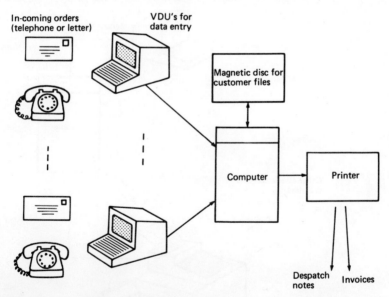

Figure 1.3 Order system (transaction processing).

Systems in which data are entered via a keyboard with the data then placed onto discs are known as 'key-to-disc' systems.

1.5   General information systems

An information system is one in which data are collected and stored and retrieved as required (an information-'retrieval' system). There are many existing examples of this, e.g. library information systems, museum catalogue systems, hospital information systems, police information systems, health and social security systems. In some cases special input peripherals are used; in others VDU's are adequate. The main reason for developing these systems is to reduce paper work and files and aid cross-referencing. Generally, there is a large amount of data to be stored and this can be held on *magnetic tapes* or *magnetic discs*.

A hospital information system, for example, collects information regarding patients to assist the overall running of the hospital. Records are kept of the patients, their treatment and progress, perhaps on a day-to-day basis. A modern hospital computer system has VDU terminals in each ward, in clerical offices and research laboratories, maybe connected to a central computer or via several local computers. There may be over 50 terminals to handle admissions/discharges, and clerical laboratory procedures.

Records can be kept on the availability of beds, operating theatres, X-ray rooms, and nursing 'manpower'. Waiting lists can be stored and managed. Statistical information can be produced.

The police information system installed at Scotland Yard holds records of two million fingerprints in addition to information on stolen vehicles, wanted and missing persons, disqualified drivers, people convicted or on suspended sentences, and some types of stolen property. This is held on disc stores and is available for retrieval from numerous terminals throughout England, Scotland and Wales.

A library information system is in some ways similar to the point-of-sale system described previously with a special optical character recognizer (say) for reading details of books lent as they are taken out. Here the customer's library membership card may provide the 'customer code'.

1.6 Patient monitoring

In the previous section a computer system in a hospital was outlined for collecting information. A computer can be used in a more active role for monitoring individual patients' medical parameters such as ECG (electrocardiograph) readings, blood pressure, body temperature, and activating alarms if certain conditions occur. Such a system is shown in Fig. 1.4. The peripheral input device for such systems (usually based on mini-computers) is the *analogue-to-digital converter* (*ADC*), which converts analogue signals such as voltages and currents from sensors placed on the patient to digital form for subsequent processing. One computer may service several patients. There may be a link to a larger computer system that holds the patients' records.

1.7 Process control

The process-control industry particularly lends itself to control by computers. This industry is involved in the production of steel, paper, oil, cement, chemicals, and the direct control by computer means that pneumatic valves and switches are controlled by the computer. Certain inputs are read, for example temperature

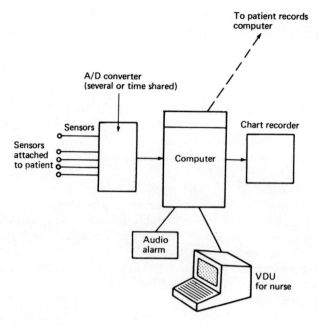

Figure 1.4 Patient monitoring.

and pressure (Fig. 1.5). Between the process and the computer there need to be peripheral devices to convert voltages and currents (analogue quantities) to digital values and vice versa, i.e. *analogue-to-digital and digital-to-analogue converters (DACs)*.

The type of control possible can be very advanced; the control of the final product may depend upon temperature and pressure and on the amount and condition of catalysts which may be altered during the process. There may be alternative products that can be produced; for example in the production of a mixture of ethylene and propylene there is a choice of different blends according to market demands.

1.8 Computer-aided design (CAD)

Computer-aided design is the use of a computer in the design of engineering products, e.g. cars, bridges and integrated circuits.

The peripheral device associated with this application is the *graphic display* which enables drawings to be displayed. The images can be created and input by causing a small symbol known as a cursor to move around the display area drawing shapes. The cursor movement can be specified by, for example, moving a 'mouse' device across the surface of a table. The mouse movement causes a corresponding movement of the cursor. Figure 1.6 shows a computer system with a graphic display and mouse. Diagrams can be produced on paper using a *graph plotter.*

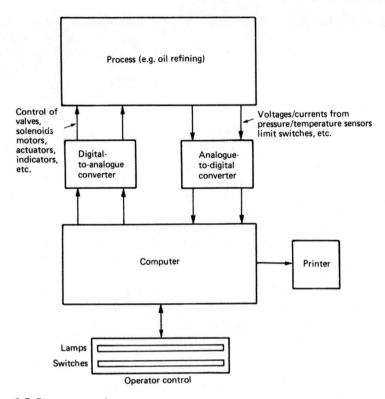

Figure 1.5 Process control.

1.9 Scientific calculations

Often in scientific work large and complex calculations are required; computers came into being to meet the requirements of complex calculations. This led to the development of large computers capable of operation at very high speed, and naturally at extremely high cost. These large 'number crunchers' were characterized by the mode of operation of accepting programs from a number of users in 'batches', running the jobs, and producing the results at some time later for the users to pick up. The computer would run continuously (hopefully) through the night, working on the jobs submitted. The method of submission for batch operation was by punched cards, loaded on a card reader by the operators. Results were printed on a single *high-speed line printer*.

Today there are generally two modes of operation for these machines, the original batch mode and the on-line or interactive mode. In the latter mode programs are entered by the user on terminals. Results appear on the terminal within a short period of time. The two modes operate concurrently (background/foreground operation).

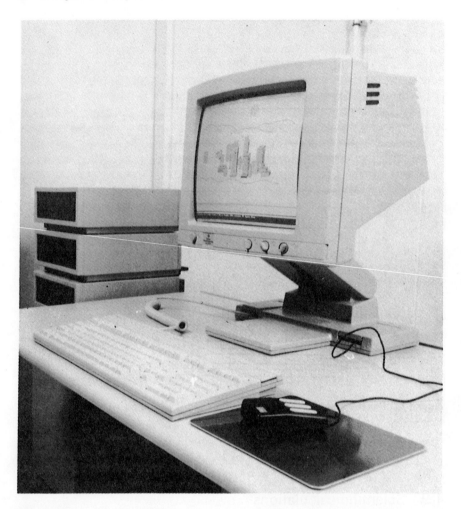

Figure 1.6 'Explorer' Artificial Intelligence Workstation (Courtesy of Texas Instruments Ltd).

A large computer system (Fig. 1.7) has perhaps the largest and widest selection of peripherals to cater for the user's needs. Apart from peripherals connected locally around the central processor, there may be a second processor unit known as a front end processor to control large numbers of other peripherals (Fig. 1.8) and communications units to transfer information from other computer sites.

1.10 The microprocessor

We leave this chapter with a mention of the most important device produced in the last few years; the *microprocessor*. This is a central processor in one integrated circuit (Fig. 1.9). With the additions of integrated circuits for storage and control of the peripherals, and the peripherals themselves, a small but very powerful

Figure 1.7 A very large computer room. (Courtesy of International Computers Ltd.)

micro-computer can be formed (Fig. 1.10). One particular peripheral has been associated with the micro-computer; the *floppy disc* unit, a magnetic-disc backing store where the disc is flexible and small (8 in (20 cm) or less).

An application of the micro-computer (the microprocessor with additional components to make a computer) is office word processing. Word processing is the name given to computer office equipment designed to assist the office typist in typing documents. The basic operations are typing of the original document, storage and editing of text and subsequent printing of the document. Early equipment to store and retrieve text from typewriters used punched paper tape and later magnetic tape and magnetic card. Due to technological advance of the microprocessor, it is now possible to produce highly sophisticated, though inexpensive, computer systems for individuals or groups of typists, providing editing and many other facilities. Text is initially entered on a visual display unit. Storage is by means of floppy discs and printing by a high-quality character printer. The whole system is controlled by the microcomputer.

Facilities that can be incorporated into a computer-based word processor include insertion of characters, words, lines and sentences, conformation to standard paragraphs, pagination and justification (straight left and right-hand margins).

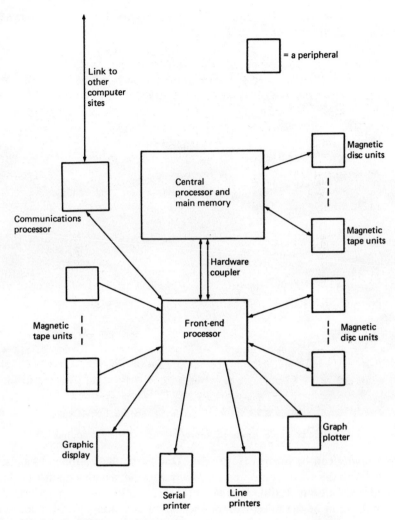

Figure 1.8 A typical large computer system.

Figure 1.9 A microprocessor.

Figure 1.10 Microcomputer Systems (Courtesy of IBM United Kingdom Ltd).

Throughout this book reference will be made to the microprocessor as a component used to enhance the facilities of peripherals. For example, the microprocessor is used in printers to give higher printing speed. The microprocessor makes decisions on how the characters are to be printed.

2

The connection of peripheral to computer

2.1 Introduction

2.1.1 Components of a stored-program digital computer

A digital computer executes instructions given to it. These instructions are first entered into the computer and held in a store (the term 'memory' is often used synonymously with 'store'). There is a unique location in the store for each instruction and each location is identified by an *address* A coherent collection of instructions is called a *computer program*. To perform the tasks specified by the program, a part of the computer known as the *central processing unit* (CPU), or central processor, takes the first instruction from the store and executes it. The next instruction is then taken and executed, and this is repeated for all the instructions in the program in order – unless an instruction is encountered which involves a change in the order of execution. This will of course, alter the sequence of instructions. Some instructions alter the sequence if certain conditions occur. The data required for any of the operations are also held in the store.

This then is a brief description of the principle of stored-program operation, basic to all digital computers.

The essential components of a stored-program digital computer are shown in Fig. 2.1, with the computer proper enclosed by a shaded area. The other components are peripherals. The input unit is used to enter programs and data, the output unit to output results and other information, the main store to hold the program and data and the central processing unit to execute the instructions held in the main store. Usually there is a backing store, which is used to hold programs and data not currently required.

Between each of the peripherals and the computer is electronic computer-pheripheral interface circuitry.

2.1.2 Computer instructions

The computer can execute many instructions (known as machine instructions) which are loaded into the main store. Traditionally these instructions are divided into various classes characterized by the task performed, e.g.

Load/store   Transfer data from locations within the processor (processor registers) to the main store and vice versa.
Arithmetic/logical/shift Perform operations upon data held in registers such as addition, subtraction, logical AND, shift bits left or right.

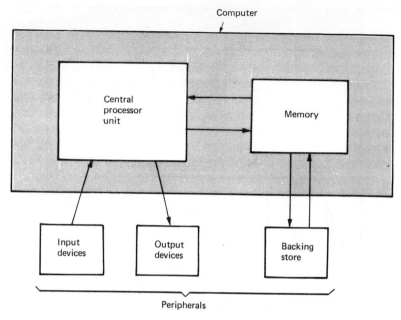

Figure 2.1 Components of a digital computer.

Jump/branch	Jump to an instruction not next in the program; may be conditional upon certain factors.
Input/output	Instructions concerned with the input of information from peripherals and output to peripherals.

Only the last class will be dealt with but the jump/branch instructions are sometimes needed to implement fully the input–output instructions. The reader is referred to books cited at the end of the chapter for treatment of the other instructions. Knowledge of the general operation of computers is assumed.

In accordance with common practice, mnemonics will be used with associated addresses and numbers where applicable to represent the machine instructions. Comments following the mnemonics serve to explain the mnemonics.

2.1.3 Central-processor highways

Very commonly a computer-peripheral interface unit joins onto the central processor via a common input–output (I/O) *highway* or *bus* as shown in Fig. 2.2. A further refinement is to have a common highway for both the peripheral interfaces and the memory, as shown in Fig. 2.3. This is the usual method employed by microprocessors. A consequence of adopting a single bus structure is that since it must now do two jobs the overall throughput of the computer is not as great.

The highway is a collection of wires that enables data to pass between a source and destination. With input devices and output devices attached via the highway,

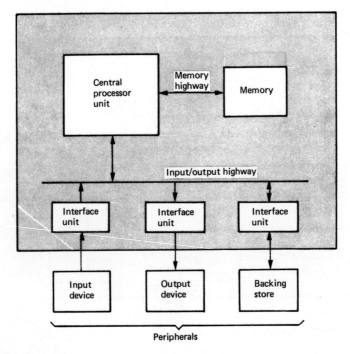

Figure 2.2 Highways.

the highway needs to be bidirectional, and able to pass data from an input device to the CPU or from the CPU to an output device. In both cases the peripheral device is selected by an address (a number) using address signals that pass down the highway to the device. In addition to data, and address lines, there are control lines that pass signals to enable timing and other operations to take place.

The following sections deal with the software and hardware aspects of the peripheral to computer connections.

2.2   Computer input–output operations

2.2.1   The interface unit

Figure 2.4 shows, in a little more detail, the usual arrangement for connecting peripheral devices to the computer input–output highway, or buses. An interface unit is needed to ensure compatibility between the bus and the peripheral. Conceivably all the interface unit circuitry could be included within the peripheral device, but the latter would then only be compatible with other computers having exactly the same I/O bus characteristics. Interface units are therefore usually built into the computer itself and the points on the interface unit where the peripheral devices are connected are often called *I/O ports*.

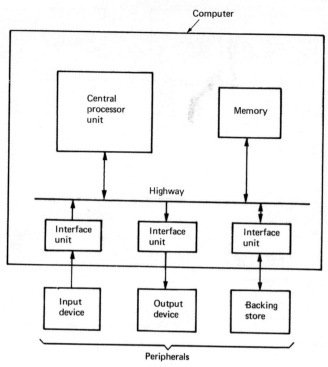

Figure 2.3 Single highway.

Several types of interface are used in practice and are discussed further in Section 2.4. However, typically each would comprise:

(i) *Transmit data and receive data registers* A register is a piece of electronic circuitry which can store several bits of data. Two registers are used here to hold and pass data to and from the peripheral device. The registers act as buffers and are needed because in general data are put into the interface unit by the CPU (or peripheral device) and taken out by the peripheral device (or CPU) at different points in time. In some interface units these two registers are combined into a single bi-directional data register, the direction of which (transmit or receive) is set by the control register. This is the arrangement indicated in Fig. 2.4.

(ii) *A control register* Separate bits of this register are used to 'flag' the presence, or not, of individual control conditions originated by the CPU. These can be intended for the peripheral device, for example 'activate peripheral device', or for the interface unit itself, for example to set the bidirectional data register in the 'data read' or 'data write' mode. The words read/write are used synonymously with input/output and receive/transmit in this context.

(iii) *A status register* This indicates to the CPU, individual status conditions. These conditions may be originated by the interface unit (for example 'ready to transmit next data word') or from the peripheral device (for example 'paper is low' on a line printer).

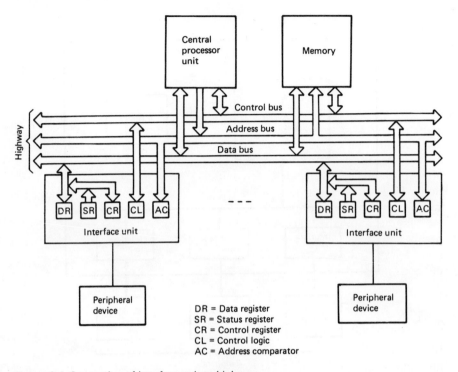

Figure 2.4 Connection of interface unit to highway.

(iv) *An address comparator* (*or address decoder*)   This allows the CPU access to the interface unit registers. Typically, each register is given a unique address. The main part of the address corresponds to an address for the interface unit, and two bits or so of the address are used to select a particular register within. The CPU then gains access by placing the appropriate address code on the address bus, and the address comparator connects the required register to the data bus. Alternatively, one or two of the more important status flags (say *busy or done* (see later)) may be given individual bus lines and the remaining register contents then accessed via the data bus.

(v) *Internal logic gates and circuitry*   Among other tasks, these monitor the registers and alter the various status and control flags as conditions dictate. For example, if an error is detected in the received data, then the appropriate error flag is set in the status register. Also included could be necessary hardware to handle interrupts (see Section 2.2.3).

The exact significances attached to the various control and status flags depend on the particular computer manufacturer and also on the type of peripheral device and the way its associated signals are defined. These details are not important in this discussion, but of course are known when the computer-system software is originally created and taken account of in the various software that controls the peripherals, etc.

Interface units in some computers may vary somewhat from the description given above while achieving the same ends.

Small computers often have a single set of buses, which are used for both main memory and I/O. The possible conflict that can arise here because memory locations and I/O interface units share the same addresses can be resolved by fitting an extra I/O signal in the control bus, which is set by the CPU. This indicates whether the address is intended for memory or I/O. Alternatively a group of addresses in the memory-addressing range can be reserved for the I/O and not connected to by main-memory hardware. The I/O devices are then said to be *memory mapped*. In this case the CPU gains access to I/O simply by using its memory-reference instructions, thus avoiding the need for special I/O instructions. This can be an advantage where there would be difficulties because the small computer is constrained to have a limited instruction set.

Computer input–output does not therefore usually take place directly with peripheral devices, but via various interface units. Computers vary in the way I/O is achieved, and the following should be taken as broadly representing the methods used.

2.2.2   Programmed I/O

In this case all data transfers between CPU and peripheral are completely under program control. The CPU instruction set contains four types of I/O instruction:

  (i) input data to CPU from peripheral;
 (ii) output data from CPU to peripheral;
(iii) set individual control flags in the I/O interface unit;
 (iv) test individual flags in the I/O interface unit.

Output of a data word to the peripheral is straightforward. The CPU addresses the interface unit and tests the status register. If the relevant flag in the status register shows that the peripheral is *ready* (it is not ready if it is busy handling the previous piece of data), then the CPU puts the data into the interface unit transmit-data register via the data-bus, causing the setting of one of the control flags to show that there are some new data for the peripheral device.

On the other hand, the input of data to the CPU is a little more involved. Here the peripheral places its data in the received data register and sets the ready status flag. The CPU is made to step periodically through all input peripheral addresses and test each ready status flag in turn, and in this way discovers the address of the ready peripheral. This is called *software polling*. The CPU uses this address and its I/O instructions to transfer data from the interface unit to the CPU. The programs that do this are called *device handlers* or *service routines*. The order in which the peripherals are polled imposes a priority on them. A peripheral can be given a higher priority by connecting it to an interface unit with an address which is early in the sequence. A refinement is to use a software polling table in main memory, which contains a list of interface unit addresses in some preferred order. The table contents are accessed sequentially to poll the peripherals. This allows the device priorities to be readily altered under software control.

The disadvantage of software polling is the amount of time that can be taken up when polling a large number of peripherals. This can significantly reduce the time available to the CPU for its other work.

Programmed I/O instructions

The mnemonic for the programmed output instruction is often OUT, meaning transfer the lower bits of the number held in A register (within the processor) to the peripheral device identified by the device number following the mnemonic. For example in the Z-80 microprocessor,[1]

$$\text{OUT (4), A}$$

outputs the 8 bit number held in the A register to device number 4 (i.e. address 4).

The mnemonic for the programmed input instruction is IN A, meaning input into the A register from the device identified by the device number following. For example,

$$\text{IN A, (5)}$$

inputs from device 5.

Prior to each of the above instructions, it is necessary to test whether the device is ready to receive data in the case of an output instruction or to test whether the device has provided new data in the case of an input instruction. In each case there will be a flag which indicates the state of the device at the interface unit, and designated a *ready* flag or a *busy* flag. The actual interpretation of these flags depends upon the machine. A flag is a single bit variable set to a 1 to indicate a particular condition.

In a *programmed output transfer* operation, the transfer of data is firstly from an internal storage location (normally a specified processor register) to the output interface and then automatically to the peripheral device when the peripheral is ready. These actions occur after an output instruction is executed. Usually storage is incorporated in the interface for data waiting to be sent to the peripheral. With *double buffering* (see Section 2.4.5), it is possible to load the interface unit with new data before the peripheral device has received the previous data. The ready flag of an output interface indicates that the data can be sent to the interface and will be accepted. Another flag can be provided to indicate that the transmission of data is taking place between the interface and peripheral device.

In a *programmed input transfer* operation, the transfer of data is firstly from the peripheral device to the input interface under the control of the peripheral and interface, and then to an internal storage location (normally a specified processor register) after the appropriate input instruction is executed. For example, information is transferred from a keyboard (Chapter 3) to the interface when a key is pressed. The interface *data received flag* is set when the interface has received new data. The new data can be read using a programmed input instruction, which, normally, causes the data received flag to be reset. An error flag (overrun flag) is set if the interface receives more data while the data received flag is set. Other input error conditions include a parity error condition. Extra storage can be provided in the input interface to store input data waiting to be read, and then the overrun flag is set only when no storage is left for new data.

In some early computers, special instructions were provided to examine particular interface flags. However, more commonly the flags are part of the information held in an interface status register which can be read as any other input/output register using IN instructions. For example an interface ready flag could be the least significant bit in the interface status register, i.e.:

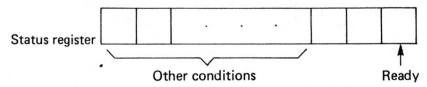

To determine whether this bit is set, the status register is first read using an INA instruction, and then 'ANDed' with the number 000 . . . 01. If the result is zero, then the flag must be '*0*', and if not it must be '*1*'. The sequence to execute this could be:

```
L1:  IN   A, (14)     ;read in status register of device 4
                      ;say designated address 14
     AND   0001       ;'AND' A register contents with 0001
     JP   Z, L1       ;repeat ready flag zero
     OUT  (4), A      ;copy contents of A register to device 4
```

A similar sequence is required for a programmed input transfer operation. Firstly, the appropriate flag is examined. When indicating new data, a programmed input instruction is used to obtain the data, and the flag is automatically reset. In the Z-80, a special BIT instruction is available to check a specified bit in a register (or memory location) and the instruction AND 0001 can be replaced with the instruction BIT 0, A (check bit number 0).

In some systems, such as 68000 microprocessor systems,[2] input/ouput is memory-mapped and normal memory reference instructions are used instead of input/output instructions. (The 68000 does have a specialized input/output instruction but the addresses of peripheral interfaces are still taken from the memory address space.)

The above gives typical examples of programmed I/O using special I/O instructions. Given a memory-mapped system the IN and OUT instructions would be replaced by normal memory reference instructions (LDA, load A register from a memory location and STA, store A register in a memory location).

Examples for specific peripherals are given in the following chapters.

2.2.3   Interrupts

Interrupt schemes are an improvement on programmed I/O principally because the address of the peripheral device which has data ready for transfer can be passed quickly to the CPU without the need for polling.

When the peripheral device presents data for transfer a flag is set in the interface unit, which in polling would be interpreted as *ready*, but is now interpreted by the CPU as *interrupt request*, IREQ. The CPU may be doing something more important, but when ready, it returns *interrupt acknowledge*, IACK. At the same time CPU working register contents are saved. A last-in first-out 'stack' of registers is often used here. The interface unit contains logic gates which, on receipt of the interrupt acknowledge, place the address of the interrupting peripheral on the data bus where it is copied into the CPU. This is then used to access in memory the appropriate software service routine. On completion, the service routine adjusts the interface unit control register and returns the original CPU register contents from the stack so that the previous program continues execution from the point where it was interrupted. Some further time can be saved if on receipt of IACK the interface unit returns the start address of the service subroutine instead of its own address. This automatic transfer of program control in response to an interrupt is often called *vectored interrupt*.

Interrupt schemes are also used for data output, especially when the rate at which data can be taken up by a peripheral device is low. In this case the CPU loads a data word into the interface unit and is then free to do other computations. In the meantime, these data are transferred to the peripheral device, and when this process is completed, an IREQ is raised on the CPU. The CPU loads in the next data word, and so on.

For a computer system with a small number of peripheral devices, programmed I/O methods are usually entirely adequate. Whereas in a system with a higher number of busy peripherals, such as a multi-user system, it is common practice for all I/O transactions to be effected by interrupts; the processor is said to be *interrupt driven*.

Priority schemes

Priority schemes are needed for two reasons. Firstly, in the simple interrupt scheme described above, if more than one peripheral device simultaneously requests an interrupt, then something will have to be done to stop the returned IACK from causing several units to attempt to place their addresses into the one CPU register. Secondly, during the execution of one of the interrupt service routines, a more important peripheral may request service and it would be desirable to respond to this request rather than risk loss of data. This requires extra priority logic hardware, and Fig. 2.5 shows one arrangement. Ignore for the moment the mask register. Simultaneous interrupt requests may originate from internal interrupts from within the computer ($IREQ_0$) or from any peripheral ($IREQ_1$ to $IREQ_N$). Internal interrupts carry the highest priority, since they call for an immediate response to such conditions as failure of power supply, memory fault, real-time clock, etc. The priority logic then selects that request which has the highest priority; that is, the one with the lowest IREQ-number in the range 0 to N and issues a single IREQ to the CPU.

When it is ready to accept the request, the CPU acknowledges this with IACK. The priority logic cancels IREQ (this enables subsequent requests to be passed to the CPU provided they have higher priority, or if the current interrupt service

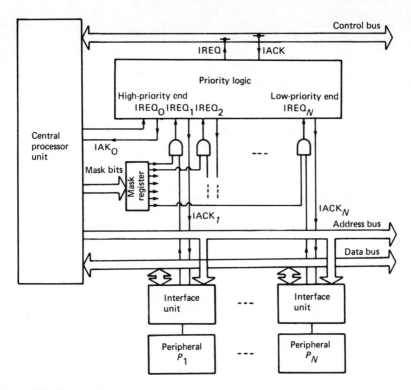

Figure 2.5 Priority scheme.

routine has been completed), and passes the appropriate interrupt acknowledge ($IACK_0$ to $IACK_N$) to the interrupting interface unit. This interface unit then places its own address, or service-routine address-vector, onto to the CPU data bus, and execution of the peripheral service routine then follows. By saving the CPU working register contents on a stack each time an interrupt is accepted, many nested levels of interrupts are allowed. A typical sequence is shown schematically in Fig. 2.6, where it is assumed that priority A exceeds that of B.

The device priorities are determined by the order in which peripherals are connected to the interface units. Some degree of software control of priority is possible using a register which is referred to as the *mask* register. The CPU can place any desired bit-pattern of ones and zeros into the mask register. Each of the zeros that feeds into an AND gate then stops, that is 'masks', the associated interrupt request from entering the priority logic, and in this way interrupts from particular devices may be suspended if desired. Assuming the mask register length is the same as the word length of the CPU, then typically 16 levels of priority can be handled on a small computer.

A greater number of levels can be obtained by having a second hierarchical level of priority-logic units. That is, the pair $IREQ_1$ and $IACK_1$ are not directly connected to an interface unit as shown in Fig. 2.5, but to the top of another priority-logic unit which can have up to 16, say, peripheral devices feeding into it.

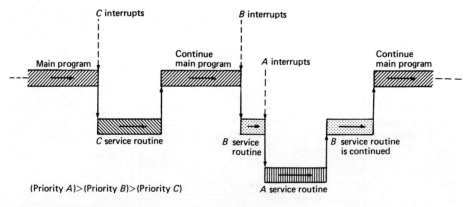

Figure 2.6 Nesting of interrupts: typical program sequence.

Doing this on other interrupt lines can allow up to 256 levels (that is 16^2) to be obtained on a small computer.

An alternative way to connect several peripheral devices to a single IREQ/IACK pair is to 'daisy chain' several devices together as shown in Fig. 2.7. All interrupting requests on the daisy chain are paralleled and a joint request sent to the CPU. If the request is accepted, IACK is returned to the first peripheral P_A in the chain. Extra logic circuitry in each interface unit tests its own IREQ flag, and if this is not set, passes the acknowledgement to the next peripheral. Hence the acknowledgement passes down the chain until it is trapped by the first interface unit with an interrupt request. This interface unit then sends an address to the CPU to start the service routine.

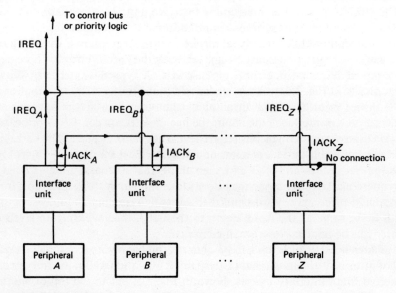

Figure 2.7 Daisy chain.

A disadvantage of daisy chains is that devices at the end of the chain may be starved of attention.

2.2.4 Block data transfer

To transfer a data word between memory and peripheral takes about ten instructions, or about $20\mu s$ in time, in a small computer. This sets an upper limit on the transfer rate of 50 000 data words per second. There are many cases in which it is required to transfer blocks of data words from, or to, consecutive addresses in main memory at much higher rates than this – for example, from disc files to main memory. There are several ways to do this, but in one way or another, each requires the following information to be specified.
1. peripheral device address;
2. starting address of the block allocated in memory;
3. number of data words in the block;
4. direction of transfer (that is memory to peripheral or vice versa).

(a) *CPU-controlled block data transfer*
Here the CPU instruction set is provided with special block-data transfer instructions. The use of these reduces the average time taken to transfer each data word. This can be further improved by using a special type of interrupt called a *data break*. It turns out that on block-data transfer, the CPU working registers need not be affected and the use of a data break saves the time taken to transfer CPU register contents to a stack as with normal interrupts. This results in a net increase in speed of data transfer.

A disadvantage is that the CPU is not free to do other tasks in this mode of block-data transfer, unlike direct memory access, which is now discussed.

(b) *Direct Memory Access (DMA)*
DMA is often preferred to CPU-controlled block data transfer. A hardware *DMA controller* is required, which can be thought of as an interface unit with additional registers and logic. In response to a CPU command, or peripheral interrupt, the DMA controller is loaded with information (1)–(4) mentioned above. The DMA controller then takes command and overrides the CPU whenever both compete for the use of the bus. This causes the CPU to hesitate and the process is called *cycle stealing*. In single bus structures the CPU is unable to use the bus during DMA transfer of a data word which is a hinderance. An improvement is to attach the DMA controller to the memory bus in those computers with separate memory and input/output buses. Less hesitation occurs in computers where those parts of the machine cycle in which main memory is not active can be used by DMA. Other computers employ two-port main memory with DMA connected to the alternative access port.

In effect, the DMA controller is a small processor separate from the CPU. Hence it is sometimes designed to do arithmetic operations on the data as well as simple data transfer. DMA priority systems are employed where there are several high-speed peripherals each needing its own DMA controller.

2.3   Codes

Data passing between the computer and peripheral comprise groups of bits. On many occasions these data represent letters of the alphabet and other characters in connection with keyboard devices and printers, etc., and agreed coding schemes are used for this.

Groups of bits were used to code printed characters for use in telegraphy, etc., long before the modern computer was developed. Over the years many different coding schemes have been used, as new data terminals and transmission practices have been evolved. The maximum size of the character set is determined by the number of bits in each character. For example, a seven bit coding scheme allows 2^7, that is 128, different characters to be defined. The characters in a code fit into the following groups:

1. Numeric (0 to 9)
2. Alphabetic (upper and lower case)
3. Special characters (punctuation marks, brackets, etc.)
4. Control characters (used by equipment on both ends of the link to control data flow).

The two most widely used codes in data transmission between computer and peripheral device are ASCII and EBCDIC. The seven-bit ASCII (American Standard Code for Information Interchange) was originally put forward by the organization now called ANSI (American National Standards Institute). This was developed by the International Standardization Organization, ISO, and Comité Consultatif International Téléphonique et Télégraphique, CCITT, and as the International Alphabet No. 5 (IA5) was agreed in 1968, and is shown in Table 2.1.

Items in parenthesis are for ASCII usage. Notice that two of the bits, b_6 and b_7, define the groups: control; special and numeric; upper-case alphabet; lower-case alphabet. This makes it easy for the computer to decide on whether a code word is a control character (both bits zero) or a graphics character both bits not zero). The code is usually used with an eighth *parity* bit.

Parity bits are used for error checking. There are two types: *odd parity* and *even parity*. In the former, a parity bit is appended to the data word such that the total number of 1s is odd, while in even parity an even number of 1s is produced. There is little to choose between the two methods. Examples are as shown in Table 2.2.

Parity checks are simple to implement, and allow all single-bit errors to be detected that may occur during, say, data transmission or when the data are stored on media which contains blemishes. For example, if odd parity is being used and the word 10111000 is received, then since there is an even number of 1s, it is certain that an error has occurred, and retransmission should be requested. The presence of single and odd numbers of bits in error can be detected; however even numbers do not change the parity condition, and so go undetected. Other methods of error detection and correction are discussed in Chapter 10.

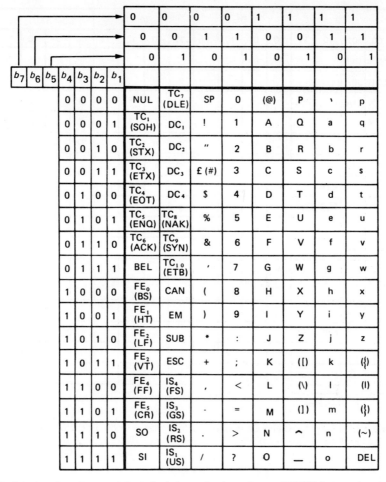

b_7				0	0	0	0	1	1	1	1
b_6				0	0	1	1	0	0	1	1
b_5				0	1	0	1	0	1	0	1
b_4	b_3	b_2	b_1								
0	0	0	0	NUL	TC₇(DLE)	SP	0	(@)	P	`	p
0	0	0	1	TC₁(SOH)	DC₁	!	1	A	Q	a	q
0	0	1	0	TC₂(STX)	DC₂	"	2	B	R	b	r
0	0	1	1	TC₃(ETX)	DC₃	£ (#)	3	C	S	c	s
0	1	0	0	TC₄(EOT)	DC₄	$	4	D	T	d	t
0	1	0	1	TC₅(ENQ)	TC₈(NAK)	%	5	E	U	e	u
0	1	1	0	TC₆(ACK)	TC₉(SYN)	&	6	F	V	f	v
0	1	1	1	BEL	TC₁₀(ETB)	'	7	G	W	g	w
1	0	0	0	FE₀(BS)	CAN	(	8	H	X	h	x
1	0	0	1	FE₁(HT)	EM	)	9	I	Y	i	y
1	0	1	0	FE₂(LF)	SUB	*	:	J	Z	j	z
1	0	1	1	FE₂(VT)	ESC	+	;	K	([)	k	({)
1	1	0	0	FE₄(FF)	IS₄(FS)	,	<	L	(\)	l	(|)
1	1	0	1	FE₅(CR)	IS₃(GS)	-	=	M	(])	m	(})
1	1	1	0	SO	IS₂(RS)	.	>	N	^	n	(~)
1	1	1	1	SI	IS₁(US)	/	?	O	_	o	DEL

Table 2.1 American Standard Code for Information Interchange (ASCII)/International Alphabet IA5.

Data	Odd parity added	Even parity added
1001011	10010111	10010110
0010101	00101010	00101011

Table 2.2 Parity bits for error checking.

The eight-bit EBCDIC (Extended Binary Coded Decimal Interchange Code) is used primarily in IBM Co. computers and compatible equipment from other manufacturers. The bits are numbered b_0–b_7. Table 2.3 shows a version of EBCDIC used for the IBM 3270 display system. Other versions have different control-character functions in the first four columns of the table.

Bits 0,1 →	00				01				10				11			
Bits 4567 / Bits 2,3 →	00	01	10	11	00	01	10	11	00	01	10	11	00	01	10	11
0000	NUL	DLE			SP	&	.									0
0001	SOH	SBA					/		a	j			A	J		1
0010	STX	EUA		SYN					b	k	s		B	K	S	2
0011	ETX	IC							c	l	t		C	L	T	3
0100									d	m	u		D	M	U	4
0101	PT	NL							e	n	v		E	N	V	5
0110			ETB						f	o	w		F	O	W	6
0111			ESC	EOT					g	p	x		G	P	X	7
1000									h	q	y		H	Q	Y	8
1001		EM							i	r	z		I	R	Z	9
1010					¢	!	¦	:								
1011					.	$	,	#								
1100		DUP		RA	<	.	%	@								
1101		SF	ENQ	NAK	(	)	_	'								
1110		FM			+	;	>	=								
1111		ITB		SUB	!	¬	?	"								

Control characters

Table 2.3 IBM Extended Binary Coded Decimal Interchange Code (EBCDIC). Version used for IBM 3270 display system.

Although IA5 (ASCII) and EBCDIC are the most commonly used, other codes are occasionally encountered. Examples are the five-bit Baudot code in telegraphy, various five–eight-bit paper-tape codes, and the 12-bit Hollerith punched-card code.

2.4 Interfacing methods

2.4.1 Duplex

Depending on the number of transmission channels, data may be passed between I/O port and peripheral device in three ways. These are, using the generally accepted meanings of the terms,

1. *Full-Duplex* (FDX) where data are transmitted simultaneously in both directions

2. *Half-Duplex* (HDX) where data are transmitted in both directions, but only one way at a time, and
3. *Simplex* where data are transmitted in one direction only.

FDX requires two channels, whereas one channel is sufficient for HDX and simplex.

2.4.2   The range of methods

Figure 2.8 shows, for a small computer system, various ways in which the CPU and peripherals may be connected via interface units and lines. Not all methods need be used in a system. Conversely several peripheral devices may be connected using interface units of the same type. A quite small computer might only require two serial and two parallel I/O ports, while larger machines could require more than a hundred I/O ports.

Practically every manufacturer has his own way of implementing interfaces, however approaches are generally similar and the following descriptions give the main features.

2.4.3   Direct connection

This is the simplest of all, in that the peripheral is connected directly to the computer buses and no actual interface unit is required. If the peripheral together with the linking lines places an appreciable electrical load on the buses, then a set of buffer gates called a *bus extender* should be used.

Direct connection is used where the functions of the interface unit are not needed; for example, plug-in extensions to main memory. Alternatively it may be used where these functions are built into the peripheral device. This may provide economies but means that the peripheral is then compatible with only the one bus configuration. This is not so important in such cases as the popular S100 bus, which is used by several microcomputer manufacturers so that there is a wide and rapidly expanding range of peripheral devices and special-purpose computer sub-systems which are directly 'plug-compatible' with the S100 bus.

2.4.4   General-purpose parallel interface

Figure 2.9 outlines the contents of a simple interface unit of this type. The parallel I/O data port commonly comprises 4, 8 or 16 data lines. Figure 2.10 shows how parallel data are transferred.

The port is set as an input port or an output port by setting the read or write bits in the control register which, via the control logic, sets the appropriate direction of the bi-directional data register.

Two peripheral control lines are shown. Depending on requirements C_1 could be used to indicate 'data ready for output', that is, there are new data from the CPU in the data register. On data input C_2 could be used to indicate that the next data word from the peripheral is on the lines, which sets a flag in the status register at the same time that the data are loaded into the data register. If

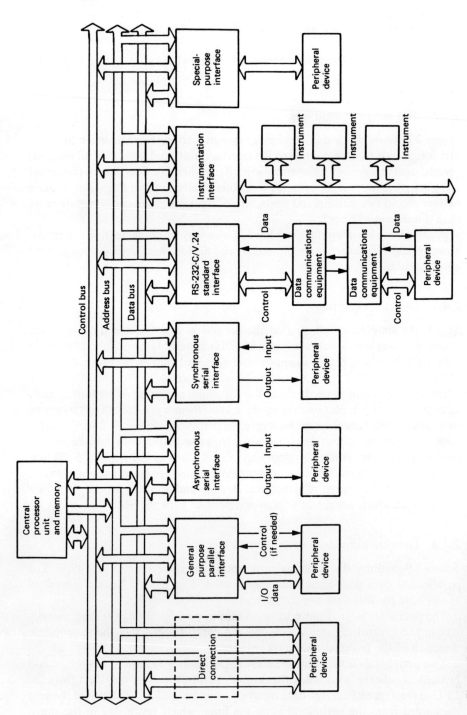

Figure 2.8 Interfacing methods.

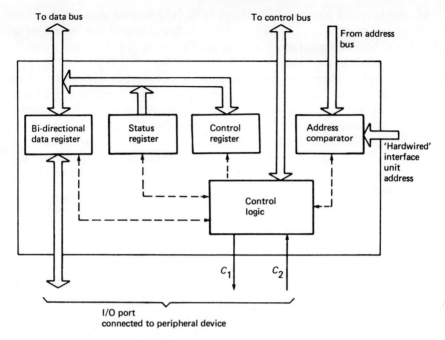

Figure 2.9 General purpose parallel interface.

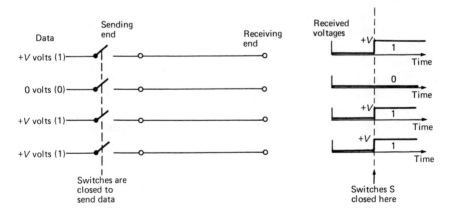

Figure 2.10 How parallel data is transferred.

programmed I/O is in operation then this flag would be the 'ready' flag; or for interrupt driven I/O it would be the IREQ signal.

Further enhancements to the basic arrangement in Fig. 2.9 can include circuitry to respond to an IACK returned by the CPU to an interrupt request, and which returns the interface unit address or service routine address vector, as explained earlier.

Programmable, as well as basic, versions are available in LSI (large-scale integration) form. In this case there are further internal registers and control circuitry. A set-up phase is used before it is used to pass data, and various facilities can be set-up under CPU control, such as the selection of individual data bits to be either input or output, the presence of multiple I/O ports, and the ability to switch to any one.

LSI parallel interface integrated circuits are not usually equipped with an address comparator but instead with a *chip select* input, together with address pins to select one of the multiple I/O ports (if present) and to access the internal registers. Addressing the interface unit is then achieved by using individual chip select lines in the computer buses, which is impractical for large numbers of interface units, or by using separate address comparators alongside the LSI circuit to form the complete interface unit. Logic to deal with interrupts would also probably be fitted separately.

2.4.5 Asynchronous serial interface

In serial transmission the bits of the data word are transmitted one after the other, on a single wire.

For ASCII codes the bit sequence normally runs from b_1 to b_7 and then the parity bit, whereas for EBCDIC the sequence is b_7 to b_0.

Some peripheral devices may move data naturally in serial form, such as teletypewriters. Others, while dealing in parallel data, are sited a long distance from the computer and worthwhile savings may be achieved on cables etc., by using single-line serial transmission rather than the multiple lines of parallel transmission. This is especially so when the peripheral is linked to the computer via telephone lines, in which case serial tansmission is always used.

A consequence of having to push more data bits down one line is that serial transmission is slower than parallel transmission.

A modern computer moves data in parallel form, and hence a parallel-to-serial convertor is needed in the interface unit. This is shown schematically in Fig. 2.11. For transmission, the parallel-data word is loaded into a shift register. A shift register has the property that the application of a clock pulse causes the data word in the register to move one place to the left and the leftmost bit is output.

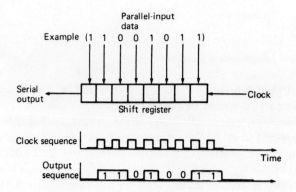

Figure 2.11 Parallel to serial conversion using shift register.

Hence for an *n*-bit data word a burst of *n* clock pulses will output the word in serial form. To receive serial data, the incoming data are connected to the right-hand side of the shift register and then clocked in. Of course the receiver clock timing has to be close to that originally used at the transmitting end, to ensure that data bits are not missed out (clock too slow), or entered twice (clock too fast).

The asynchronous character format that is generally used is shown in Fig. 2.12. In between the characters, the line is in the idle state, which is the 'MARK' or '1' condition. This comes from telecommunications practice and is convenient because a break in the line will cause the MARK condition to cease and the fault is readily detected. The first bit of the character, the 'START' bit, is in the '0' condition, and the '1' to '0' transition at the beginning is used to start the receiver clock and indicate that the character is coming. The first bit of the data could not be used as the start bit, because on those occasions that it was at a '1' it would be indistinguishable from the idle condition and so ignored by the receiver. For the data part of the character, five, six, seven, or eight bits are used in practice, with the least significant bit transmitted first. Following the data word an odd or even parity bit may be included to enable a check to be made for errors made during transmission. After the parity bit the signal returns to the idle condition and a gap is forced between this character and the next by appending one, one and a half, or two stop bits. This gap is required to allow slower-responding devices to reset and settle down before the next character. Because of this format, this type of transmission is sometimes called *start – stop* transmission.

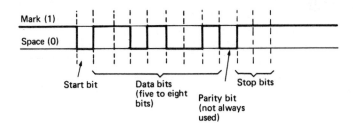

Figure 2.12 Asynchronous character format.

This format is used when characters arrive at irregular intervals, without any particular synchronism (that is *asynchronously*) as for example from keyboard devices.

Within the character the bit timings must be reasonably regular, and the following bit rates are among those commonly used: 110, 150, 300, 600, 1200, 2400, 4800, 9600 bits per second. The slower rates (e.g. 110 bits/s) are used for such devices as teletypewriters, whereas a visual-display unit would normally use one of the higher rates.

Transmission rates are sometimes expressed in *bauds*: 150 bit/s is written as 150 baud. The baud is a communication engineering unit which expresses modulation rate, and is the reciprocal of the shortest signalling element. However, generally, bauds are not necessarily the same as bits/s. For example, in a signal element which has four possible voltage levels, say 0, 1, 2, 3 V then each level can represent a pair of data bits, say 00, 01, 10, 11, and 150 baud would then be equivalent to a data rate of 300 bits/s.

The block diagram of a simple asynchronous interface unit is shown in Fig. 2.13. An LSI version is available called a UART (Universal Asynchronous Receiver/Transmitter). The transmitter section (for computer output) and receiver section (for computer input) are separate. Both of these would be used, for example, on a printing terminal with the received serial input coming from the keyboard and the transmitted serial output going to the printer.

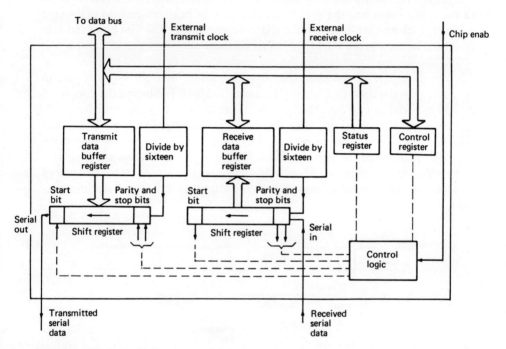

Figure 2.13 Asynchronous serial interface.

Notice that as well as a shift register, each section contains a parallel-data register. This *double buffering* is useful in the receiver section because without it the computer could have too little time to read the data from the shift register before the next character starts to arrive. The computer can now afford to wait until the next character has been entirely received and assembled in the shift register. A wait beyond this time is monitored by the UART and a *data overrun* flag is set in the status register. On the transmitter side, double buffering is helpful in keeping the transmitter fully primed with data ready to send. When the transmitter data register is empty the CPU is *flagged* by the status register.

Other status conditions indicated by the UART include: *receive data ready, receive parity error* and, *framing error* (given when the stop bits do not return to the MARK condition and indicates a possible break in the line, or other mishap).

The control register is loaded by the CPU to specify the required character format; that is, number of data and stop bits, and type of parity bit if required.

As on other LSI interface circuits a *chip select* control input is fitted, and address comparators and interrupt address-vector logic have to be provided separately.

Often external clocks running at sixteen times the required bit-rate are used. The frequency of this external clock is unlikely to be the same as that of the computer itself and so an independent *baud-rate* generator is usually coupled to the UART in a complete asynchronous serial interface unit.

2.4.6 Synchronous serial interface

Asynchronous communications require start and stop bits to allow data words to be sent at irregular intervals. However, these bits are wasteful in that they do not convey data information.

In synchronous communications efficiency is improved by transmitting data in long blocks. One simplified format is shown in Fig. 2.14. Several formats are in use, each with its own set of operating rules (called a *protocol*). This is dealt with further in Chapter 11.

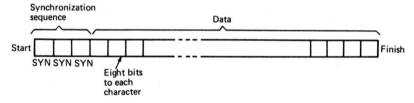

Figure 2.14 Simplified synchronous block data format.

Because the data stream in synchronous communication can be very long, the receiving end must be maintained in exact bit-synchronism with the transmitter. This is done using a separate clock lead from the transmitter. Alternatively, when modulation – demodulation methods are used over a single-line telecommunications path, the demodulator, which is local to the receiver, recovers the clock signal from the received signal and passes it over to the interface unit.

The start of the data block is indicated by a special synchronization bit sequence. In those formats in which the data block comprises a string of data characters (often eight bits each) one or more synchronization (SYN) characters are used. In ASCII the bit pattern for SYN, including parity, is 10010110 (least-significant bit on the right). If only one SYN character is used, then a random single-bit error caused during transmission could alter the meaning of SYN and recognition of the start of the data sequence could be missed. Hence up to four, or five, SYN characters are often used at the start of the data block.

After the start has been detected, the receiving end groups the bit-stream into characters.

If a random disturbance occurs during the transmission of data, the receiver could lose its position. Erroneous groups could then be formed starting part way through one character and continuing into the next, thus causing nonsense to be produced. To help recovery when this occurs, SYN characters are included at intervals within the data block. Having recognized these SYN characters, the receiving end can re-start its bit groupings at the correct positions.

The SYN characters, and various other control characters, constitute an overhead. However, because the blocks of data are long this is proportionately less than for the start – stop bits in asynchronous communication.

Again, LSI circuits are available. A simplified block diagram is shown in Fig. 2.15 and is not very dissimilar to that of the synchronous interface, Fig. 2.9. Start, stop, and parity-bit mechanisms are not required here, however. SYN-character generation and insertion circuitry on the transmitter side and SYN-recognition circuitry on the receiver side are now present. The status register flags such conditions as: received data word ready for transfer to CPU; transmitter section ready for another data word from the CPU; and various error conditions. The control register is set up by the CPU to determine such things as number of bits per word, number of SYN characters, and to force the receiver side to search for SYN characters. This latter action occurs when the CPU believes, on the basis of high numbers of received characters in error, that character synchronism is lost.

It may be necessary, as in other LSI interface circuits, to add address and interrupt logic to form the complete interface unit.

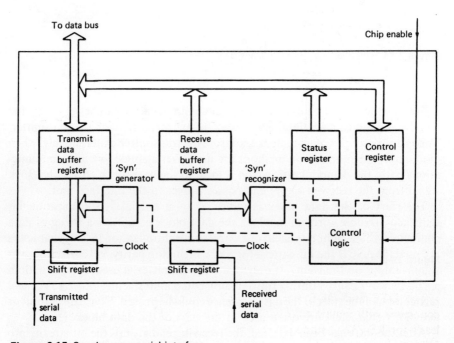

Figure 2.15 Synchronous serial interface.

2.4.7 RS-232-C/V.24 standard serial interface[4,5]

These two standards relate to the connection of a DTE (Data Terminal Equipment), such as a peripheral device, or a computer, to a DCE (Data Communications Equipment) such as a *modem*. Modems (the word is a contraction of 'modulator' and 'demodulator') are used when data is transmitted over long lines, more especially telephone lines. This is such a frequent requirement that standards have been adopted to ensure compatibility between equipment from the many manufacturers of DTEs and DCEs. The general arrangement is shown in Fig. 2.16 and it is seen the standard is used at both the computer and peripheral ends.

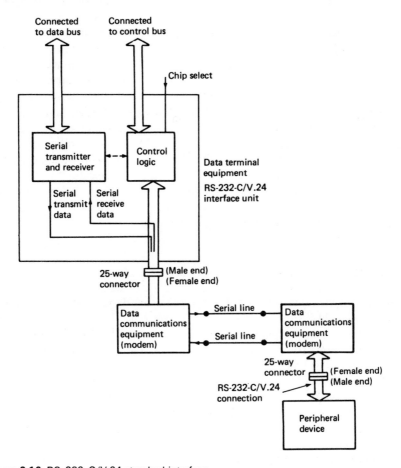

Figure 2.16 RS-232-C/V.24 standard interface.

The DTE and DCE are connected by a twenty-five lead cable, using a connector with female end associated with the modem (DCE). The connector leads for RS-232-C standards of the Electrical Industries Association (EIA), USA, have very similar meanings to those of recommendation V.24 of the

CCITT, which is widely used in Europe. V.24 does not define connector contacts but refers to circuits. The RS-232-C contact meanings are summarized in Table 2.4, with the V.24 circuit numbers in parenthesis.

Contact	Description	Contact	Description
1 (101)	Protective earth	14 (118)	Secondary transmitted data
2 (103)	Transmitted data	15 (114)	Transmitter signal element timing
3 (104)	Received data	16 (119)	Secondary received data
4 (105)	Request to send (RTS)	17 (115)	Received signal element timing
5 (106)	Clear to send (CTS)	18	Unassigned
6 (107)	Data set ready	19 (120)	Secondary RTS
7 (102)	Signal earth	20 (108)	Data terminal ready
8 (109)	Received line signal detector (RLSD)	21 (unassigned)	Signal quality detector
9	Unassigned	22 (125)	Ring indicator
10	Unassigned	23 (111)	Data signalling-rate selector
11 (126)	Unassigned	24 (unassigned)	External transmitter clock
12 (122)	Secondary RLSD	25 (unassigned)	
13 (121)	Secondary CTS		

Table 2.4 RS-232-C standard of the Electrical Industries Association.

Circuit 126 (pin 11) is unassigned in RS-232-C but designated 'select transmit frequency' in V.24.

Despite the number of parallel wires, the data are moved serially (asynchronous or synchronous) on contacts 2 and 3. Consequently, incorporated within an interface unit of this type is the kind of serial hardware outlined in Section 2.4.5 or 2.4.6. Other parts of the interface unit relate to controls between the DTE and DCE, and their use is covered by the Applications Notes to RS-232-C issued by the EIA, and also by other CCITT V-series recommendations. CCITT V.24 also describes a '200' series of circuit designations which are used for automatic calling procedures.

A selection, and not necessarily all, of the circuits are used depending on the particular equipment type. Hence the fact that a peripheral device is marked as RS-232-C or V.24 compatible does not mean it is able to work with every possible type of data communications equipment, but that it at least conforms in its electrical and mechanical aspects to the standard.

Electrical signal characteristics are specified, and are described briefly in Section 2.5.2.

The RS-232-C/V.24 interface is widely applied to peripherals and computers, and it is often convenient to use it even when the peripheral and computer are near to each other, and modems are not therefore required. This raises a compatibility problem: both ends will try to transmit data along the same circuit between number two contacts, and also will both listen for received data on the circuit between number three contacts, with 'disappointing' results. A remedy is to use a *null* modem (see Fig. 2.17), whose sole job is to cross over the transmit and receive circuits and similarly reconnect certain of the other circuits where necessary. Some manufacturers take a cheaper solution and instead supply a cable which incorporates the cross-overs.

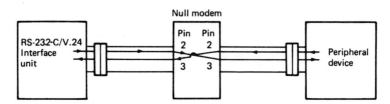

Figure 2.17 Null modem.

2.4.8 Instrumentation interfaces

(a) *IEEE standard 488*
This is issued by The Institute of Electrical and Electronics Engineers, USA, and entitled 'Digital Interface for Programmable Instrumentation'.[6] It is also known as the Hewlett Packard–Interface (HP–IB). The IEEE bus has gained widespread acceptance for computer-controlled instruments such as data-loggers, spectrum analysers, network analysers, etc. The general scheme is shown in Fig. 2.18. Up to fifteen devices may be connected on the bus. A device may be a *listener*, a *talker*, or both; one of the devices (usually the computer) must be able to control as well as talk and listen.

A large number of instruments from different manufacturers are now available which can be plugged onto the IEEE 488 bus. There is also growing interest in the use of this interface for peripheral devices as well as instruments.

The sixteen-line bus is passed from one instrument to another using a cable and specified twenty-four-way connectors. A compatible connector socket is mounted on the back of each instrument and also at the rear of the cable-plug housing, to allow all instruments to be linked in star or chained fashion. The cable length must be no more than 2 m per instrument, with a maximum total of 20 m. Conveniently, the signals are electrically the same as in ordinary gates of the TTL logic family. The connector contact and signal designations are as shown in Table 2.5.

The eight data lines DIO1 and DIO8 carry addresses, program data, measurements, and status bytes, in bit-parallel form. Lines DAV, NRFD, NDAC, control the transfer of data, and IFC, ATN, SRQ, REN, EOI, are for general interface management. Detailed protocols are laid down in the standard.

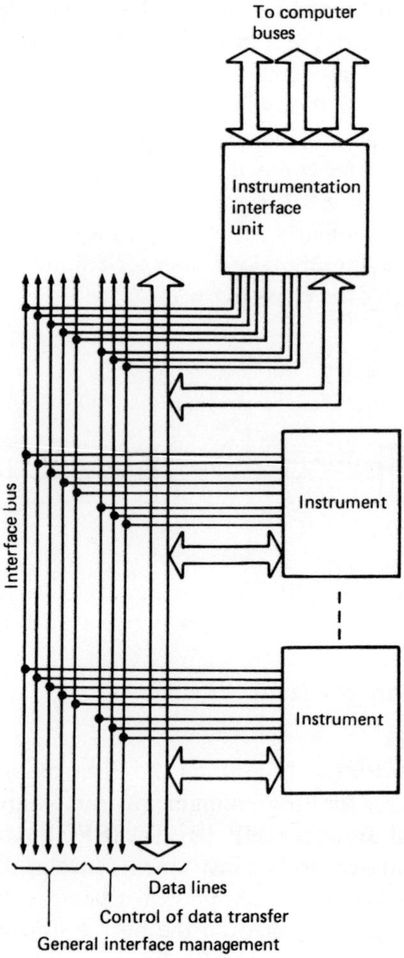

Figure 2.18 IEEE-488 instrumentation interface

LSI circuits are available to handle this interface. One of these can be incorporated directly into an interface unit in the computer, or made into an 'add-on' interface adapter to convert one of the existing I/O ports (say RS-232-C/V.24) into an instrumentation interface.

(b) *CAMAC*

The Computer Automated Measurement and Control (CAMAC)[7] Standard is a product of the nuclear instrumentation fraternity, and is somewhat similar in aims to IEEE-488. It is a modular system with instruments constructed on plug-in assemblies and then mounted into standard crates. The bus (or Dataway) comprises the back wiring that is connected to each of the 86 way sockets at the rear of each module. Common power-supply lines are also included in the bus. Voltage logic levels for Dataway signals are those of TTL with the convention

Contact	Designation	Contact	Designation
1 DIO1		13 DIO5	
2 DIO2	Data input/output	14 DIO6	Data input/output
3 DIO3	lines	15 DIO7	lines
4 DIO4		16 DIO8	
5 EOI	End-or-identity	17 REN	Remote enable
6 DAV	Data valid	18 Gnd (6)	
7 NRFD	Not ready for data	19 (Gnd (7)	
8 NDAC	Not data accepted	20 Gnd (8)	
9 IFC	Interface clear	21 Gnd (9)	Signal ground return for the contact
10 SRQ	Service request	22 Gnd (10)	number indicated
11 ATN	Attention	23 Gnd (11)	
12 SHIELD	Cable shield	24 Gnd logic	

Table 2.5 IEEE standard 488 Bus.

that voltage low is logic '1' and voltage high is logic '0'. Details of the Dataway designations and bus protocols are laid down in the standard.

2.4.9 Special-purpose interfaces

A computer manufacturer may decide that a peripheral product, brand 'XYZ', is most suited to its computer system, and will make a special-purpose unit to interface to that product. One advantage in doing this compared with using one of the general-purpose interfaces is that unwanted features and circuitry need not be built in. A second advantage is that some of the electronics that would normally be sited within the peripheral device can now be put in the interface at the computer, where regulated power supplies and control signals are close at hand.

Following such a move, other peripheral device manufacturers may make their own 'XYZ compatible' devices. Also other computer manufacturers may in turn make I/O ports to fit XYZ compatible products and so a 'de facto' interface standard is born. An example of such standards is the Centronics 8-bit parallel interface for printers, which has become accepted. IBM has produced several of its own 'standards'.

2.5   Line drivers and line receivers

2.5.1   Maximum bit rate versus line length

The interface unit at the computer is coupled to a peripheral by one or more lines. The lengths of these lines may be a couple of metres long, or less if the peripheral device is near to the computer; or it could be hundreds of metres, and more, if it is sited in another room or building. It is found that the maximum reliable transmission bit rate that can be sustained is smaller for longer line lengths. Typical relationships are shown in Fig. 2.19, with curve B representing a higher-quality link than curve A. Several factors affect the position of the curve, such as type of cable, line driver, line receiver, and also how much electrical noise impinges on the line. However, the general shape remains the same.

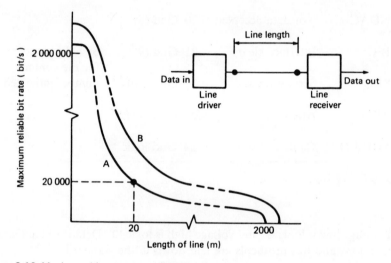

Figure 2.19 Maximum bit-rate versus line length.

At very short line lengths maximum bit rate is quite high and the flat portion of the curve indicates that the upper limit is set more by the speed of response of the driver and receiver circuitry than by the line length.

As the line is increased in length, the capacitance of the line becomes important. This capacitance has to be charged up and down as the data sequence is transmitted, and constitutes a load on the driver, so that the signal amplitude arriving at the receiver will be reduced. If the bit-rate is increased, then the capacitance-charging current is also increased until a maximum bit-rate is reached, at which the loading effect is such that the receiver cannot reliably interpret the signal. Now this capacitance is directly proportional to line length, and so there is an inverse relationship between maximum bit-rate and line-length as indicated in the curved portion of the characteristics in Fig. 2.19.

This figure also shows that an upper limit exists on line length, beyond which the maximum bit rate rapidly falls to zero. This effect can be caused by electrical interference, from signals on nearby lines etc. The magnitude of this interference increases with line length until a point is reached where the line receiver is confused by this noise and gives incorrect output. Also, at long line lengths, the resistance of the line causes signal attenuation in addition to that due to capacitance, which thus accelerates the decline in maximum reliable bit rate. For distances greater than this, techniques such as modems (see Chapter 11) or optical fibre lines (section 2.5.6) are necessary.

The line drivers and receivers are usually built into the peripheral device and also the interface unit at the computer. Several techniques are available, some of which are governed by standards. Descriptions of some of these techniques now follow.

2.5.2   Single-ended line driver and line receiver

As can be seen from Fig. 2.20 the term 'single-ended' is used because the line is connected at a single point on the driver and receiver at each end of the line.

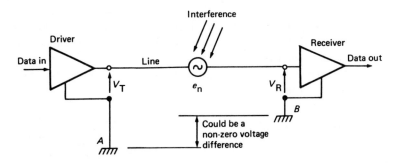

Figure 2.20 Single-ended line driver and receiver.

The simplest way is to use a direct connection, with line drivers and line receivers being normal logic gates of the type used within the computer and peripheral. Transistor-Transistor-Logic (TTL) gates or TTL-compatible gates are most often used and the voltage levels are shown in Fig. 2.21. To ensure that the receiving end does not misinterpret the driver gate output sent at the start of the line it is necessary that $V_{OH} > V_{IH}$ and $V_{OL} < V_{IL}$. That is, adequate *noise margins* are needed. If the line is too long then attenuation of the line, or additive voltages picked up on the way, can cause logic levels to fall inside the indeterminate region at the receiver end and therefore risk misinterpretation.

Additive voltages can occur in two ways. Firstly, interfering radiation can be picked up from nearby electrical activity. This is marked as e_n on Fig. 2.20. Secondly, the receiver input voltage is sensed with respect to its local earth, B, which may not be at exactly the same potential as A. The difference could amount to several volts, if the driver and receiver are some distance apart and especially if they are energized from different points in the power distribution system, and it effectively puts a large offset on the received signal. This can easily cause the receiver to give an incorrect output.

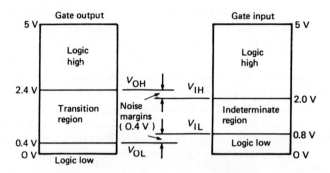

Figure 2.21 Voltage levels for transistor-transistor-logic (TTL).

The situation is improved if larger margins are used (see Fig. 2.22) as in the electrical specification of the EIA standard RS-232-C, or the closely related CCITT recommendation V.28. Full details can be obtained by referring to the published specifications. A driver circuit is required here which accepts input data at normal logic levels, and transmits at the voltages shown to a receiver at the far end which outputs data at normal logic levels. A capacitance load on the receiver of less than 2500 pF is specified, which for a typical line capacitance, of say 125 pF/m would limit the permitted length of line to 20 m. It can be seen from Fig. 2.18 that by sacrificing bit rate it is possible to use a longer line, but operation is then outside the standard.

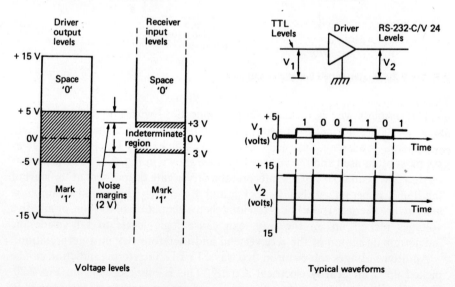

Figure 2.22 Voltage levels for RS-232-C.

2.5.3   Differential line receiver

Here the line receiver circuit, unlike the single-ended receiver, is able to sense the difference in two voltages, neither of which needs to be at zero volts. When used as shown in Fig. 2.23, this can overcome two of the difficulties of single-ended receivers that were mentioned above. Firstly, the transmitter earth A is conveyed to, and used by, the differential receiver. This eliminates the problem caused when earth B is not at the same potential as earth A. However, there is a limit to how much of this offset can be accommodated, since both input voltages, V_1 and V_2, must remain within the working range of the receiver circuit. Secondly, provided the two lines are laid close together, preferably twisted, any electrical interference will induce almost identical voltages, e_n, into each line. Hence at the receiver $V_1 = V_T + e_n$, and $V_2 = e_n$. However, the receiver senses the difference:

$$V_R = V_1 - V_2 = (V_T + e_n) - (e_n) = V_T,$$

which is independent, ideally, of interference effects.

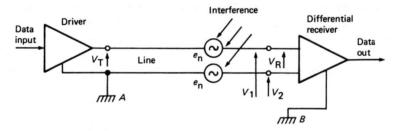

Figure 2.23 Differential line receiver.

This type of driver/receiver combination is covered by EIA standard RS-423-A and allows transmission at higher data rates than RS-232-C.

2.5.4 Balanced driver and differential receiver

The arrangement is shown in Fig. 2.24. Here the driver has two outputs, one of which, labelled $+V_T$, is similar to that of the single-ended drivers mentioned above. For the second output, labelled $-V_T$, the driver circuit generates the complement of $+V_T$. That is if one output is in the MARK state the other is in the SPACE state.

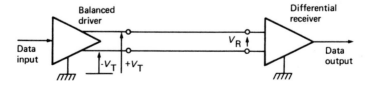

Figure 2.24 Balanced driver and differential line receiver.

One advantage here is that the effective transmitted voltage between the lines is twice that of the single-ended driver/differential-receiver arrangement. Hence a greater signal attenuation and therefore line length can be tolerated.

A further advantage is that the complementary signals will cause radiation fields which cancel each other out. This attacks the problem of interference at source, and when all lines in a cable use balanced drivers there is lower 'cross-talk' which again benefits maximum line length.

This type of configuration is covered by EIA standard RS-422-A.

The EIA standard RS-232-C is now joined by RS-449 to allow higher data rates to be obtained. For data rates above 20 kbit/s certain circuits are designated to be used with balanced RS-422-A electrical characteristics. For data rates less than this RS-423-A is designated.

2.5.5   The 20 mA current loop

The transmission of serial data by 20 mA currents is often associated with electromechanical types of peripheral device such as teletypewriters. Figure 2.25(a) shows the basic principle of operation. At the receiver end is a voltage source E, a current-limiting resistor R, and a current-sensitive device. At the transmitter, the switch in the open position corresponds to a SPACE. A MARK is generated when the switch is closed, thus forming a loop and current flows.

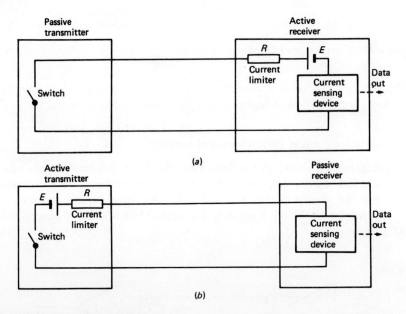

Figure 2.25 The 20 mA current-loop.

The voltage source and resistor are chosen to give a typical current of 20 mA (60 mA current loops are also encountered in practice). A glance at Ohm's law $(I = V/R)$ reveals that many different values of V and R can be used, and are used, to give the required 20 mA current. At the receiver the current-sensing device detects the presence of the current and indicates a MARK condition. From the location of the voltage source, the receiver is said to be *active*, and the transmitter *passive*.

An alternative, and equally valid, arrangement is to have a passive receiver and active transmitter, as in Fig. 2.25(b). It is sometimes convenient to use both methods, as in the two-way connection of a teletypewriter to a computer where both active ends are energized by the computer.

In non-electromechanical devices such as a computer, electronic circuits and components are used for the elements of the current loop: switch, current limiter, active source, and current-sensing device.

With the trend away from electromechanical peripheral devices the use of the 20 mA loop is becoming increasingly rare.

2.5.6 Optical-fibre cables

In recent years improvements on materials and manufacturing techniques have made the use of optical fibres cost effective in many applications requiring the transmission of data.

Figure 2.26 shows the general arrangement. Data signals are taken by the driver, which activates the light-emitting diode (LED) to send pulses of light down the fibre. The thin optical fibre is coated so that light cannot enter or escape. At the receiving end the optical pulses are converted to electrical signals by the photo-diode and receiver circuit.

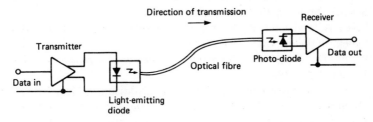

Figure 2.26 Optical-fibre arrangement.

Precise coupling techniques are required where the fibre joins the LED and photo diode, and also where sections of cable are joined, to avoid unacceptable loss of light.

The use of optical fibres can have several advantages. The fibres are intrinsically unaffected by electrical interference, which makes this method very suitable for electrically noisy industrial environments. A second advantage is that high data rates can be achieved; typically 50 Mbit/s can be obtained using LEDs and even higher is obtained using more costly lasers.

Modern glass materials have low optical attenuation and cable lengths of typically 10 km or more can be used before regeneration of the pulses is needed.

References

1. *Z80-CPU Z80A-CPU Technical Manual*, Zilog Inc., Cupertino, California Inc., 1978.
2. *MC68000 16/32-bit Microprocessor Programmer's Reference Manual* (4th ed.), Motorola Inc., Geneva, Switzerland, 1984.
3. Stone, H. S. (ed.), *Introduction to Computer Architecture*, Science Research Associates, Chicago 1975.
4. *CCITT Recommendation V.24, Green Book*, Vol. III, 1972.
5. *EIA Standard RS-232-C, and Application Notes*, Electronic Industries Association, Washington DC, USA, 1969.
6. *IEEE Standard Digital Interface for Programmable Instrumentation*, (IEEE Std. 488-1975), The Institute of Electrical and Electronic Engineers, New York, 1975.
7. IEEE Standard Modular Instrumentation and Digital Interface System (CAMAC). (IEEE Std. 583-1975), The Institute of Electrical and Electronic Engineers, New York, 1975.

Further reading

1. Bartee, T. C., *Digital Computer Fundamentals* (6th edn.), McGraw-Hill, USA, 1985.
2. Hebditch, D. L., *Data Communications, An Introductory Guide*, Elek Science, London, 1975.
3. Lesea, A., and Zaks, R., *Microprocessor Interfacing Techniques*, (2nd edn), Sybex, Berkeley, USA, 1977.
4. Pritty, D., *Practical Interfacing to Popular Microprocessors*, Addison Wesley, USA, 1985.
5. Stone, H. S., *Microcomputer Interfacing*, Addison-Wesley, USA, 1983.
6. McNamara, J. E., *Technical Aspects of Data Communication*, (2nd edn) Digital Press, for Digital Equipment Corporation, 1982.
7. Senior, J. M., *Optical Fibre Communications*, Prentice-Hall International, UK, 1985.

3

Displays, keyboards and visual display units

3.1   Introduction

The communication with a computer at the lowest level is by means of the engineers' panel which comprises a number of switches and a number of lights mounted on the central-processor cabinet. A switch in one position represents a 1 and in the opposite direction a 0. Thus, binary numbers can be entered into the machine using these switches. A light illuminated represents a 1 and extinguished a 0. Thus binary numbers can be 'output' from the computer.

The normal inter-human communication is via the medium of words and numbers. It is therefore natural that the communication with computers should be through alphabetic and numeric characters (alpha-numeric characters). The basic peripheral for entering alpha-numeric characters is the keyboard, and the basic peripheral for displaying them is the alpha-numeric display. The two, the keyboard and the alpha-numeric display, can be combined to form the basic man–machine communication device, the visual display unit (VDU).

This chapter is concerned with alpha-numeric (and numeric) displays, keyboards and the VDUs, and begins with single character displays and character representation.

Numeric symbols are the symbols 0, 1, 2, . . . , 9, together with $+$, $-$, and (decimal point). Alpha-numeric symbols are the numeric symbols, the letters of the alphabet, A, B, C, . . . , Z, punctuation symbols (,.:;!?), together with special symbols such as @, £, \$ and %. The letters of the alphabet may additionally include both upper case and lower case.

3.2   Character displays

In this section, displays capable of showing single characters are examined as a necessary prologue to the text displays that are composed of several character displays. Additionally, character displays find applications as indicators in peripheral devices proper.

3.2.1   Character fonts

For character displays, there are two principle styles (fonts): dot matrix and segment. Dot matrix representation is used also in text displays and printers.

47

(a) *Dot matrix*

The dot matrix representation consists of a matrix of dots, in the case of character displays usually a 5×7 matrix. Selected dots are illuminated to give clearly recognizable symbols (Fig. 3.1). For greater clarity, usually with text displays, 7×9, 10×14 or greater matrix sizes can be used. Lower-case letters can be accommodated by an extra one, two or three rows for the character tails (of *g*, *j*, *p*, *q*, *y*). For example, a 5×7 dot matrix typically becomes 5×9 dot matrix for upper and lower case, a 7×9 dot-matrix becomes a 7×12 dot matrix. Foreign language symbols can be accommodated with a dot matrix. For example, Arabic symbols can be represented.

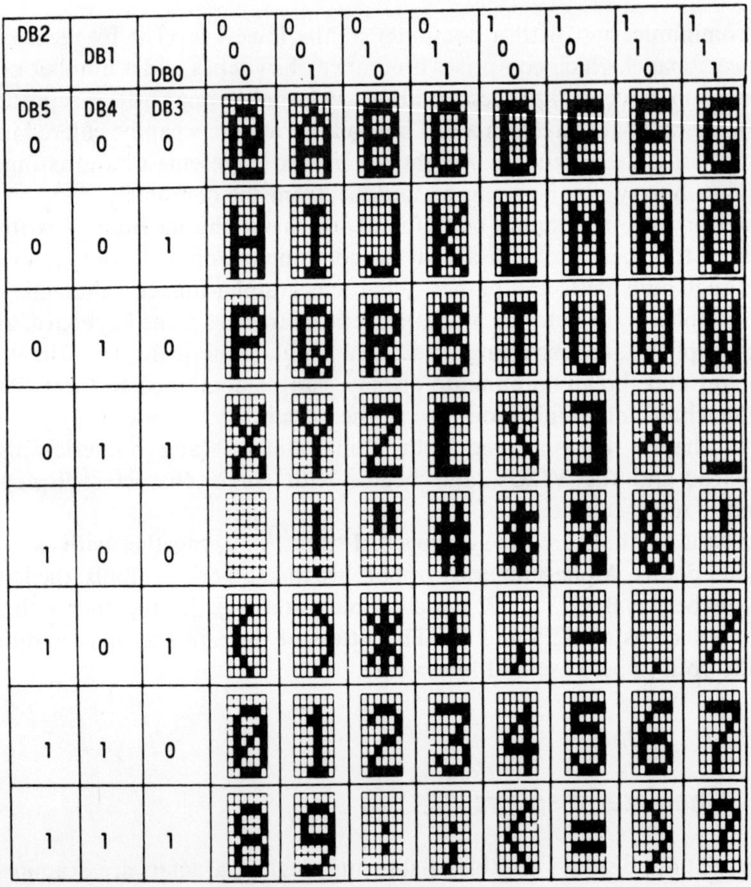

Figure 3.1 5×7 dot-matrix characters.

(b) *Segment*

Segment representation is usually only used for character displays. For numeric symbols, the 7-segment font (Fig. 3.2) has found wide use and is perhaps known mostly for its use in calculators. The seven segments are conventionally labelled *a*, *b*, *c*, *d*, *e*, *f* and *g*.

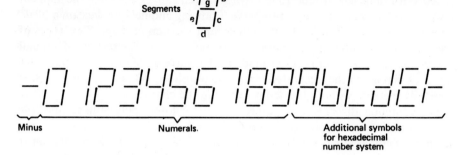

Figure 3.2 Seven-segment characters.

The 9-segment font has also been used and is similar to 7-segment with extra vertical segments, one centrally placed in the upper area and one placed in the lower area. This provides a limited alpha-numeric representation. There are also 14- and 16-segment arrangements. The 16-segment font for alpha-numeric representation is shown in Fig. 3.3.

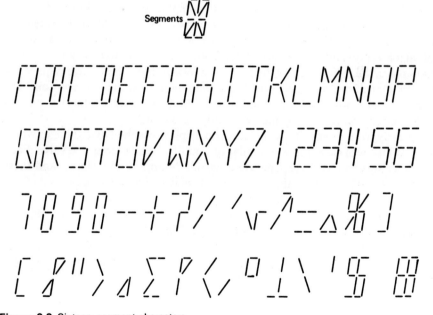

Figure 3.3 Sixteen-segment characters.

3.2.2 Incandescent-filament displays

The incandescent-filament display is based on the familiar electric light bulb. The character font used is often 7- or 16-segment and there is a single filament for each segment. Often each filament is a single helix of tungsten or tungsten alloy. When current passes through a filament, the filament heats to a high temperature (2500°C for tungsten, around 1350°C for tungsten alloys), such that the filament glows. The filaments are treated to prevent bowing and held in place on a black substrate and contained in an evacuated, high-vacuum package. Two types of package are common; the cylindrical glass envelope similar to that of a small thermionic valve with connections made to the 'valve' base, and the rectangular *flat pack* similar to the integrated-circuit dual-in-line package. The flat pack is generally metallic with a glass front exposing the character.

For computer displays, the requirement is for low supply voltage and low power consumption. Typically, the supply is 5 V and the filament current (for one segment or dot) as low as 8 mA. To obtain reasonable life, the filaments are run at less than the maximum current. A 100 000 h life is typical in this mode.

The initial current flowing when cold filaments are switched on may be ten times the normal operating current. Current-limiting resistances are sometimes used in series with the filaments to limit the switch-in current, thus protecting the filament from being burnt out.

3.2.3   Gas-discharge displays

Gas-discharge or plasma displays comprise a glass envelope filled with a neon-gas mixture, which is ionized by a high potential difference (around 180 V) between an anode and cathode in the envelope. The gas mixture is principally neon with the addition of argon to reduce internal oxidation, krypton to aid initial ionization and mercury to reduce in ionization potential. When ionization takes place, the region around the cathode glows orange. The voltage required to sustain ionization is considerably less than that to initiate ionization. The segment font is often used, and in this case there are several cathodes, one for each segment, which can be independently activated.

An early form of gas-discharge numeric display was the Nixie tube, in which the envelope was glass and was similar to that of a small thermionic valve. Each character was formed by a separate electrode of appropriate shape, and these were separated from each other so that the display had to be viewed directly from the front.

The planar gas-discharge display is a recent development. A seven-segment planar-gas discharge display is shown in Fig. 3.4. Metallic segments are deposited onto a glass plate which is mounted above the ceramic base, using spacers. The space between the glass plate and the base is filled with a neon-gas mixture, thus completing the construction.

3.2.4   Light-emitting diode displays

The binary semiconductor compound, gallium phosphide, formed into a p–n diode, emits red light when forward biased. This phenomenon was first discovered in the 1950s, originally using point-contact diodes. In the ensuing 20 years, intense development has resulted in a light source that is presently used in about half of all display applications (computer and non-computer).

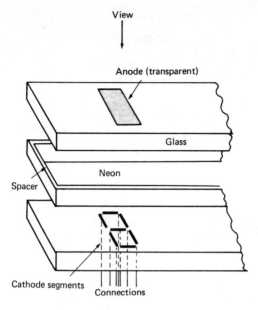

Figure 3.4 Planar gas-discharge display.

The red colour of the light emitted from a gallium phosphide *light-emitting diode* (LED) is due to impurities. A pure GaP diode emits green light. It has been found that the ternary compound, gallium arsenide phosphide (GaAsP), also emits red light. By varying the mix of gallium arsenide phosphide from GaP to GaAsP, any light from infra-red to green can be obtained. Various colours and greater efficiency can be obtained by doping the compounds (with nitrogen, for example). Other gallium compounds are under development.

The construction of an LED display is shown in Fig. 3.5 and consists of a substrate of GaP or GaAs onto which an epitaxial layer of GaP or GaAsP is grown, and a p–n junction formed by diffusion into the epitaxial layer. A metallic contact is formed on the top and bottom of the chip.

The chip size needs to be small to keep the display cost down. To obtain a seven-segment display, each segment can be produced by one chip and the light reflected and diffused to produce a bar (Fig. 3.5(b)). This is used in small displays mounted on dual-in-line packages. Dot matrix LED displays are also available.

Typically, the red-light-emitting diode is operated at 10 mA forward current and gives a voltage drop of 1.9 V, and interfaces easily with logic circuits. The life expectancy is greater than 20 years; there is a gradual reduction in the light output over this period to around 50%.

3.2.5 Liquid-crystal displays

Liquid crystal displays (LCDs) employ an organic liquid which has a high degree of molecular order. When an electric field is applied across the liquid, the molecular order is disturbed and this changes the optical properties. The liquid in

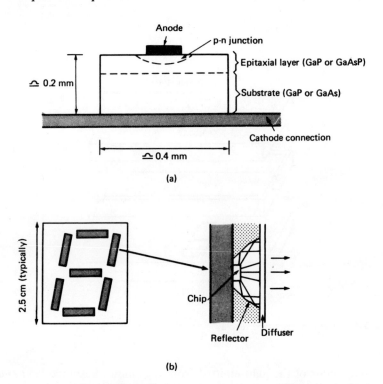

Figure 3.5 Light-emitting diode display: (a) chip; (b) seven-segment LED display.

a liquid-crystal display is contained between two parallel glass plates, and the inner surface of the plates coated with transparent conductive film electrodes, such as indium oxide. A potential applied between the electrodes produces the desired electric field across the liquid.

The first commercial liquid-crystal display employed the *dynamic scattering* effect shown in Fig. 3.6(a). When the display is unenergized the molecules are arranged perpendicularly, and light can pass through the liquid. When energized, the molecular structure is disrupted by the ionic current, causing light to scatter. The liquid is lightly doped with electrolyte to provide the ionic conduction. Generally, a low-frequency (30 Hz) a.c. voltage in the region 15–30 V r.m.s. is used to energize the display, rather than a d.c. signal, to reduce electrolysis. Complete reliability has not yet been achieved with this type of liquid-crystal display, due to electrolysis, material defects and instability.

Present liquid-crystal displays are generally based upon the *twisted nematic field effect*. The display (Fig. 3.6(b)) is manufactured so that the liquid-crystal molecules are aligned parallel at the surface on one electrode and parallel at the surface of the other electrode, but rotated through 90° so that the molecules twist between the upper and lower electrodes. This has the effect of twisting polarized light through 90° as it passes through the liquid. The twisting of the molecules and hence of the light polarization can be removed by the application of an electric field. The light first passes through a sheet of polarizer, then through the

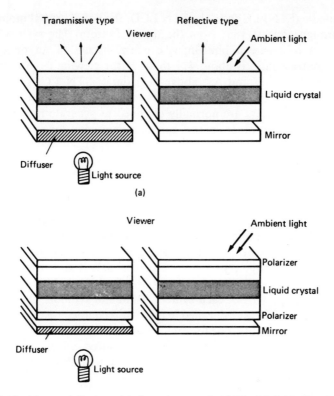

Figure 3.6 Liquid-crystal displays: (a) dynamic scattering LCD; (b) field-effect LCD.

liquid crystal and finally through another sheet of polarizer, with the plane of polarization 90° to the first, such that when the device is unenergized, light passes through the display unheeded. When energized, the light will not pass through the second polarizer. This is the transmissive type of field-effect display. This results in a dark character on a light background. A light character on a dark background can be obtained using polarizers with the planes of polarization aligned together. Additionally, a mirror can be added behind the second polarizer to send the light back to the front. This is known as the reflective type of field-effect display. The electrodes can be driven with in-phase sine or square waves to get no potential difference, and out-of-phase signals to energize the display. Very low currents are required, typically 0.3–0.5 μA. The liquid is made resistive and high reliability obtained.

Original liquid crystals that were used exhibited the liquid-crystal state only in a narrow range of temperatures, but recent mixtures have ranges as wide as $-10°$ to $+70°$C.

The optical switching times are in the region 100–150 ms.

The basic twisted nematic (TN) LCD suffers from rather poor contrast ratio (about 3:1 at 15° for viewing from normal) and viewing angle (20° wide, 60° above horizontal), which have adversely effected the acceptance of LCD displays. Both contrast ratio and viewing angle have been improved in the supertwisted nematic (STN) LCD. In the STN LCD, the liquid crystal molecules are twisted through at least 180° from the top to bottom. The system still uses polarizers but to create a birefringence effect instead of an on–off effect. Maximum contrast ratio is about 4:1 to 4.5:1 for viewing from normal, and viewing angle 65° wide and 45° above horizontal. STN LCDs have slower response times in the region of 200–300 ns but this does not appear to be a major disadvantage. STN LCDs are normally designed to generate blue dots with a yellow background but other colours can be generated at lower contrast ratio.

3.2.6 Encoders

Each numeric or alpha-numeric character has a binary code. Typically, seven-bit ASCII is used. In the case of a 5×7 dot matrix, each seven bits need to be translated into 35 signals. Each signal is associated with a particular dot and is a '1' if the dot is to be illuminated and is a '0' if the dot is not to be illuminated. In the case of a seven-segment display, there are seven signals representing the segments *a* to *g*. The circuitry to provide such signals is known as an encoder.

Dot matrix encoders usually employ a ROM (Read Only Memory) arranged to hold the 35-bit pattern of each symbol. With 128 symbols, there would be 35×128 bits stored. The ROM, called in this case a character ROM, is generally organized with five outputs (one for each column in the matrix), and two sets of inputs. One set is used to select the character required, which in the case of a complete ASCII character set would be one of 128, and a seven-bit input is required. The other set is used to select one of the rows of the matrix. For seven rows, a 3 bit input is required.

The design of a binary to seven-segment code encoder is a simple logic-design exercise. Integrated-circuit encoders are available.

3.3   Text Displays

3.3.1   Multiple-character displays

A line or even a page of text can be displayed using an individual character display for each character position. Plasma (gas discharge) displays, LED displays, and liquid-crystal displays, in particular, can be constructed with several characters in one package, and several such packages can be mounted side by side.

If each dot or segment of each display is driven independently, a large number of drivers is necessary. This can be reduced by using a smaller number of drivers shared between particular dots or segments of all the displays. This is known as multiplexing.

Consider a number of (numeric) 7-segment plasma or LED displays; the same cathode segments of each display are connected together and driven by one of seven drivers as shown in Fig. 3.7. Each display is produced sequentially by applying an appropriate voltage to the anode of the display with the required segments energized. If the displays are operated at a sufficiently high repetitive rate (greater than 30 Hz), the complete display appears to be non-flickering.

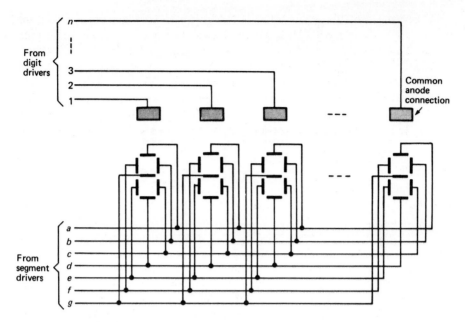

Figure 3.7 Multiplexed seven-segment display.

Planar gas-discharge displays are often constructed with several numeric characters on one substrate and there is an additional cathode called a *stay-alive cathode*, kept active continuously. This cathode provides an internal ion source that reduces ionization time and aids multiplexing. Plasma displays may also need *cathode blanking* when multiplexed. The cathodes are turned off during each transition period to eliminate difficulties caused by premature ionization, and to ensure that the circuit voltages decay below the ionization potential on one display before they rise to the ionization potential on the next.

Dot matrix LED displays could be multiplexed by selecting a particular column and energizing the rows which are made common to all displays. However, with a number of displays, say, n, the percentage of the total time each LED was activated (the duty cycle) would be $1/5n \times 100\%$. Thus, with only two displays, the duty cycle would be only 10% and the intensity would be quite low. To overcome this problem multiple dot matrix LED displays are available with integral shift registers as shown in Fig. 3.8. For a four-character display, there are four seven-bit shift registers, each holding the pattern required for one column of each display. Like columns are selected together. The pattern for all column 1's is loaded into the shift register and the column energized. Then the pattern for all column 2's is loaded into the shift register and column 2 energized. This is repeated for all the columns and the whole process repeated continually.

3.3.2 Cathode-ray tube

(a) *Construction and operation*
The cathode ray tube (CRT) consists of a glass funnel-shaped tube which is evacuated so that the air pressure is less than 10^{-6} mm Hg. Contained within the

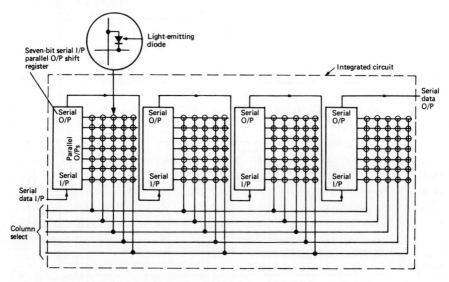

Figure 3.8 Four-character 5 × 7 dot-matrix LED display.

tube are several electrodes as shown in Fig. 3.9. A cathode, made from nickel, coated with an oxide (a mixture of barium, strontium and a little calcium), is heated indirectly by a filament heater, and raised to a temperature (around 1100°K) that causes electrons to be emitted from the surface of the cathode. These electrons are focused into a narrow beam by electrostatic or magnetic fields, and accelerated to a high velocity by an electrostatic field so as to strike a screen coated with a phosphor. The phosphor is caused to fluoresce where the electron beam strikes.

The phosphor coating is made from oxides and sulphides of cadmium, zinc and manganese, together with metals such as silver. Particular combinations give particular fluorescence and phosphorescence (fluorescence after the beam has been removed). For example, the phosphor, P4 (with the formula $ZnS + Ag + Zn_8BeSi_5O_{19} + Mn$, used in monochrome television CRTs) gives a white fluorescence/phosphorescence and the time for the intensity to delay to 1% of 0·005 s. The beam can be deflected by applying two mutually perpendicular electrostatic or magnetic fields controlled by electrodes in such a way that images can be formed on the screen.

The controlling electrode which regulates the 'size' of the beam and hence the brightness of the fluorescent spot on the screen is known as the *grid*. The grid is situated immediately in front of the emitting cathode and has a small hole through which electrons can pass. Placing a negative potential on the control grid with respect to the cathode repels the (negatively charged) electrons, and given a sufficient potential (around −20 to −100 V), electrons can be prevented from passing through the control grid at all. Thus whether the beam of electrons exists or not is determined by the control grid (as is the brightness). The beam of electrons, if there is one, after leaving the grid converges to a point and then diverges towards the attraction of a positive potential anode A_1 (at about 300 V), through which the electron beam passes. The beam then passes through the focusing and deflection systems, and is accelerated to a very high velocity by a positive potential final anode (at around 2–20 kV). This anode is generally a circular disc with a hole for the electron beam to pass through, and is located before the deflection system. The wall of the CRT is coated in the inside with a conductive material and this may be connected to the final anode. The electron beam may be accelerated after the deflection system, utilizing conductive material on the inside surface of the CRT.

Electrostatic focusing and deflection is used in the CRT of Fig. 3.9(a). Focusing is obtained by the electrostatic fields produced between a cylindrical anode, A_2, placed between the first anode, A_1, and the final anode, A_3. Typically a voltage range of 10–100 V on A_2 is required for focusing. To deflect the beam, two pairs of plates generate electrostatic fields at 90° to each other and these can deflect the beam in the X-direction or the Y-direction, or a combination of both. The pairs of

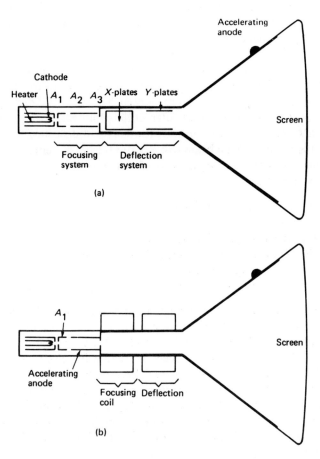

Figure 3.9 Cathode-ray tube construction: (a) with electrostatic focusing and deflection; (b) with magnetic focusing and deflection.

plates may be parallel or inclined to give more sensitive deflection. For parallel plates, the deflection sensitivity is given by

$$\frac{\Delta X}{V} = \frac{LD}{2V_a d} \text{ cm/V,}$$

where ΔX is the deflection on the screen
  V is the voltage across the plates to obtain ΔX
  L is the length of the plates
  D is the distance from the plates to the screen (measured from the centre of the plates)
  V_a is the accelerating voltage (on A_3)
  d is the distance between the plates

Thus, the sensitivity is proportional to the distance of the plates from the screen. It is usually required, given a choice, that the X-deflection be more sensitive than the Y-deflection: This is obtained by having the X-plates placed further from the screen than the Y-plates.

Magnetic focusing and deflection are used in the CRT of Fig. 3.9(b). Magnetic fields are produced by coils around the outside of the neck of the CRT. Electrons are affected by magnetic fields but in a different manner from that experienced with electro-static fields. An electron beam experiences a force at right angles to a magnetic field and at right angles to the direction of motion of the beam. The action of the magnetic focusing field is to cause the electrons to spiral about the axis and also inwardly, focusing on the screen. The magnetic deflection system comprises two mutually perpendicular coils producing two approximately uniform fields, one for X-deflection and the other for Y-deflection. In the presence of uniform fields, the electron beam will move in the arc of a circle and on leaving the field will continue on a straight path, striking the screen in such a way that the deflection is given by

$$\Delta X \simeq lDH \sqrt{\left(\frac{e}{2mV_a}\right)}$$

where l is the width of the coil (and field)
  D is the distance from the centre of the field to the screen
  H is the field strength (in gauss)
  e/m is the electron charge/mass ratio.

A comparison often made between magnetic and electrostatic deflection is that in the former, the deflection is proportional to $1/\sqrt{V_a}$, whilst in the latter it is proportional to $1/V_a$. Thus, for a given accelerating voltage, greater deflections can be obtained with magnetic deflection than with electrostatic deflection (though for linear deflection in magnetic deflection, the coil winding needs to be properly distributed). Magnetic deflection is often employed in wide-angle tubes for televisions, alpha-numeric and graphic displays. However, it is slower than electrostatic deflection, the limit in the speed of operation being set by the rate of change of current in the magnetic deflection coil. This is given by

$$\frac{di}{dt} = \frac{V_c}{L}.$$

where V_c is the voltage supplied to the coil

L is the inductance of the coil.

An important criterion, especially in graphic displays (described in Chapter 7), is the size of a focused spot on the screen. Generally, magnetic focusing is superior to electrostatic focusing in this respect, and typically 0.25 mm can be achieved, which would allow a 36 cm square screen to be divided into a matrix of $2^{10} \times 2^{10}$ points separated by 0.4 mm (i.e. just resolvable).

Apart from a purely electrostatic focusing and deflection system as in Fig. 3.9(a), or a purely magnetic focusing and deflection system as in Fig. 3.9(b), electrostatic focusing with magnetic deflection is often used and, of course, magnetic focusing with electrostatic deflection is possible. In attempts to obtain the advantages of both techniques, it is possible to have both electrostatic and magnetic deflection in a combined system, and to have both electrostatic and magnetic focusing in a combined system.

Colour CRTs employ red, blue and green phosphors arranged in dots (or strips) on the inner surface of the screen, and three electron guns. The beam of each electron gun is directed to phosphor dots of one colour. A perforated metal mask, known as a *shadow mask*, is placed in front of the phosphors to ensure that each beam strikes the required colour as shown in Fig. 3.10. The diameter of each electron beam is actually several times greater than the pitch of the shadow mask holes so that a proportion of the beams pass through several holes simultaneously. In computer applications generally, the electron guns are arranged in line rather than in a triangular form because the in-line configuration more readily produces three beams which intersect at the plane of the shadow mask (i.e. the

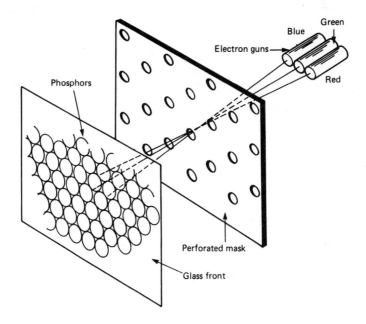

Figure 3.10 Shadow mask colour CRT

configuration with suitable focusing/deflection coils tends to be self-convergent). Colour CRTs are most often used in graphic displays (see Chapter 7) but they can find application in alpha-numeric displays. For example, text could be high-lighted in different colours by using a colour CRT.

The resolution of colour CRTs as used in domestic televisions is quite low, allowing only up to about 256 points across the screen. Such low-resolution CRTs are not really suitable to display 80-column text as they tend to lead to eyestrain. Higher-resolution CRTs with up to 600 points across the screen can be produced which are more suitable as computer displays.

(b) *Use of a CRT as an alpha-numeric display*
Alpha-numeric CRT displays usually employ the raster-scan technique, as used in televisions. The image is composed of a number of lines, and each line a number of dots. The dot matrix character representation is universally used, originally 5 × 7 dot-matrix, but greater sizes are now normally used. A 7×9 dot matrix requires nine 'raster' lines for a complete line of text (see Fig. 3.11), and seven dot positions for each character position. An additional dot position is reserved for the space between the characters. There will be one or two blank raster lines between each line of text.

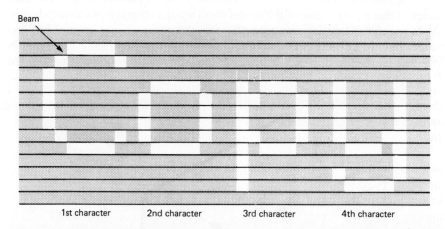

Figure 3.11 Raster-scan technique

As the CRT beam moves along the first raster line, the top row of the 7×9 dot matrix for each character on the line of text is successively produced. As the beam moves across the second raster line, the second row of the matrix of the same characters is successively produced. This is repeated for the other rows. Then the next line of text is subjected to the same procedure.

The seven-bit code of each character displayed on the screen is held in a read–write *character* store. With 24 lines of 80 characters, the character store has $7 \times 24 \times 80$ bits (13440 bits) organized as 24×80 words (seven-bit words). The seven-bit word output addresses a character pattern ROM (Fig. 3.12).

To display the text, the first character is read out of the character store and the first row selected to give the first seven dots on the first raster line. The next

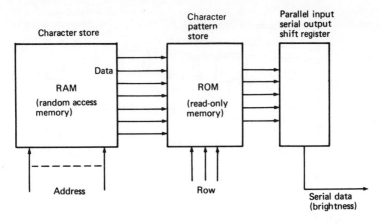

Figure 3.12 Raster-scan character pattern generator.

character is accessed to give the first seven dots of the second character. This is repeated for all 80 characters on the first line. The row counter is incremented and the process repeated with the same characters for all the rows.

The above is repeated for each of the 24 lines, and the total cycle repeated typically 50 times a second to refresh the screen.

The display may be a TV monitor type which requires a video signal. In this case, the ROM output is coupled with other circuitry to produce the video signal. With a standard TV raster scan, one raster line takes 60 μs and with 80 characters on the line, the time allowed between generating one character row and the next character row is 600 ns. This is a major design consideration and demands 600 ns as the maximum access time of both the read–write character store and the character pattern ROM.

Early (late 1960s) alpha-numeric CRT display systems used MOS (metal-oxide–silicon) shift registers for the character store, arranged as a re-circulating store with the output of the shift registers fed back to the input. Sometimes there was a fast re-circulating line consisting of 80 seven-bit words (for 80 characters on the line and 128 different characters), and a slower recirculating page store which updates the line store after each line of text has been fully displayed.

Present display systems employ semiconductor random-access memory and incorporate microprocessors.

3.3.3 Plasma panels

Large plasma discharge text displays or plasma panels, capable of displaying 512×512 dots, have been produced. As with small plasma displays a neon mixture gas is enclosed between two glass plates, but in this large variety the plates measure 21 cm square. Onto the plates, gold electrodes are deposited. A dielectric glass layer covers the electrodes. There are 512 X-electrodes vertically formed on one plate, and 512 Y-electrodes horizontally formed on the other plate. This is shown in Fig. 3.13. If a voltage is applied to specific X- and

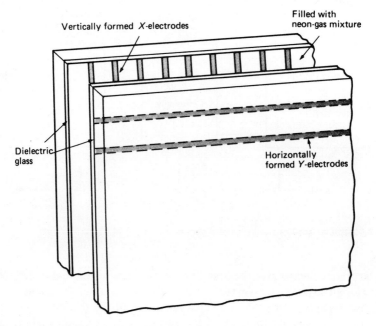

Figure 3.13 Plasma panel.

Y-electrodes, such that the summation of the voltages is greater than the ionization potential, then at the intersection of the electrodes, the gas between the electrodes will ionize and a plasma glow produced. The voltages may be reduced below the ionization potential and the glow will continue. Thus the display can be maintained by applying a continuous a.c. sustaining voltage to the electrodes (of about 100 V), and updated by pulsing selected $X-Y$ locations. The glow can be erased by reducing the potential below the sustaining potential. This is done by applying anti-phase a.c. voltages to electrodes.

3.3.4   Large panel LCD displays

Large panel LCD displays are manufactured to compete with CRTs, especially in the portable computer market. A large panel LCD for a portable computer commonly displays 25 lines of 80 characters each, requiring a matrix of 640×200 dots (using an 8×8 matrix overall for each character). The displayed 'dots' on a display are called picture elements, which is abbreviated to *pixels*. Pixels in the LCD are selected by *X*- and *Y*-address lines formed in the vertical and horizontal directions respectively as in the plasma panel. Each pixel is switched from light to dark in sequence for a short period and the process repeated after all pixels have been switched.

Unfortunately as the size of the display increases, less time can be made available to switch the LCD pixels and with large displays the LCD may not have time to switch fully, reducing the contrast. The LCD screen can be divided into two halves and each half driven simultaneously to improve the contrast ratio.

However, the effect can be eliminated by incorporating a transistor and storage capacitor at each pixel site to hold the pixel in the dark condition after been pulsed by the select lines. The transistors can be constructed with thin-film techniques using, for example, amorphous silicon. However, a very large number of transistor circuits is required. A 640×200 pixel array would require $128\,000$ transistors, most of which must work correctly to obtain an acceptable display.

Colour LCD displays (i.e. displays with various colours at each pixel site) can also be manufactured. Colour LCDs can be used in small colour televisions and here the full television pixel resolution need not be implemented. Colour is created from the LCD by the use of very small red, blue or green filters, placed at the pixel sites. Each pixel can be placed in the dark condition by switching on a thin-film transistor integrated within the pixel site. If a red colour is required, blue and green pixels are set dark so that only red is seen. In a similar fashion blue or green can be obtained. Various other colours can be obtained by partially allowing selected primary colours. Black is obtained by switching on all the transistors.

3.3.5   Electroluminescent displays

Electroluminescence is the name given to the phenomenon that a phosphor layer will emit light if subjected to a high electric field. Electroluminescence has been known for over fifty years. It is thought that a high electric field causes electrons in the phosphor-insulating layer junction to accelerate in the phosphor. Some of the electrons strike the manganese exciting them to emit yellow light.

Electroluminescence can be achieved with d.c. or a.c. voltages. The construction of an a.c. electroluminescent display consists of a sandwich of materials on a glass substrate. A transparent electrode is mounted on the glass surface. On top of the transparent electrode is an insulating layer, a thin layer of manganese-doped zinc sulphide (ZnS:Mn) phosphor, an insulating layer and finally a second electrode. An a.c. voltage is applied across the electrodes. Typically a voltage of about 150 V is necessary to cause light to be emitted. The voltage necessary to sustain emission is less than the voltage to initiate the emission as in plasma displays.

3.4   Keyboards

3.4.1   General

The keyboard, as a means of entering information into a computer, is very widely used. Pressing a key on the keyboard generates an n-bit code that represents the character associated with the key. For *ASCII* representation, the code is seven bits. This code is transmitted to the computer. Figure 3.14 shows the layout of a typical alpha-numeric keyboard. The numerical and alphabetical symbols are found in the same position as on a typewriter. In addition, there are 'control' codes that can be sent to the computer by the depression of the control key (CTRL), together with another key(s). For example, pressing the CTRL key and

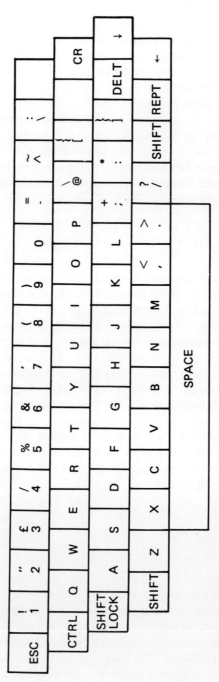

Figure 3.14 Alpha-numeric keyboard.

at the same time pressing the U key causes the code 0010101 to be transmitted (assuming ASCII representation). This might be assigned the meaning: 'disregard the current line being typed in'. (It does mean this on the Open University DEC SYSTEM-20 system.) Table 3.1 shows the relationship between the key(s) pressed and the codes produced for ASCII representation. Keyboards are used in conjunction with an output device, principally the CRT display, though historically with a printer. In the case of the CRT display, the complete unit is known as a visual display unit (VDU), and in the case of a composite

Mnemonic	ASCII code	Hexadecimal equivalent	Keys to depress
NUL	0000000	00	control, shift and P
SOH	0000001	01	control and A
STX	0000010	02	control and B
ETX	0000011	03	control and C
EOT	0000100	04	control and D
ENQ	0000101	05	control and E
ACK	0000110	06	control and F
BEL	0000111	07	control and G
BS	0001000	08	control and H
HT	0001001	09	control and I
LF	0001010	0A	control and J
VT	0001011	0B	control and K
FF	0001100	0C	control and L
CR	0001101	0D	control and M
SO	0001110	0E	control and N
SI	0001111	0F	control and O
DLE	0010000	10	control and P
DCI	0010001	11	control and Q
DC2	0010010	12	control and R
DC3	0010011	13	control and S
DC4	0010100	14	control and T
NAK	0010101	15	control and U
SYN	0010110	16	control and V
ETB	0010111	17	control and W
CAN	0011000	18	control and X
EM	0011001	19	control and Y
SUB	0011010	1A	control and Z
ESC	0011011	1B	control, shift and K
FS	0011100	1C	control, shift and L
GS	0011101	1D	control, shift and M
RS	0011110	1E	control, shift and N
US	0011111	1F	control, shift and O

Table 3.1 Keyboard control codes (ASCII)

keyboard-printer, the most popular unit is known as a Teletype, both of which will be discussed later. These peripheral devices are known as alpha-numeric terminals.

The desirable qualities of a keyboard are reliability, quietness and light operating pressure. Here we shall be discussing modern electronic keyboards, and Sections 3.4.2–7 deal with various types of switches that are used in keyboards.

3.4.2   Contact switches

Though effort has been taken to obtain better methods, contact switches as shown in Fig. 3.15 are widely used. Pressing the plunger causes the contacts to touch (or maybe separate) and thus one of two voltages can be produced, representing a '0' or a '1'. The contacts in some cases may 'bounce' between touching and not touching each other after depression of the plunger, for a short period (a few milli-seconds), and this will produce a series of '1's and '0's. Circuitry may be necessary to eliminate this effect. The contact resistance is typically 0.1 ohm and this will gradually increase over the operating life.

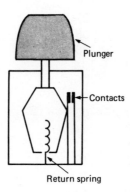

Figure 3.15 Key switch—contact type.

The *membrane switch* is a recent form of contact switch. This switch generally contains three layers of a material such as polyester or polycarbonate film which are separated by spacers, the whole assembly being 1 mm thick or less. The bottom layer is fixed, the inner layer flexible, and the top layer, also flexible, contains legends. The switch contacts are formed on the inner surfaces of two lower layers by screen printing a conductive polymer. Pressing the top layer causes the inner layer to press against the bottom layer, forming an electrical contact. When the top layer is released, the contact is broken. Membrane switches are inexpensive, thin, inherently sealed, and can be waterproof. The legends can be illuminated from the back, and some designs can include tactle feedback with an appropriately shaped dome as the top layer. The switches are often used for user switches on peripherals such as printers, and complete keyboards can be manufactured.

3.4.3 Hall-effect switches

Of the non-contacting switches, Hall-effect switches are popular. The Hall effect is the generation of a voltage across a slab of semiconductor when current is flowing through the semiconductor and there is a magnetic field which is at 90° to the current flow. The generated voltage is at 90° to both the magnetic field and the current flow (Fig. 3.16). The plunger of the switch brings a small permanent magnet close to a small slab of semiconductor. The Hall voltage is detected and amplified to represent a '1'.

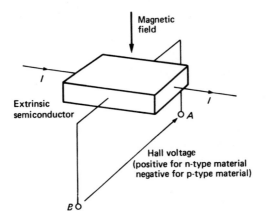

Figure 3.16 Hall-effect.

3.4.4 Capacitive switches

A capacitive switch is shown in Fig. 3.17. Two plates are mounted on the base of the switch. The plunger holds a third plate which is brought close to the two fixed plates when the plunger is depressed. An a.c. signal is applied to one fixed plate and sensed on the other fixed plate when the plunger is depressed. As there is no

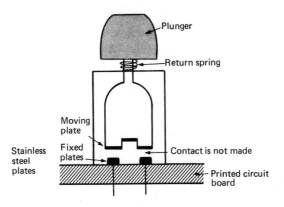

Figure 3.17 Capacitive switch.

physical connection between the plunger and the fixed plates, there is no contact wear. They are adversely affected by foreign particles lodged between the moving and fixed plates, so the whole assembly needs to be encapsulated.

3.4.5   Magnetic-reed switches

A magnetic reed switch has a pair of contacts enclosed in a glass envelope. The contacts can be made to open and close by the influence of an external magnetic field. This magnetic field can be produced by a permanent magnet attached to the plunger of the switch, in the same way as in the Hall-effect keyboards. The contacts can bounce in the same way as some contact switches. Because the contacts are enclosed, they have a longer life.

3.4.6   Ferrite core switch

An annular ferrite core is used here, mounted on the base of the switch, with two wires, a drive wire and a sense wire, passing through the centre of the core. A current pulse is applied to the drive wire and due to transformer coupling, a signal is obtained on the sense wire. In the influence of an external magnetic field the core magnetically saturates, causing no coupling between the drive and sense wires.

A magnetic field is obtained by a pair of permanent magnets attached to the plunger and arranged so as to clear the core only when the plunger is depressed, thus bringing the core out of saturation and signal is then obtained on the sense wire.

This type of switch is non-contacting, with zero bounce and long life.

3.4.7   Mercury-contact switches

This switch contains a flexible tube with mercury inside and with one pin at two edges of the tube. When the plunger is depressed, the flexible tube is compressed and causes the mercury to make electrical contact with the two pins. These pins are brought out as terminals. Mercury-contact switches tend to have lower contact bounce than normal contact switches (about 2 ms rather than 4 ms) whilst retaining about the same operating life. Contact resistance is in the order of 1 ohm.

3.4.8   Keyboard encoder

A keyboard encoder is attached to the keyboard switches to produce the key codes. A keyboard and simplified encoder is shown in Fig. 3.18. The encoder (enclosed in dotted lines) is available in integrated-circuit form. The keys are wired electrically as a matrix, often with 9 rows and 10 columns. The encoder has the task of detecting when a key has been depressed, identifying it and generating the corresponding key code as an output.

A row is activated or enabled by placing a voltage on it, and a column sensed for a voltage. If the switch at the intersection of the row and column has been

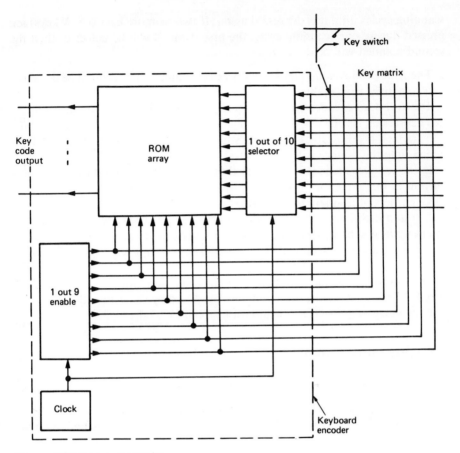

Figure 3.18 Keyboard encoder.

depressed, this will be sensed as the row voltage is transmitted to the column input. The row and column select signals are used to address a ROM (read only memory), which holds the code for each key. The process is repeated for each row and column combination in order to determine whether a key has been pressed, and the complete cycle repeated continuously. A scanning cycle typically takes 900 μs (10 μs clock period × 90 keys).

There are two basic modes of operation to cater for these instances when more than one key is depressed:

(*i*) *N-key Lockout* In this mode, the first key depressed is detected and any others depressed before the first is released are ignored (locked out). If two or more keys are pressed during one scanning cycle, the first scanned will be detected, and all the others ignored until the first is released. Each key ignored needs to be pressed again to produce its character code.

(*ii*) *N-key Rollover* In this mode keys pressed one after the other will be detected in the correct sequence as long as each depression occurs in a different scanning cycle. Once a key depression has been detected it will be ignored in subsequent scanning cycles until it is depressed again. If two or more keys (i.e. *N* keys) are pressed during one scanning cycle, the first scanned will be detected, then the second scanned will be detected and so on.

The *N*-key rollover enables *N* keys pressed in quick succession to be detected. 2-key rollover is available.

The keyboard encoder usually has the ability to eliminate key bounce. Once a key depression is detected, the scanning cycle is stopped for a period of typically 4 ms (which is adjustable). The key is ignored until the end of this period, by which time the bounce will have ceased.

In the rollover mode it is necessary that the switches are unidirectional (pass current in one direction) because if, for example, three keys are depressed on three corners of a square in the matrix, there will be conductivity at the fourth corner and it will appear as though a fourth key has been depressed when the intersection is sensed. One diode can be inserted in series with each switch in order to make it unidirectional. To isolate 90 keys completely, eighty diodes are necessary.

The output of the keyboard encoder provides standard key codes (such as ASCII). Special key codes are sometimes produced by using an additional read-only memory addressed by a standard keyboard encoder.

3.5   Visual display unit

3.5.1   General

A visual display unit (VDU) (Fig. 3.19) consists of a text display and an alpha-numeric keyboard, which together provide the principal man-machine commun-

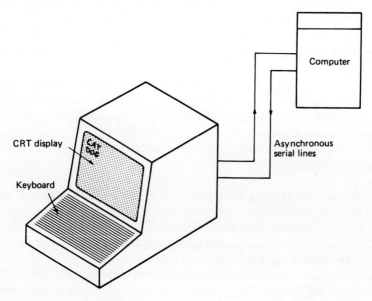

Figure 3.19 Visual display unit.

ication peripheral. The display is almost always a CRT type, though plasma-panel systems are available.

Historically, the VDU was designed to replace the extremely successful printing terminal, the Teletype (a printer with a linked mechanical keyboard). Today the VDU is regarded as the basic terminal device where a permanent record is not required. Specific printing is often performed with a systems printer. The original Teletype has been superseded by an improved printing terminal, composed of a fast printer such as a needle printer (see next chapter), with an electrical keyboard. The printing terminal would be employed in less common situations where 'hard copy' of the input information is required.

The modern VDU can be a simple 'teletype alternative' terminal providing the minimum requirements for man-machine communication, or the full potential of the display and keyboard can be exploited by adding many extra facilities.

The CRT tube used is always a magnetically deflected, wide-bandwidth type typically 12, 14 or 15 in (30.5, 35.6, 38.1 cm) in size (diagonal measurement). The phosphor is usually P4 (white) or less commonly P31 (green). A filter is often used in front of the screen to provide an anti-glare high-contrast image.

Often 24 lines of text can be displayed with 80 characters of the dot matrix font on each line. The character size is typically 2 mm × 5 mm.

A 7 × 9 matrix is often used and produces acceptable upper-case and lower-case alpha-numeric characters. Larger matrices can be used to give extra definition.

Figure 3.20 shows the basic internal architecture of a typical microprocessor-based VDU. The microprocessor, program memory, data memory, character display memory, character pattern memory, display controller and keyboard encoder/interface logic interconnect through a bus (see Chapter 2). The character display memory holds the codes (normally ASCII codes) representing the characters displayed. This memory needs to be accessed by the microprocessor to load new characters into the memory, and also accessed continually by the display controller. The display controller reads the stored characters in sequence and generates the appropriate signals for the CRT display to maintain a flicker-free image.

In the following, the display area on the screen is called a page (of text). The actions described are 'typical' but may vary from VDU to VDU. It can be expected that VDUs will become more sophisticated as hardware becomes cheaper. Generally most actions that can be initiated by the keyboard can also be initiated by sending the equivalent (ASCII) code to the VDU. A few keyboard-initiated operations do not affect the display; for example, the ESCAPE key causes the equivalent (ASCII) code to be transmitted from the VDU but generally has no internal action. The BREAK key causes the communications line to go to a 0 for a specified period.

The original Teletype had a 'bell' which rang when the end of the line was being approached (as on a typewriter). The equivalent also exists on many modern VDUs. An electronic 'beep' sounds for a short period when, say, the 70th character on a line is reached. The BELL code when transmitted to the VDU also causes the same sound. Table 3.2 (page   ) gives typical responses to control-key operations or control codes received from the computer.

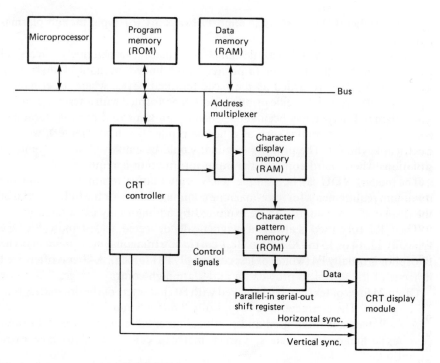

Figure 3.20 Microprocessor-based VDU block diagram.

3.5.2 The cursor

The cursor is a symbol whose position on the screen denotes where the next character input (either via pressing keys or via the interface) is to be displayed. Symbols used include:

1. ▲ appearing below the position to be marked;
2. an underline (one character in length);
3. a reducing underline that extends from the current cursor position to the edge of the screen (the line reduces as it gets closer to the edge):
4. ≡ .

When the cursor (of type (1) and (4)) is over an existing character, it is made to flash on and off 10 or 15 times a second.

As text is being entered, the cursor automatically advances across the screen. On reaching the end of the line, or when carriage-return–line-feed characters or a return character have been received, the cursor positions itself at the start of the next line. On reaching the bottom line, there are two possibilities for advancement which are selectable:

(*i*) *Page mode* In the page mode, after the bottom line is complete, the cursor moves to the first position of the top line.
(*ii*) *Roll mode* In the roll mode, after the bottom line is complete, the whole page of text is moved up one line, with the top line vanishing, and the bottom line

ASCII Code sent to VDU	Keyboard	VDU-Response
0 0 0 0 0 0 0		
0 0 0 0 0 0 1	Clear	Clears screen of unprotected characters and 'homes' cursor
0 0 0 0 0 1 0		
0 0 0 0 0 1 1		
0 0 0 0 1 0 0		
0 0 0 0 1 0 1	Send	'Homes' cursor and transmits message block
0 0 0 0 1 1 0		
0 0 0 0 1 1 1		
0 0 0 1 0 0 0	←	Moves cursor left one character position
0 0 0 1 0 0 1	→	Moves cursor right one character position
0 0 0 1 0 1 0	Line feed	Moves cursor down one character position
0 0 0 1 0 1 1	↓	
0 0 0 1 1 0 0	Home	Moves cursor to top left-hand character position
0 0 0 1 1 0 1	Carriage return	Moves cursor to left-hand end of next line
0 0 0 1 1 1 0	↑	Moves cursor up one line
0 0 0 1 1 1 1	Local	Data written onto screen from keyboard only
0 0 1 0 0 0 0		
0 0 1 0 0 0 1		
0 0 1 0 0 1 0		
0 0 1 0 0 1 1		
0 0 1 0 1 0 0	Page	When cursor moves downwards from bottom line, it re-appears on
0 0 1 0 1 0 1		first line.
0 0 1 0 1 1 0	Roll	When cursor moves downwards from bottom line, it re-appears on
0 0 1 0 1 1 1		first position on bottom line, and text moves
0 0 1 1 0 0 0		upwards one line
0 0 1 1 0 0 1		
0 0 1 1 0 1 0		
0 0 1 1 0 1 1		
0 0 1 1 1 0 0		
0 0 1 1 1 0 1		
0 0 1 1 1 1 0		
0 0 1 1 1 1 1		

Table 3.2 Typical VDU responses to control codes.

becoming empty. The cursor positions itself at the beginning of the bottom line.

After one page of text has been entered in the page mode, further text will overwrite that existing from the top line downwards. In the roll mode, at any instant, the last page of text entered will be displayed.

The cursor can be moved one position in any direction by the use of the cursor controls:

↑ which moves the cursor up one line;
↓ which moves the cursor down one line;
← which moves the cursor left one character position;
→ which moves the cursor right one character position.

The ability to move the cursor directly to a specific location on the screen is an advanced feature known as an *addressable cursor*. After the code indicating *addressable-cursor movement* is received, the next two items of data are interpreted as the x- and y-co-ordinates of the location the screen to which the cursor is to be moved. The cursor moves to the desired position after receipt of the three items. With 24 lines and 80 characters on a line, the x-co-ordinate has a value between 1 and 80 and the y-co-ordinate has a value between 1 and 24. The current cursor position can sometimes be transmitted from the VDU, either initiated by operating a key or by a specific control code transmitted to the VDU.

The *home* position on the screen is the first position on the first line. The cursor can be moved from its current position to the home position by the 'home' control. The screen can be cleared of characters and the cursor returned to the home position by the use of the 'clear' control (but see protected fields below .

3.5.3   Data transmission

If the VDU is connected to the computer locally (that is within a 100 m or so) it is usually connected via two asynchronous serial lines, one line to transmit data to the VDU and one line to receive data from the VDU. There is also an earth line. The signals may be voltages according to CCITT V24 or a 20/60 mA current loop. Both are usually provided by the VDU. The data rate is often switchable (between 75 and 9600 bits/s or exceptionally 50 and 19.6K bits/s). Parity (odd, even or none) and half/full duplex are often also switchable. The character code is usually 7-bit ASCII.

Data can be transmitted from the VDU one character at a time as it is typed in. Specific characters can be transmitted by positioning the cursor over the character and using the character-transmit key. The cursor moves one position right after such an operation and specific words can be transmitted by repeated use of the character transmit key.

All the characters from the current cursor position to the end of the line can be transmitted at a high rate by the single depression of the 'transmit line' key. The cursor re-positions itself at the start of the next line. The complete line of text is transmitted if the cursor was originally at the beginning of a line.

All the characters from the current cursor position to the end of the page (to the last position of the last line) can be transmitted by the single depression of the transmit-page key. The cursor re-positions itself in the 'home' position. A complete page of text can be transmitted if the cursor was originally at the home position.

Occasionally the transmit line operates from the beginning of the line to the cursor position, and the transmit page operates from the beginning of the page to the current cursor position.

If the VDU is in the local mode, then data are written from the keyboard to the display, but not transmitted from the VDU proper. No data can be received by the VDU.

If the VDU is in the on-line mode all data are transmitted and all data received is displayed.

Sometimes there is a printer interface on a VDU which enables a printer to be attached and the displayed data to be printed (from the top of the page to the current cursor position).

3.5.4 Editing

The ability to edit text prior to transmission is one of the most powerful facilities of a VDU. A line or page of text can be prepared and corrected by using the insert/delete-character and insert/delete-line keys (when available) in conjunction with the cursor-positioning keys, whilst in the edit mode. The insert-character key, when depressed, causes the character displayed at the current cursor position and all characters to the right on the same line, to move one position to the right, leaving a space where the cursor is. For example, if

THIS IS MY ESSAGE

has been typed (and is displayed), the insertion of M in 'ESSAGE' can be performed by backspacing the cursor to be under the E:

THIS IS MY E̲SSAGE

and the insert key pressed:

THIS IS MY E̲SSAGE

followed by the M key:

THIS IS MY ME̲SSAGE

The delete-character key, when depressed, causes the character above the cursor to disappear and all the characters to the right of it to move one position left. For example, 'IS MY' could be deleted as follows, the cursor is positioned as:

THIS I̲S MY MESSAGE

and the delete character key pressed five times to get:

THIS _̲MESSAGE

The insert-line key, when depressed, causes the line on which the cursor lies, together with all lines above it, to move one line position upwards, leaving the cursor on a blank line, and the original top line is lost. The delete-line operation is the reverse; all lines above the cursor are moved downwards one line position and the original line of text on which the cursor lies is lost.

3.5.5 Other features

(a) *Protected fields*

With the protected-field facility, specific characters can be made not alterable and not erasable. The cursor will not stay over a protected character and will quickly move to the right when an attempt is made to place it over a protected character. This facility allows text to be sent to the VDU which cannot be deleted by the user whilst the protect facility is activated. This may find application when formatted data are being displayed, an example of which is shown in Fig. 3.21. Here NAME, ADDRESS and spaces shown by a hyphen are sent from the computer. The other spaces are left for the user to enter data.

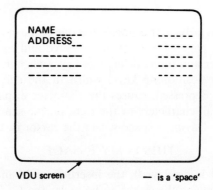

Figure 3.21 Protected characters.

Generally, each character displayed has an extra 'protect' bit associated with it, and the character store has extra storage for these protect bits (i.e. instead of, say, 1920×7 bits, 1920×8 bits). From the keyboard, the protect bit is set by using the set-protect key. Those characters with their protect bits set can be protected by activating the protect facility. This can be done by pressing the protect-on key. The protect facility can be de-activated by pressing the protect-off key, and re-activated at will. Similarly, these actions can be performed by sending the appropriate codes to the VDU.

(b) *Blinking fields*
With the *blink* facility, specific characters can be made to flash on and off typically two times a second. As with protected characters, there needs to be an extra bit associated with each character. This bit, the *blink bit*, is set to a '1' if the character is to blink; otherwise it is set to a '0'. A blink-on key will cause subsequent characters entered to have their blink bit set, and the blink-off key will cause subsequent characters to have their blink bit reset. Similarly, blink-on/blink-off codes can be sent to the VDU. The blink facility is one method of causing certain characters to be conspicuous.

(c) *Inverted characters*
An inverted character is a black character on a white background as opposed to a white character on a black background (green instead of white if a green phosphor is used), as shown in Fig. 3.22. The term 'inverse video' is employed in context with inverted characters. To obtain inverted characters, the video signal is inverted, that is, the 'on' level becomes the 'off' level and vice versa. The brightness level is usually set at around 50% for inverted characters to obtain an even overall appearance.

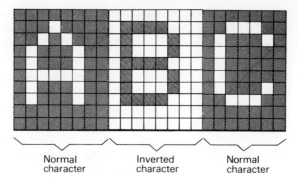

Figure 3.22 Normal and inverse video characters.

Again an additional bit needs to be associated with each character for this facility, set with an 'invert-on' key and reset with an 'invert-off' key, operating on characters entered subsequent to pressing the key.

Blink and inverted characters may be capable of being overwritten with non-blink/non-inverted characters (depending on the VDU).

(d) *Tabulation*

On an ordinary typewriter, the tabulation key enables the carriage (or print head) to move directly to chosen set points in order that columns of figures or words can be typed quickly. The set points are selected by the use of a tab-set key, and the mechanism reset with a tab-clear key.

Tabulation can be brought over to VDUs though this is not widely found. Generally, tabulation is coupled with the protected fields ((a) above). In this case, the tabulation key causes the cursor to move directly to the nearest unprotected field on the current line.

(e) *Normal/low intensity*

Sometimes characters can be displayed at less than full brightness. For this an additional bit is associated with each character to specify normal or low intensity. There is little demand for various levels of brightness. Dual level (normal/low) allows certain words and letters to stand out.

(f) *Foreign-language characters*

The character set depends on the character pattern ROM. It is a simple matter to alter this. Most languages can be accommodated including Arabic.

(g) *Word generation*

In this facility, commonly used words may be generated by pressing a single key.

3.6   Using a microcomputer as a terminal

A microcomputer can be used as a terminal; indeed the cost of a small microcomputer with keyboard and display may be similar to a terminal and the flexibility to use a microcomputer to stand alone or act as a terminal to another system may be useful. The hardware design of a small microcomputer is very similar to that of a dedicated microprocessor-based VDU. There are a number of *de facto* standard terminals and the microcomputer may need to emulate the terminal in some applications. However, in many applications, all that is often necessary for the conversion is to provide suitable software to transmit keyboard data from the unit, including control codes, and to display received data. In fact, the basic keyboard and display operations probably already exist within the existing microcomputer software. Editing functions contained within a VDU are not used very much in practice. Most editing functions are provided by the host computer using keyboard control codes.

4

Printers

4.1 Introduction

A printer produces characters on paper.

One situation in which printed output (known as hard copy) is required when the output is produced at a distance from the user and maybe at an undefined or inconvenient time as in an off-line batch-processing system. Such systems require high-speed printing in large quantities and typically employ a 'line' printer (that is a printer that prints a line at a time).

A printing device is also essential in a commercial system, for example, producing payrolls. In this case the printing may be performed on perforated pre-printed stationery and generally a line printer is again employed.

The smaller scientific systems employing mini computers often operate in an interactive on-line mode with VDU terminals. Printing in this case is required for final results and this maybe achieved again by a 'systems' printer as in the batch-operated systems.

In this chapter the mechanisms for printing will be described. These can be divided into two basic types, impact printing and non-impact printing. In the former case a print head strikes carbon ribbon placed in front of a roll of paper and characters are formed on the paper. Various print-head designs exist and these are described, and there are various features which are described separately. Any particular printer may use one of the print heads described with some or all the features described.

The printing terminal is composed of one of the printers to be described together with a keyboard. In the USA the printing terminal was in the past also known as a teletypewriter, and in the UK a teleprinter. The first printing terminal to gain widespread use was given the product name Teletype (a contraction of teletypewriter). This employs a *cylinder* head and a mechanically linked keyboard. The cylinder head has not generally been employed for other than in a Teletype. Another early teletypewriter employed a standard typewriter mechanism with a *golf-ball* print head. Again the golf-ball print head has not found wide use as a separate print mechanism. The Teletype is outlined in Section 4.6.1 for historical interest.

Printing terminals have generally been replaced by display terminals (an alpha-numeric display with a coupled keyboard) for man-machine communication. Hard copy, when required, is produced by a separate printer.

4.2   Impact serial printing

4.2.1   General features

Impact printing is achieved by the action of a print head striking an inked ribbon which is located between the print head and the paper. This action causes characters to be printed on the paper in ink. Impact printing can be divided into serial impact printing and line impact printing. In the former, each character is formed in one or more actions, one character at a time sequentially across the paper. In line printing (to be dealt with later) a complete line is printed in one or more actions, with part or complete characters printed simultaneously across the page. Naturally serial printing is slower than line printing. Serial printing is usually in the range 10–500 characters/s whilst line printing is usually specified in lines/min, typically in the range 300–2000 lines/min. Typically 10 characters are printed in 1 in (2.5 cm) length with 74 to 132 characters on a line depending upon the width of the paper (20–35 cm). There are often 6 lines per inch vertically.

Printing may be character by character as the character codes are received by the printing device or after a complete line has been received. In the latter case a line buffer is necessary to hold all the characters to be printed. The final character on the line is indicated by either the carriage-return, line-feed or new-line characters, or when the full number of characters for a line, say 80, has been received. Generally, when the full number has been received, subsequent characters are printed on the next line, thus ensuring no data are lost. Bidirectional printing will be described later, this being a recent technique to obtain higher speed of operation.

(a) *The ribbon*
Generally a new portion of the ribbon is presented to the head on each occasion the head strikes the ribbon. The ribbon (standard $\frac{1}{2}$ in (1.27 cm) wide typewriter ribbon) is usually of the nylon fabric type; carbon ribbons cannot be used with certain heads (e.g. needle heads). Figure 4.1 shows two ribbon configurations. In Fig. 4.1(a) the ribbon is carried in reels held to the head for each print action in a similar way as on an ordinary typewriter. Some ribbons are contained in cartridges and are continually re-lined. In Fig. 4.1(b) the head moves across the page and the spools are in fixed positions mounted in the body of the printer. The second approach is mechanically easier, because the mechanism holding the head does not have the extra load of the spools of ribbon, and consequently this approach is becoming increasingly popular. The direction of travel of the ribbons is automatically reversed once one spool has been rewound by sensing metal eyelets located at either end of the ribbon, or by other means. The reel of ribbon holds about 36 m of ribbon and this will have a life of greater than 4 million characters. A printer operating at 180 characters/s could achieve this in 8 h of continuous operation.

(b) *The paper*
The paper is either in rolls (around 13 cm diameter) or fan-folded (Fig. 4.2) around 20 cm to 35 cm wide. There are two principal means of feeding the paper

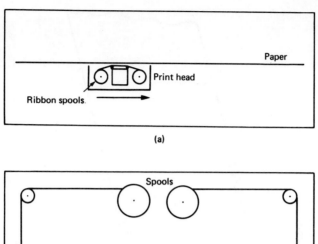

Figure 4.1 Ribbon configuration: (a) attached to print head; (b) fixed spools (both viewed from above).

past the heads, as shown in Fig. 4.3. In Fig. 4.3(a) the paper is driven past the head by means of friction rollers that grip the paper. In Fig. 4.3(b) it is necessary for the paper to have holes pierced along each edge which then locate into sprocket pins. The pins are mounted on the periphery of small wheels that rotate accurately, driving the paper past the head at constant speed.

The sprocket feed is necessary if multiple copies are required to hold the copies firm. Copies can be obtained using carbon paper or specially prepared paper backed with a copying film. Two or more separate sheets or 'forms' can be held side by side using split platens. Typically 2–5 copies can be produced with the impact printers to be described.

Within the paper feed mechanism, there is generally a 'paper-low' detection device which produces a signal for transmission from the printer when the paper is about to be exhausted.

(c) *Control operations*
Apart from printing characters initiated by character codes sent to the printer, several 'control' operations can be carried out. Fundamental ones are:

1. carriage return   brings the print head back to the left hand margin;
2. line feed   moves the paper up one line;

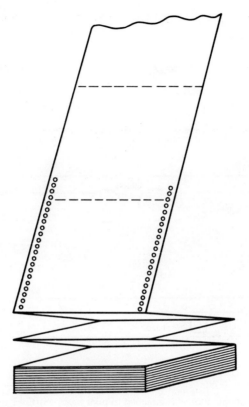

Figure 4.2 Fan-fold paper.

3.	space	moves the print head right one position without printing a character;
4.	backspace	moves the print head left one position without printing a character;
5.	form feed	mechanism to move the paper to the top of the next page.

(d) *Print heads*

Print heads are to be considered in some detail in the following section. They can be divided into two principal types, characterized by whether each character is formed by an inverted embossed character contained on the print head, giving a high-quality print, or by the printing of dot-matrix characters (see Fig. 3.1) providing adequate but poorer quality.

Without exception, the head moves rather than the carriage (as opposed to typewriters with print arms). The movement of the print head is typically by means of a toothed-belt drive and an optical system or electromagnetic system detects the current position of the head.

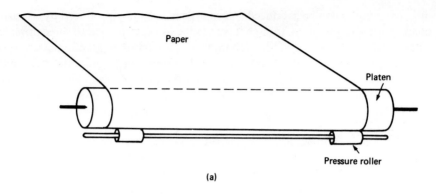

(a)

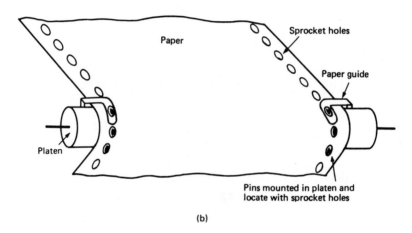

(b)

Figure 4.3 Paper-feed mechanisms: (a) friction feed; (b) sprocket feed.

(e) *Printer noise*

Printer noise has become a significant factor in printers, especially for office applications. Impact printers inherently produce noise by the printing mechanism. Some reduction in noise can be achieved by careful design of the print head, for example lighter needles in matrix printers. However, the main attempts to reduce noise concentrate upon using sound-absorbing materials. Sound-absorbing materials can be applied to the inside surface of the printer case, and the case can be sealed except for opening for the paper. The print mechanism can be mounted on a synthetic rubber. The whole printer can be placed in a soundproof enclosure.

(f) *Colour printing*

Colour printing can be achieved with impact printers by the use of ribbons with stripes of three primary colours, magenta, cyan and yellow. By superimposing pairs of colours with equal intensity gives red, green and dark blue, and seven different colours can be produced. Black type is normally produced by a fourth black stripe on the ribbon, though it is possible to superimpose all three primary colours to obtain black. This technique is also used in graph plotters (see Chapter 7). However, the colours on striped ribbons tend to migrate and it may be necessary to print the lightest colour first, to reduce ink migration. Note that in colour printing, light is absorbed and the primary colours are subtractive. In a colour CRT light is emitted and additive. Red, green and blue light is used in such systems.

Usually the ribbon has horizontal strips and one colour is printed first across a line. Then the whole print head is moved up to meet the next colour and this printed, and again for a third colour. However, the ribbon can consist of lengths of each colour and the ribbon wound onto the next colour after each pass of the print head.

The non-impact thermal transfer printers (see Section 4.4.2) also use a ribbon and colour printing can be achieved here with a multicoloured ribbon.

4.2.2 Daisy wheel head

The daisy wheel head is shown in Fig. 4.4 and consists of a number of spokes held on a spindle. The spokes are like petals on a daisy, hence the name of the

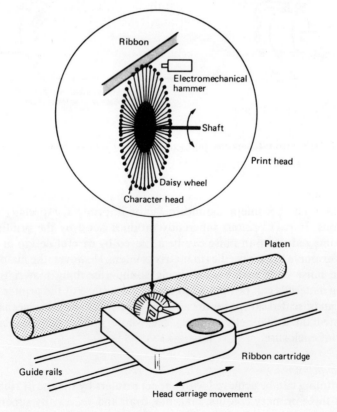

Figure 4.4 Daisy-wheel print head.

head. At the end of each spoke there is an embossed symbol. Usually 96 characters and hence 96 spokes are provided. In front of the daisy wheel is the ribbon and paper, and behind it is a narrow electromechanical hammer. The hammer consists of a solenoid with a shaft which is driven onto a spoke.

The impact of the hammer on the spoke causes the spoke to bend and strike the ribbon, thus causing a symbol to be printed on the paper. Different symbols are obtained by electrically rotating the wheel prior to the hammer action. The rotation of the wheel may be clockwise or anticlockwise (up to 180°). The direction is chosen to give the shortest distance to the next symbol to be printed (see also Section 4.2.4). The most commonly used symbols may be carried by spokes near each other to reduce the amount of rotation required.

The wheel is often made of plastic, but for better quality heavier metal wheels can be used. Metal wheels are used, for example, in word-processor applications. The daisy wheel can be removed and replaced as required.

Microprocessors permit very complex control which will be described later (Section 4.2.4). Specific actions are connected with this head and illustrate the possibilities with any head. The direction of rotation of the wheel mentioned above is one example of microprocessor control. With the wheel motor directly controlled by the processor the speed can be controlled and the velocity arranged to be a function of the distance to be travelled. The solenoid current of the hammer can also be controlled such that the energy impacted to the hammer is accurately controlled. Then it can be arranged that the energy imparted for large-outline characters such as the letter M is appropriately larger than that for smaller outline characters such as a full stop.

4.2.3   Dot-matrix printers

(a) *Needle print head*

The needle print head forms the basis of the 'needle' printer. Characters are formed from a matrix of dots, typically a 7×7 matrix or 9×7 matrix. A complete column of dots is formed by a number of 'hammers' comprising wires driven head-long onto the ribbon/paper by electromechanical solenoids. With 7 dots per column there are 7 solenoids; with 9 dots, 9 solenoids. Once one column has been printed, the head moves to the next column position and that column is printed. Thus with 7 columns, 7 movements are required. Once these movements have taken place, completing the printing of one character, the head moves to the next character position and the process is repeated until the complete line has been printed.

The solenoids need to be quite powerful and therefore bulky, so that they cannot be mounted without the need to bend the wires. Early needle heads had solenoids mounted in line, as shown in Fig. 4.5(a), but there is now a general preference for mounting them radially (Fig. 4.5(b)) or in two rows (Fig. 4.5(c)) so that the flexing of the wires is reduced and the reliability and life is increased. The wires are usually made from tungsten (about 10 cm long) and stand about 10^8 operations. The tips tend to wear over a period of time and become shorter, resulting in lighter, blurred printed characters.

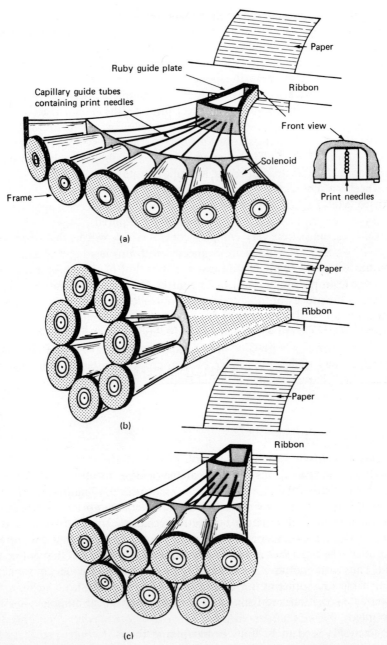

Figure 4.5 Needle print heads: (a) solenoids in line; (b) solenoids radial; (c) solenoids two in line.

The needle printer has become an industry standard for slow and medium-speed printing, providing reasonable clarity and great flexibility of the dot-matrix format. It is easy to alter the character set by altering a character pattern ROM (within the electronics of the printer). Double-height (or indeed any height) characters can be obtained by passing the head across the paper more than once. Two passes would give a 14 dot column (with 7 solenoids) so that a 14×14 sized character could be printed. The width of the character can similarly be altered, double width (7×14) being common. Figure 4.6 shows some possibilities. Graph plotting is also possible.

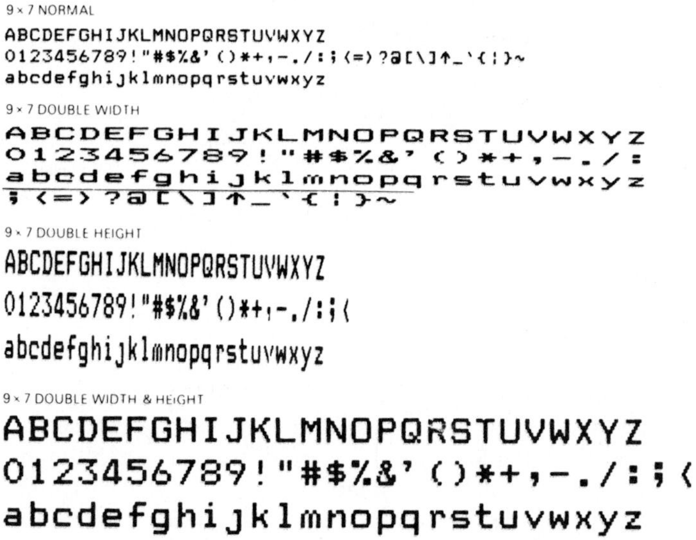

```
9 × 7 NORMAL
ABCDEFGHIJKLMNOPQRSTUVWXYZ
0123456789!"#$%&'()*+,-./:;(=)?@[\]↑_`{|}~
abcdefghijklmnopqrstuvwxyz
```

```
9 × 7 DOUBLE WIDTH
ABCDEFGHIJKLMNOPQRSTUVWXYZ
0123456789!"#$%&'()*+,-./:
;<=>?@[\]↑_`{|}~
abcdefghijklmnopqrstuvwxyz
```

9 × 7 DOUBLE HEIGHT
ABCDEFGHIJKLMNOPQRSTUVWXYZ
0123456789!"#$%&'()*+,-./:;(
abcdefghijklmnopqrstuvwxyz

9 × 7 DOUBLE WIDTH & HEIGHT
ABCDEFGHIJKLMNOPQRSTUVWXYZ
0123456789!"#$%&'()*+,-./:;(
abcdefghijklmnopqrstuvwxyz

Figure 4.6 Matrix printer characters.

(b) *Ballistic print head*

The necessity of flexible wires in the needle print head is a major disadvantage. The ballistic print head has been designed to avoid this problem. In the ballistic head (Fig. 4.7), rather than having the print wires attached to the solenoid core, the wires are separate and are propelled 'ballistically' onto the ribbon and paper by hammers. These hammers can be mounted close enough for the wires not to be bent. The guidance is simpler and the wire life longer. Additionally, it is claimed that the electromagnets that activate the hammers use only a small fraction of the power that solenoids require and hence there is less heat generated. This enables the print head to operate longer and faster (180 characters/s).

This head has the feature of inherently compensating for multiple copies. With several copies, the wire has less distance to travel before reaching the paper and its kinetic energy is greater. Thus the hammer action is stronger, providing the greater impact required for printing multiple copies. The design is such that no feed adjustment is required for between one and six sheets. This means that split forms with different numbers of copies can be printed.

(c) *Print quality*

The quality of the printed characters in a dot-matrix printer is dependent upon the number of dots provided in the matrix. In an attempt to obtain the print

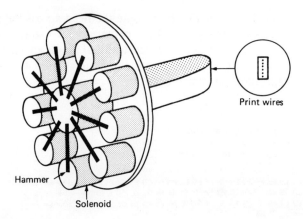

Figure 4.7 Ballistic print head.

quality of daisy wheel printers, more dots are printed in each character matrix. The term *letter quality* (LQ) is used to indicate printed characters of a quality to be suitable for business correspondence. Daisy wheel printers achieve letter-quality printing but at relatively slow speed (up to about 55 characters/s). Dot-matrix printers can achieve letter quality or *near letter quality* (NLQ) by the use of 18 or more dots in a row. Print heads can have 18 or 24 needles to print one row simultaneously. The matrix size for LQ/NLQ is typically 18×36, or greater. Matrices found include 18×36, 18×25, 18×50 using 18 needles. Such matrix printers can have two modes of operation, high-speed draft printing using a 7×9 matrix (say) printing at perhaps 200–500 characters/s, and a slower LQ/NLQ mode printing at say 100–200 characters/s.

A resolution of 240 dots/inch gives good characters, while to achieve text which compares well with typeset characters, 400 dots/inch is necessary. Printers with this resolution find application in in-house publishing. Higher resolution is necessary to give grey scale levels.

4.2.4   Microprocessor control

Most modern printers incorporate a microprocessor for control and to effect the communication from the transmitting device.

The printing speed can be improved by *optimized operation*, whereby the printing is maybe either left to right across the paper or right to left depending upon which gives the least movement of the head from one line to the next. This means that a complete line of text must be received prior to printing (as in the case of a line printer) so that when the present line has been printed, it can be determined whether the next line should be printed right to left or left to right. In the former case, the head moves to the end of the line to be printed. In the latter case, the head moves to the beginning of the next line (left-hand margin generally). This mechanism reduces the need for high-speed carriage return and increases throughput (see Fig. 4.8). Carriage return is generally a slow, noisy and

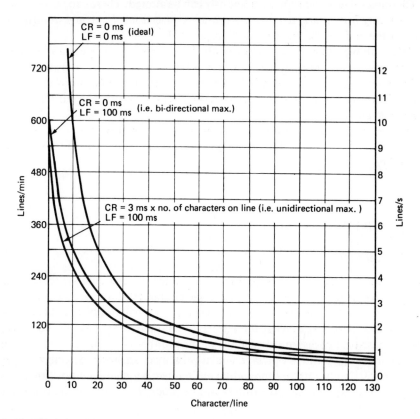

Figure 4.8 Performance of serial printing.

mechanically complex process taking in the order of 300 ms. To obtain increased speed, multiple spaces can be combined into one operation.

Printing and input of data can take place simultaneously if there is a data store.

Vertical formating is traditionally performed electromechanically. With the inclusion of a microprocessor, this too can be done by software and can be altered by the host computer. One method is to make a direct equivalent of the paper-tape loop of the electromechanical vertical format unit, with the codes on the tape held in a store that is read cyclically. Naturally more sophisticated methods are possible. The facilities typically provided are: user-defined page size, skip to specified line' orders and 'skip to a channel number' orders, where specific lines can be allocated one or more channel numbers.

Horizontal formating can be added. This includes tabulation, margins (form width), perforation skip-over, direct addressing of print-head position (both horizontal and vertical). In this latter context, the print-head movement can be controlled by a stepper motor (see Section 7.6.1) so that the head can be stepped across the page in small increments (typically 0.2 mm). This gives the possibility of graph plotting. Vertical movement is typically 0.6 mm.

Character size as mentioned previously can be altered. There can be a choice of line spacing and character pitch. Automatic insertion of carriage return – line feed at the end of the line can be incorporated.

All the above can be initiated by a control-data input sequence in a similar way as the set-up of additional features on a VDU.

Diagnostic test routines can be incorporated allowing continuous printing of the entire character set or any selected character, and there can be self-tests on the electronic circuitry.

In conclusion, microprocessor control enables extra features to be included with little extra cost, whilst reducing hardware complexity and improves reliability.

4.3   Impact line printing

4.3.1   General

A line printer prints a complete line of characters in one composite action as opposed to printing a line of characters one character at a time as with a serial printer described in Section 4.2. With a line printer it will not be possible to print a single character any quicker than a line of characters because this composite action must be completed irrespective of the number of characters on the line. Some impact line printers will have similar print mechanisms as described impact serial printers, only with one individual mechanism per character position across the page of paper. These line printers will be much quicker than the equivalent serial printers.

Generally line printers are faster than serial printers. Whereas the serial printers operate in the range 10–500 characters/s, which is regarded as the slow-to-medium speed, line printers operate in the range 200 characters/s to 2000 characters/s (medium-to-high speed). Because a complete line has to be printed in one operation, line printer speeds are specified in lines/min; hence the above range is around 10 lines/min to 1000 lines/min (132 characters per line).

4.3.2   Chain/belt printer

A chain printer is shown in Fig. 4.9. A continuous chain holds the character fonts. This is held between two gears which move the chain horizontally across the paper. Ribbon is located between the chain and the paper and a set of hammers on the opposite side of the paper to the chain. Each hammer is individually activated when the required character is correctly located behind the paper. More than one complete set of characters is held on the chain. A complete line of characters can be printed when one complete set of characters has passed across the page.

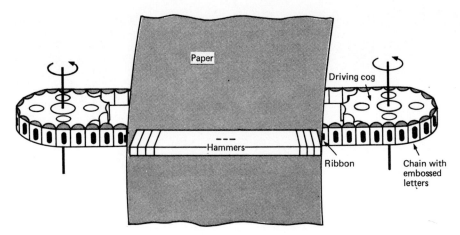

Figure 4.9 Chain printer.

A belt or band printer is similar but with the chain replaced by a flexible metal band with the letters embossed on the band.

The spacing of characters printed is typically 2.5 mm, so the hammers need to be the same (but see below). The spacing of the characters on the chain or belt may be greater than this, in which case the hammer timing can be quite intricate.

Sometimes the hammer design is such that 2.5 mm spacing cannot be achieved. In this case a smaller number of hammers than characters on the page are used and the hammers oscillated across several character positions to cover the whole width of the page. This is applicable to drum printers also.

4.3.3 Comb printer

The comb printer is a matrix printer. The printing mechanism of the comb printer is shown in Fig. 4.10. The comb is of flexible metal with teeth, one tooth for each character position. On the end of each tooth is a hard steel ball which is used as a hammer to form the dots. The comb is located laterally across the page, with the ribbon between the comb and the paper. In front of the comb is a set of small electromagnets, one for each tooth of the comb. In one action the first dot on the top row of each character is printed by activating the electromagnets which pull the individual teeth to the magnets. Upon deactivating the electromagnets, the teeth are relaxed and impact upon the ribbon and paper, thus forming the dots. If a particular dot is not to be printed, the appropriate electromagnet is not activated. Then the comb is moved laterally one column position right and the process repeated until all the dots are produced of the the first row of each character matrix. Each electromagnet is such to pull a tooth if it is in any of its character column positions.

After one row of dots across the page has been printed, the paper is advanced vertically one row position and the process repeated to print the next row of dots. To reduce the movement of the comb; alternate rows are printed right to left rather than left to right, i.e. the printing is bi-directional. Once all the rows for the characters have been printed, the mechanism can advance to the next line.

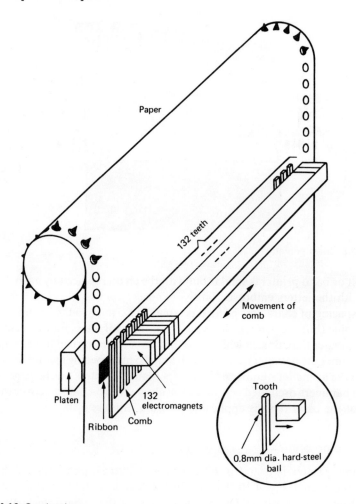

Figure 4.10 Comb printer.

Printing speed with this mechanism is generally in the range 125 lines/min to 300 lines/min or exceptionally 400 lines/min.

The print mechanism is particularly simple, resulting in high reliability. The comb motion is obtained using a stepper motor (see Section 7.6.1), the shaft of which rotates and drives the comb horizontally. As the shaft oscillates back and forth, the comb moves left and right.

4.3.4   Needle line printer

The needle line printer mechanism is shown in Fig. 4.11. A number of solenoids are mounted on a bar held across the length of the paper. The requirement for wire bending is avoided and the wires are fairly short (about 2 cm). Typically there are 22 solenoids which allow 22 dots to be printed simultaneously. The bar is moved laterally in the same fashion as the comb in the comb printer to enable

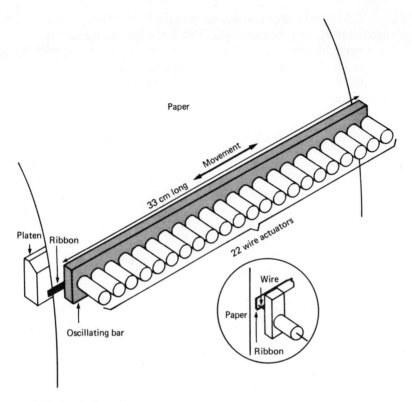

Figure 4.11 Needle line printer.

the other dots to be printed across the paper. With 132 characters, with each character a 5×7 dot matrix, 30 operations (5 dots $\times$ 132 characters $\div$ 22 solenoids) are necessary to complete a row and seven such operations. to complete the line of characters.

Greater reliability is claimed for this printer than the serial needle printer, due to the simpler mechanics, less concentrated heating of the solenoids, and particularly the avoidance of bending the print wires. The print wires can be made of stronger material. The printing speed is typically 125 lines/min (275 character/s) and the life of the head greater than 500 million characters.

4.4   Non-impact printing

4.4.1   General

Non-impact printing uses a variety of printing methods with the common factor of not requiring mechanical hammers or print heads striking paper, rather forming printed characters in a quite non-mechanical manner. As with impact printing, certain non-impact printing techniques can be applied both for serial printers or line printers, though particular techniques are only practical for line printing.

A second characteristic of non-impact printing in some cases is the potential high speed of operation, being devoid of slow mechanical operations.

Often a major disadvantage of non-impact printing is the requirement for special paper (though this is offset by not requiring ribbons).

Non-impact printers have not been sub-divided into line and serial printers in the following sections.

4.4.2   Thermal and thermal transfer printers

A thermal printer is based on locally heating special heat-sensitive thermographic paper. This paper is white and develops colours (either black or blue) when heated above a threshold value of approximately 110°C. The print head comprises a number of small heater elements that can produce segment or dot-matrix characters when pressed against the thermographic paper by pressure pads, or solenoids, and selectively energized. The temperature of the energized head needs to be higher than 110°C, perhaps in the region of 200°C or more, to overcome imperfect thermal coupling.

The heating elements are often arranged in a dot-matrix (typically 5 × 5) as shown in Fig. 4.12. A 7-segment configuration can be used for printing numbers only.

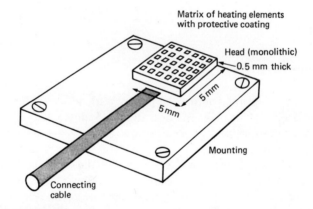

Matrix of heating elements
with protective coating

Head (monolithic)
0.5 mm thick

5 mm

5 mm

Mounting

Connecting
cable

Figure 4.12 Thermal print head.

Thermal printers can be serial, operating in the region of 10–30 characters/s, or with several character heads in parallel operated as a line printer at speeds in excess of 1000 lines/min. Generally, though, thermal printing is a relatively slow process. A serial printer operates with a single print head that is held against the paper whilst heating and forming a character. Then it is lifted away and moved to the next character position for the process to repeat. Typically there are 80–140 character positions or columns across the page.

Thermal printing is generally limited to data logging applications and very low-cost computer printing systems. In contrast, the *thermal transfer* printer is suitable for general printing applications, particularly in offices. In the thermal transfer printer, a solid polyester film ribbon is used which is manufactured to melt under the influence of heat (about 65°C). The print head typically consists of 24 elements which are pressed against the ribbon to produce printed characters on ordinary paper. Various colours can be achieved with a ribbon consisting of segments of the primary colours magenta, cyan and yellow. The thermal transfer printer produces good quality printed copy and is quiet.

4.4.3 Electrosensitive printers

Electrosensitive printers also employ special paper; paper with a very thin surface coating of aluminium (0.025 mm or less). Between this coating and a paper base, there is a layer of coloured dye (normally black, but it can be red or blue). The printing operation involves selectively removing the aluminium by electric discharge to reveal the dyed undercoat. This is done by pointed styli that touch the aluminium. A low voltage (typically 35 V) minimal current pulse is applied which generates a spark that erodes the aluminium to form dot-matrix characters.

Electrosensitive printers can be serial with the head moving across the paper as shown in Fig. 4.13, operating in the region of 200 to 2000 characters/s, or line printers with styli mounted across the length of the paper and operating at speeds in excess of 3000 lines/min.

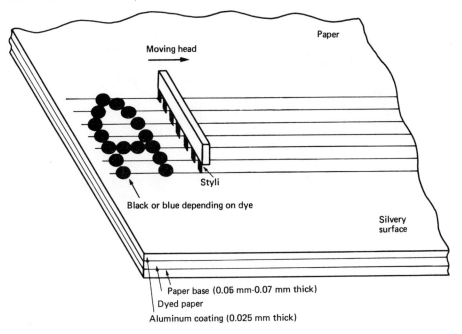

Figure 4.13 Electrosensitive printer.

Usually electrosensitive printers are limited to those with 80 columns or less and find application in low-cost systems where a silvery paper surface is acceptable (calculators, low-cost microprocessor systems, cash registers, and instrumentation).

Electrosensitive print out boasts of permanency which is generally unaffected by light, heat, or humidity.

4.4.4 Electrostatic printers

Electrostatic printers employ dielectrically coated paper. Electrostatic charge is imposed on this paper by an array of charging nibs. After a line of characters is formed, this is sprayed with liquid toner which has suspended charged particles, for example carbon particles suspended in an iso-paraffin dispersant. These particles adhere to the charged areas on the paper and produce an image. Surplus toner is removed and generally the paper dried before being handled.

Electrostatic printers are universally of line-printer type, with a row (or rows) of nibs mounted across the paper (Fig. 4.14), and produce high speeds in the region of 500–3000 lines/min. These printers find application as general system printers and graph plotters (see Section 7.6), though the dielectric paper tends, as yet, to have a poor grey appearance and this tends to limit applications.

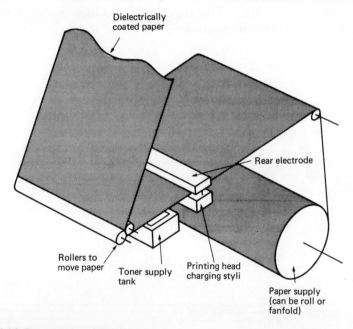

Dielectrically coated paper

Rear electrode

Rollers to move paper

Toner supply tank

Printing head charging styli

Paper supply (can be roll or fanfold)

Figure 4.14 Electrostatic printer.

There is a small air gap of about 0.6 mm between the array of nibs and the dielectric side of the paper. An electrode touches the other side. A voltage of 550–750 V d.c. is applied between the electrodes. The higher the voltage, the darker the image, and this can generally be adjusted. The charged areas are negatively charged, and the ions on the toner positively charged.

The dot-matrix spacing is typically 0.25 mm. To increase the printing density, each dot row is sometimes printed twice. In this case the paper is incremented by 0.125 mm after each print operation. The nibs may be mounted in a staggered manner and activated accordingly, with odd dots printed one row in front of even dots. This can produce touching or overlapping dots.

Typically there are 132 characters across the page and 8 dot positions for each character, requiring a total of 1056 nibs and one high-voltage driver per nib.

4.4.5 Magnetic printing

Magnetic attraction can be utilized instead of electrostatic attraction. In this a magnetic image is formed and this is developed with magnetic ink. The ink is then transferred to a sheet of paper. Speed of operation and quality of print is similar to that of electrostatic printing.

4.4.6 Ink-jet printer

The basic components of an ink jet printer are shown in Fig. 4.15. Conductive ink is forced through a very small nozzle to produce a high-speed stream or jet of drops of ink. The size and spacing of these drops are made constant by vibrating the nozzle compartment at an ultrasonic frequency with a piezo crystal mounted at one end of the cavity. The vibrating frequency is around 100 kHz, the drop diameter is typically 0.06 mm, and the spacing 0.15 mm. Each drop of ink, after

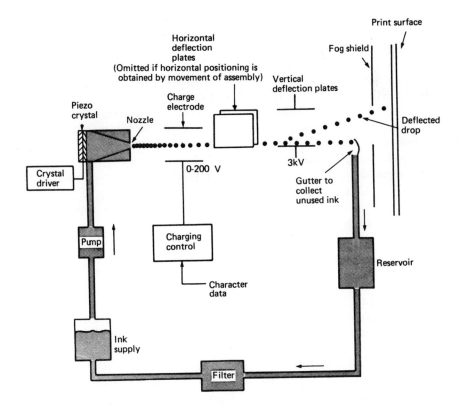

Figure 4.15 Ink-jet printer.

leaving the cavity, is given a specific amount of electrical charge as it passes through a charging electrode structure, which is located at the point at which the stream breaks up into drops. The drops are deflected vertically by a second electrode structure and strike the printing surface. The horizontal position of impact can be determined either by making the system movable and thus positioned as required (by sweeping across the page) or by using another pair of plates to deflect the jet horizontally.

The amount of deflection is determined by the charge originally imparted to the drop. With no charge imparted, there is no deflection and these drops are subsequently collected in a gutter mounted just before the print surface. The maximum deflection is obtained with a maximum amount of charge, which occurs with voltages in the region of 200 V on the charging electrodes. The voltage on the deflection system is held constant at around 3 kV.

Characters are formed from a dot-matrix. The character pattern is stored digitally (in a compressed form) and subsequently controls the charging electrode. Typically there are 10^3 drops per character for high quality printing. With 10^5 drops per second released from the nozzle, 100 characters/s can be printed. The first ink-jet character printer became available in about 1967 and several innovations have taken place since. For example, one patent describes a system whereby successive drops can be made to print in non-adjacent positions. This avoids irregularities due to electrostatic repulsion between ink drops.

Systems exist using magnetic (ferrofluid) ink (magnetic ink-jet printers).

The ink-jet printers described are called *continuous* ink-jet printers as ink droplets are produced continuously. The ink is deflected into a gutter when not required. An alternative mechanism is used in the *on-demand* ink-jet printer which produces ink droplets only when required on the paper, and hence no gutter or deflection system is required. A piezoelectric element can be used to produce the droplets on demand but this process is relatively slow. An on-demand ink-jet printer has been introduced, called the *bubble jet printer*,[1] which ejects ink by locally heating ink within a print head capillary tube, which causes the ink to vaporize. An ink droplet is ejected after the temporary formation of a bubble within the tube. A bubble jet printer typically has 24 vertical nozzles and achieves 170–220 characters/s.

Ink-jet printers produce their best results on very absorbent paper, though such paper need not be used.

4.4.7   Electrophotographic printing

In the early 1970s Xerox corporation, famous for Xerographic (Xerox) or electrophotographic printing, presented a modified office copying machine for computer print-out. Electrophotographic printing involves the use of a photoconductive material, such as selenium. Photoconductive material is an insulator in darkness and a conductor in light. A drum coated with this material is initially charged in darkness and then an image required to be produced is projected onto the drum as it revolves, one revolution for a page. This selectively removes the charge, and using toner as in electrostatic printing, as ink copy can be produced on the drum which is then transferred onto paper by contact.

For a computer printer, the images that are shone onto the drum are particular letters selected by the input data in a manner reminiscent of the drum printer, as shown in Fig. 4.16. Negative transparencies of the character images are arranged around a drum with lamps inside the drum which are selectively flashed as the required characters are in position, projecting the image onto the selenium-coated drum. The particular organization chosen is with 132 character positions across the page, divided into 22 zones of 6 characters each. Each zone is controlled by one lamp and the character in each zone appropriately staggered on the character generator drum. Thus with one revolution a complete line of characters is produced.

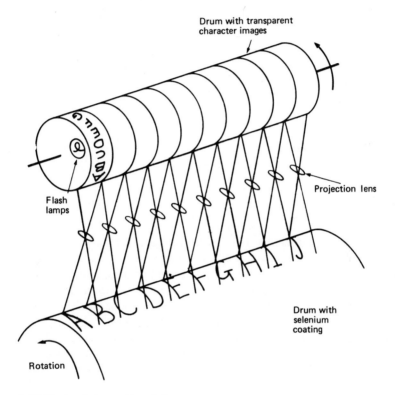

Figure 4.16 Electrophotographic printing.

The original Xerox printer was arranged for an off-line operation using magnetic tape input (see Section 7.6.4).

4.4.8 Laser printers

The electrophotographic printer technique described in the previous section was subsequently combined with a laser device to produce the so-called laser printer, perhaps the fastest printer yet developed.

Referring to Fig. 4.17, again a photoconductive drum is employed which is initially charged before being exposed to a coherent monochromatic light beam

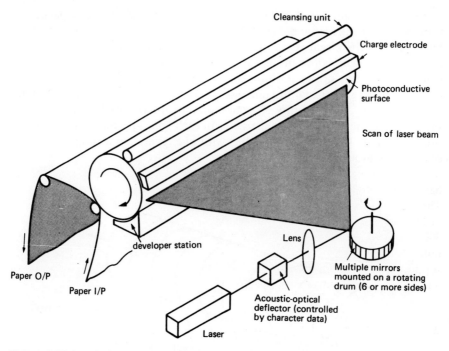

Figure 4.17 Laser printer.

from a helium–neon laser. The light beam scans parallel to the axis on the photo-sensitive drum using a rotating polygonal mirror (a many-sided mirror). As the beam hits one face of the mirror, the movement of the mirror causes one scan across the drum. The drum and mirror system are continuously revolving in synchronism so that the beam scans the whole surface of the drum. Dot-matrix characters are formed in a similar scanning manner as with a visual display unit. In this case the light beam (rather than the electron beam) is switched on and off, by an acoustic-optical deflector, inserted between the laser and the mirror system. Typically an 18×24 dot-matrix is employed with the dots partially overlapping to obtain a high-quality image. Two or three dots are used to produce a line, each dot about 0.25 mm diameter and seven dots/mm.

The light beam selectively discharges areas on the drum and then toner material is spread over the surface to form an ink image. This is then transferred to a roll of paper (rather than sheets of paper in the previous system) and finally made permanent by heat. By splitting the beam into a number of beams, several dots can be formed simultaneously in a vertical line, thus increasing the speed of operation.

Electrophotographic printing has the advantage of being able to superimpose fixed information (for example, account formats) by an additional projection system. This can consist of a revolving drum that holds the required super-imposed image and the image projected onto the photoconductive drum by flash lamps and lens systems.

The original laser printers were designed for very high-speed, high-volume printing, operating at about 100 pages/minute, and costing £100 000 or more. Such a printer finds application in very large systems. Subsequent developments include less expensive laser printers designed for more modest printing requirements. These printers operate in the region of 10 pages/minute. The lower-cost printing mechanisms have a limited life and are not designed for continuous printing. A low-cost laser printer operating at say 10 pages/minute is typically suitable for printing 3000 pages/month, (10 min/day). The electrophotographic printers can use a row of LEDs instead of a laser, or a CRT to project an image onto the print drum. LED imaging array printers are manufactured with resolutions of 240 dots/inch for good character representation. It is possible to have 400 dots/inch for characters which compare well with typeset characters. The drum itself can be made from a low-cost non-toxic organic photoconductor instead of selenium. Organic photoconductor drums have surface lives of 3000–5000 pages compared to 50–100 000 pages for selenium. Typically, though not necessarily, it is arranged that organic drums are replaced when the toner supply needs to be refilled. The lost-cost laser printer with high resolution now makes 'desk-top publishing' possible.

4.5 Connection of a printer to a computer

There are two common physical methods of transferring data to a printer from a computer locally, by asynchronous serial data transmission (Fig. 4.18 (a)), and by parallel transmission (Fig. 4.19). Both these methods are used. For really high-speed printers, parallel transmission may be mandatory. For slower printers, only asynchronous serial connection may be provided.

A typical asynchronous serial connection may consist of a 9.6 K bits/s data line, together with a READY line and a BUSY line, both to the CPU, the READY signal indicating the printer is turned on, and generally operational (loaded with paper etc.), and the BUSY signal indicates when the printer cannot accept any more data, due to the buffer(s) being full or/and actual printing of a line. Thus the BUSY signal is used to stop transmission of data. With these definitions of the signals, the printer can both be READY and BUSY. A typical sequence of events is illustrated in Fig. 4.18 (b) for a line printer with a single data buffer to hold a line of characters. Here the printer loads each character into a buffer as it is received. When a complete line has been received, indicated by a terminator received such as 'new line', 'carriage return' or 'line feed', or by the 132nd character received (with 132 characters on a line), the BUSY signal is set to a '1' to indicate that further characters should not be sent. The line is printed and the BUSY reset and the process repeated. The BUSY may also be set to a '1' whilst each character is in the process of being loaded into the buffer.

Figure 4.18 (c) shows the effect of having a double buffer. Here, after the first line has been received and loaded into a buffer, it can be printed. Whilst this printing is taking place, the second line can be loaded into a second buffer in preparation for this to be printed. This process is continued so that data to be printed is taken alternately from the first and the second buffer. An equivalent

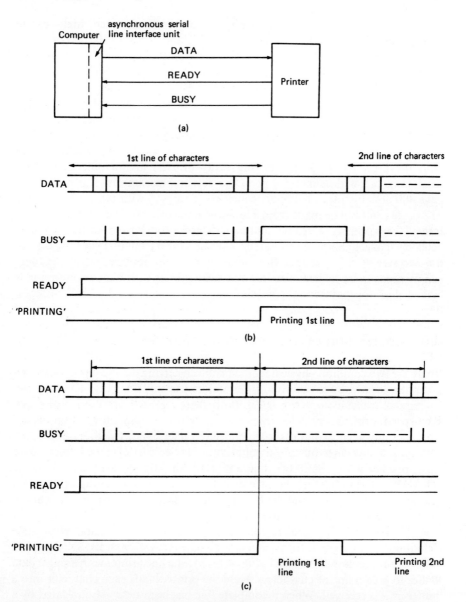

Figure 4.18 Asynchronous serial data transmission: (a) electrical interconnection; (b) signals with single line buffer; (c) signals with double line buffer.

arrangement is to take data always from the second buffer and always load incoming data into the first buffer. Data are then transferred from the first to the second buffer when the first buffer is full and the second is empty. (The process of transferring data from the registers causes them to become 'empty'.)

If the speed of transmission is such that printing a line takes less than the transmission of 132 characters, then the BUSY line is never activated and a continuous stream of data can be sent. If, on the other hand, the speed of

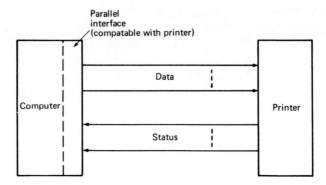

Figure 4.19 Parallel connection of a printer.

transmission is so high for this not to be the case, then the BUSY signal will be activated for that period of time that the printing time is in excess of the time of transmission of 132 characters.

The BUSY signal generated by the interface unit for the CPU indicates whether data can be transferred from the CPU to the interface unit. This will depend upon the interface unit itself and the printer. The printer indicates its readiness by the printer–interface BUSY and this is combined with internal circuitry within the interface unit to produce the required BUSY signal for the CPU (either a bit in a status register or an individual bus signal). It may be that the two BUSY signals are virtually the same. The READY signal from the printer will typically set a bit in the status register.

Programmed output to a printer is as follows (see Section 2.2.2): firstly, the READY line is interrogated. This might be done after every page is produced. Then prior to each programmed output instruction, the BUSY line is checked using a 'test and repeat if set' instruction(s). This may take the form:

```
L1:  IN    A, BUSY
     BIT   O, A
     JP    Z, L1
     OUT   PRINTER, A
```

Parallel connection to a printer usually allows more information to be passed between the printer and the CPU in addition to the data signals. These might include:

SWITCHED ON
MANUAL/ON LINE
RESET (to printer)
BUFFER FULL (BUSY)
PAPER LOW
END OF LINE
FORM FEED (to printer)
CLOCK (to printer)
CLOCK (from printer)
POWER FAIL
PARITY ERROR

The information from the printer may be in the form of a status word which can be read under program control.

The Centronics parallel interface has now become a standard parallel interface for printers, especially connected to small computer systems. The signals in the Centronics interface include eight lines for parallel data, a $\overline{\text{STROBE}}$ signal from the computer to the printer and a BUSY signal from the printer to the computer. A logic pulse is generated on $\overline{\text{STROBE}}$ when the data is valid. A BUSY signal is return from the printer to the computer. The BUSY signal is activated by the printer when it is not ready to accept further data. Other signals are present as shown in Table 4.1.

Pin	Name	Description	Pin	Name	Description
1	STROBE	Pulse after data settled	19	Return	Screen return for STROBE
2	DI	Data bit 1	20	Return	Screen return for DI
3	D2	Data bit 2	21	Return	Screen return for D2
4	D3	Data bit 3	22	Return	Screen return for D3
5	D4	Data bit 4	23	Return	Screen return for D4
6	D5	Data bit 5	24	Return	Screen return for D5
7	D6	Data bit 6	25	Return	Screen return for D6
8	D7	Data bit 7	26	Return	Screen return for D7
9	D8	Data bit 8	27	Return	Screen return for D8
10	ACK	Pulse when ready to accept data	28	Return	Screen return for ACK
11	BUSY	High until new data can be accepted	29	Return	Screen return for BUSY
12	PE	High when paper short	30	Return	Screen return for PRIME
13	SLCT	High when in on-line condition	31	PRIME	Pulse to initialize printer
14	0 V	0V	32	FAULT	High indicating error condition
15	NC	No connection	33	Return	Screen return (as 19–30)
16	0 V	0V	34	NC	No connection
17	GND	Chassis ground	35	NC	No connection
18	+V	+5 V	36	NC	No connection

Notes:
PRIME and FAULT not always present
ACK, BUSY, PE, SLCT, +5 V and FAULT generated by printer
Generally either ACK or BUSY sufficient as handshaking signal
High = +5 V, Low = 0 V

Table 4.1 Centronics interface signals.

A parallel interface with 11 or 12 data lines and special control signals can be provided to be able to specify movement across a full page and across the platen. Alternatively, an 8-bit parallel interface or serial interface can be used and special control sequences sent to the printer. For example, various control functions can be set up or initiated by sequence of two or three bytes beginning with the ASCII ESC control code. A vertical-motion index and a horizontal-motion index can be first set in this way to define the increment in multiples of 1/48 inch vertically or 1/120 inch horizontally as specified by the final binary number in the sequence. Subsequent head and paper movement is specified by other ESC sequences, the final byte specifying the movement in units as given by the corresponding motion index. Control of head and paper movement applies equally to the daisy-wheel printer and the dot-matrix printer, although it is widely associated with the daisy-wheel printer. In addition, the dot-matrix printer can often be programmed through the interface to have different character sets, a very powerful feature.

Another common way to control printers and other devices such as plotters, is the Xon-Xoff protocol. Here control characters (such as DC_1 and DC_3 in ASCII) are assigned to the states Xon and Xoff. Two thresholds are set in the character buffer in the printer. One threshold corresponds to the printer buffer being nearly full and the other corresponds to the buffer being nearly empty. Data from the computer are conveyed at a faster rate than can be printed and the buffer fills up. When the upper threshold is reached the printer issues the Xoff character and computer stops sending data. The upper threshold is set somewhere below the maximum to allow the computer time to act on the Xoff induction. The buffer now empties as the characters are printed. When the lower threshold is reached an Xon character is issued by the printer and the computer resumes sending data. The lower threshold is set above the empty condition to provide characters to sustain printing while the computer responds to the Xoff character. The Xon and Xoff characters are repeated until all data from the computer are printed.

4.6 Printing terminals

4.6.1 The teletype[2]

The most successful printing terminal has been undoubtedly the model 33 Teletype shown in Fig. 4.20. When only a printer is incorporated the peripheral is known as a *receive-only* (RO) teletype, having only the ability to receive and print the received messages.

With a keyboard added, the peripheral becomes known as a *keyboard send–receive* (KSR) teletype. This has the ability to receive, transmit and print messages.

A paper-tape reader and punch can be also added, as shown in Fig. 4.20. It then becomes an *automatic send–receive* (ASR) teletype, capable of receiving and transmitting messages, producing a paper-tape copy of the messages and printed copy. Paper tape can also be read for printing or transmission. Further details of paper-tape equipment will be found in Chapter 5.

The terminal is almost completely mechanical with a mechanical keyboard, reader and punch.

Brief details of the mechanical arrangements are included for historical interest.

The cylinder print head used as shown in Fig. 4.21. The symbols to be printed are embossed in a metallic cylinder. With 64 symbols, there are four rows with 16 symbols on each row. The ribbon and paper are immediately in front of the cylinder and a hammer is positioned behind the head. The head is rotated clockwise or anticlockwise and moved vertically until the required symbol is correctly positioned next to the ribbon and paper. Then the hammer strikes the

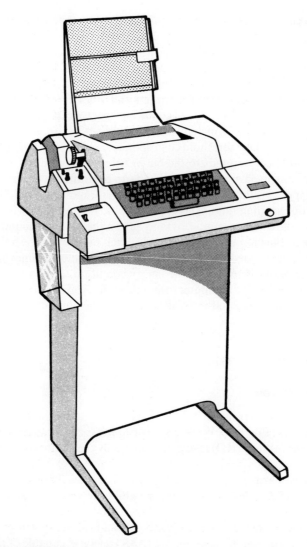

Figure 4.20 Model 33 Teletype.

back of the cylinder, forcing the cylinder to strike the ribbon. This causes the symbol to be printed on the paper. Only upper-case characters are provided, though it is feasible to have lower case.

When a key is depressed the ASCII code is produced (with or without parity) by the keyboard contacts. This is done using a pair is of code bars for each bit of the code (Fig. 4.22(a)), one of which in the pair is depressed when the key is pressed depending upon slots in the bars. There is a slot in one bar to represent a '1' and a slot in the other bar to represent a '0'. The movements of the bars are translated into switch contact movements.

When the key is released the code combination remains until another key is depressed. The appropriate bars for the new key will then move. When one bar of

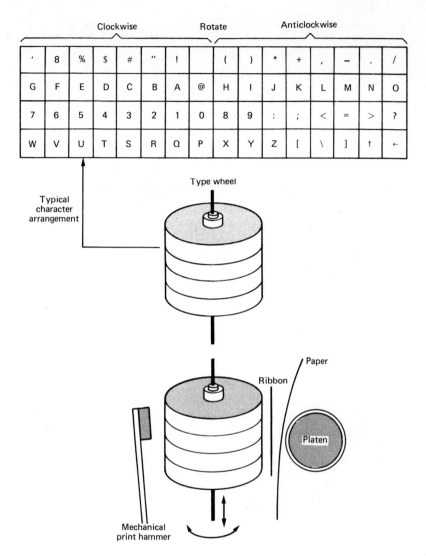

Clockwise							Rotate				Anticlockwise				
'	8	%	$	#	"	!		(	)	*	+	,	–	.	/
G	F	E	D	C	B	A	@	H	I	J	K	L	M	N	O
7	6	5	4	3	2	1	0	8	9	:	;	<	=	>	?
W	V	U	T	S	R	Q	P	X	Y	Z	[	\	]	↑	←

Typical character arrangement

Type wheel

Paper

Ribbon

Platen

Mechanical print hammer

Figure 4.21 Cylinder print head.

the pair is pressed (only those whose bit in the code is different) the other in the pair returns.

The mechanism is such that whilst one key is depressed, others cannot be depressed because the solid portion of one or more code bars prevents this (the other keys will have different codes to the one depressed). The key contacts connect to a distributor (Fig. 4.22(b)) to produce the desired asynchronous serial data output. The clutch of the distributor engages once a key is pressed and the shaft rotates once. The outer brush on the shaft moves over 10 segments corresponding to the start, 8 data, and stop bits. As the shaft rotates, the signal path through the inner brush, outer brush and keyboard contacts produces the desired mark–space (current–no current) output.

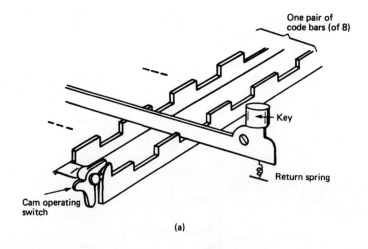

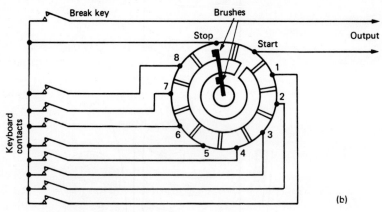

Figure 4.22 Teletype: mechanical details: (a) code-bar mechanism; (b) distributor (a parallel-to serial converter).

4.6.2   Modern printing terminals

Modern printing terminals typically employ a needle printer and electronic keyboard. Paper tape and punch equipment are not incorporated. Naturally any of the serial printers described can be combined with any of the keyboards to form a printing terminal.

Reference

1.   Thorn, G. Bubbles for Speed, *Systems International*, **41,** April 1986.
2.   (*Model*) *33 Teletypewriter Technical Manual Bulletin* 310B, Vol. 1, Teletype Corporation, USA, 1969

5

Punched cards and paper tape

5.1 Introduction

Take a piece of card or paper and punch a number of small holes, each say about 2 mm diameter, and we have a method of storing, input, and output of binary data. Each hole position can represent one bit with the presence of the hole representing a '*1*', say, and the absence of the hole representing a '*0*'. A row of hole positions thus provides a binary word. This information can be entered into the computer by feeding the tape or card through a reader which can sense the presence or absence of holes, and produced by the computer as output using a punch which perforates blank cards or paper.

The most convenient shape for punched cards is rectangular or square, one particular size (18.7 cm × 8.25 cm) being a standard, with holes punched in 80 columns, each column having 12 hole positions. A number of cards will be necessary usually to convey the information, perhaps in some cases several thousands. Paper is used in long strips of tape, between 1.746 cm and 2.54 cm wide, up to 300 m long, and wound on reels.

Both paper tape and cards pre-date computers in that they were used for other applications before computers existed; both were carried over to the earliest computers.

Punched cards and paper tape have provided major methods of loading programs and data into a computer. However, their use has been decreasing since the 1960s, and both cards and tape have been replaced in many applications by alternative forms of removable storage, principally floppy discs (see Chapter 9).

5.2 Punched cards

5.2.1 History

Joseph Marie Jacquard (1752–1834) is credited with the first use of punched cards when in 1804 he employed punched cards to control the operation of a weaving loom. This loom could weave complicated patterns as defined by a number of punched cards. The cards, each of which had holes punched in selected positions to define the pattern, were arranged in a loop that rotated. The pattern would repeat as the loop had rotated once. As one card was selected in the loop, specific threads in the loom would be lifted according to the pattern of holes on the card. This mechanism employed rods pressing against the card and the shuttle passed behind the selected threads on its forward movement. The process was repeated with each card. The cards could be replaced as required.

A small repetitive pattern would need only a few cards, whilst a portrait tapestry of Jacquard required 24000 cards. Jacquard looms became extremely popular in France with many thousand looms in operation in the subsequent years.

The story now moves to 1832 when Charles Babbage (1792–1871), a Cambridge professor, began his work on a mechanical computer named the analytical engine. This is a landmark in the history of computers, generally being a mechanical equivalent of a digital electronic computer. It comprised an *arithmetic unit* using gears to perform arithmetic operations, a *control unit* and input devices based on punched cards. It should be said that the analytical engine never worked, principally because the ideas were beyond the technology of the time. (For example, the design called for numbers to be represented to fifty decimal digits.)

So far as punched cards are concerned, cards were to be used to select the arithmetic operation (addition, subtraction, multiplication or division), and to control the transfer of the number between the arithmetic unit and the store (both sets of gears), i.e. the program. Conditional operations were to be provided. Data were to be entered using punched cards and output either by punched cards or printing mechanism (direct or some indirect means by producing printers' moulds).

In 1886 Herman Hollerith in the USA hit on the idea of using punched cards to assist the counting and evaluation of population census. Up to that time census forms were filled in by hand and collated manually. For each census, this was taking years to complete and an automated method was desperately needed. Hollerith introduced the idea of having cards punched with holes to represent simple yes/no answers to questions and also for coded information. The punched cards used today bear his name. Punched cards began increasingly to be used for a variety of sorting and counting applications, though computers were not to be introduced for another fifty years. Equipment was devised for punching the holes, reading the cards, sorting cards with the same coded information in specific columns (sorters), equipment to duplicate cards (reproducers) and other functions. Generally, all this mechanical equipment for handling cards is not required in a computer system in many instances; the basic requirement is for reading and punching cards.

The next significant event so far as computer peripherals are concerned was in 1937 when Howard H. Aiken began his design of a mechanical computer, known as the automatic sequence controlled calculator (ASCC), which had much in common with the analytical engine. This used sets of wheels to store and accumulate numbers. Interconnection was performed using gear mechanisms. In this machine paper tape was used to store the program and punched cards for numeric data and input/output. Constants were set on switches.

The pattern for digital computers was now beginning to emerge, so when the first electronic computers were built in the 1946–50 period, it was natural to use punched cards for input and output (or paper tape). This has persisted to the present day, though now punched cards are used only when they are particularly suitable.

5.2.2 Physical details and coding

Figure 5.1 shows a punched card in common usage, having 80 columns of punched-hole positions with 12 hole positions in each column. The card has a standard size of approximately 18.7×8.25 cm (and is about 0.02 cm thick). Though most often made from stiff card, plastic may be used so as to withstand repeated passage through reading equipment. Some punches cannot handle plastic, though. The holes are rectangular (an early version of this card used round holes with 45 columns).

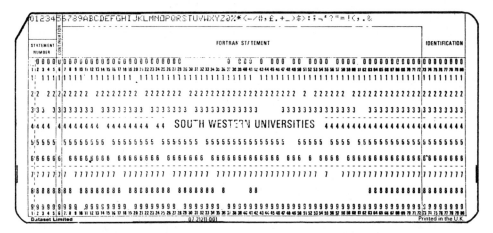

Figure 5.1 80-column punched card.

One column holds one character. Table 5.1 gives the Hollerith code that is often used. The rows are labelled 12, 11, 0, 1, 2, 3, 4, 5, 6, 7, 8, 9 from top to bottom. The coding is not efficient; with 12 rows, 4096 combinations are possible in each column but not more than three holes are used in the set shown. One hole is used in one of the rows 0 to 9 to represent the numbers 0 to 9; two holes, one in row 12 and the other in rows 1 to 9 for the letters A to I; two holes, one in row 11 and the other in rows 1 to 9, for the letters J to S; and two holes, one in row 0 and the other in rows 1 to 9, for the letters T to Z. The 'special' symbols are coded using one, two or three holes.

Naturally, efficient coding could be used, and is used, if the cards are to hold pure binary data. In this case each column could hold one 12-bit binary number. Alternatively, the words can be held in rows with 12 rows of 80 bits, i.e. 12×80 bit words can be stored.

International Business Machines (IBM) have introduced 96-column punched cards which are more compact than the 80-column cards.

5.2.3 Card preparation

(a) *Keyboard punch*

The principal device for preparing cards in a proper computer system is the keyboard-operated card punch (Fig. 5.2). This produces a punched card as

Character	Row											
	12	11	0	1	2	3	4	5	6	7	8	9
0	0	0	1	0	0	0	0	0	0	0	0	0
1	0	0	0	1	0	0	0	0	0	0	0	0
2	0	0	0	0	1	0	0	0	0	0	0	0
3	0	0	0	0	0	1	0	0	0	0	0	0
4							1					
5								1				
6									1			
7										1		
8											1	
9												1
A	1			1								
B	1				1							
C	1					1						
D	1						1					
E	1							1				
F	1								1			
G	1									1		
H	1										1	
I	1											1
J		1		1								
K		1			1							
L		1				1						
M		1					1					
N		1						1				
O		1							1			
P		1								1		
Q		1									1	
R		1										1
S			1		1							
T			1			1						
U			1				1					
V			1					1				
W			1						1			
X			1							1		
Y			1								1	
Z			1									1
.	1					1					1	
,			1			1					1	
:	1							1			1	
;	1						1				1	
%			1				1				1	
'	1								1		1	
>		1						1			1	
<		1							1		1	
=			1						1		1	
(								1			1	
)									1		1	
[		1			1						1	
]					1					1	1	
+	1				1						1	
//		1										
•		1									1	
/			1	1								
↑		1								1	1	
←			1							1	1	
10	1											

Table 5.1 80-column punched-card codes.

specified by operating an alpha-numeric keyboard, with each column of holes coded for each character depressed.

There are often extra facilities, the more common being the ability to print along the top edge of the card the characters corresponding to the holes punched.

Other features include skipping columns to enable formated data to be more easily punched, automatic punching of repetitive data and gang punching (copying a master card onto many subsequent cards).

In a manual card punch, blank cards are fed one by one from a hopper through a punching mechanism, printing mechanism and reading mechanism as shown in Fig. 5.2. The organization is such that a master card can be placed in the read station, and cards from the hopper fed past the punch/print station to form duplications of the master. The master and copy are shifted in synchronism.

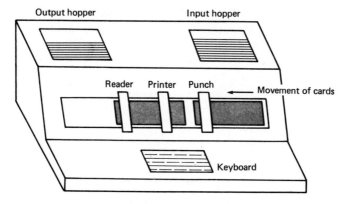

Figure 5.2 Keyboard-operated card punch.

(b) *Reproducer*
The basic keyboard punch usually has a reproducer facility whereby generally each master card has to be placed into the machine separately. In a dedicated reproducer a set of master cards is copied at high speed (100 cards/min or greater). Extra facilities include selective duplication.

(c) *Sorter*
A sorter arranges a stack of cards into separate stacks, selected by like columns. For example, all cards with the first column coded as a letter A can be placed in one stack, all cards with the first column a letter B in the next column and so on. Selector switches dictate the column examined so that with several passes through the machine complete alphabetic order sorting can be achieved of the complete or part of the data punched. The leftmost column of the characters punched is sorted first, and then the process repeated until the right hand column is reached.

(d) *Verifiers*
The process of verification is particularly applicable to data-processing applications where correctness of input data may be of paramount importance.

Verification involves keying the information in a second time after the cards have been punched. The information on the cards is compared with that keyed in and any discrepancy is reported as an error. The error may be on the original card or the subsequent verification operation, and is indicated by either marking the card with ink on a punched hole in one corner, or by a light or buzzer operating. The verification operation is often done by a different operator than the original punch operation and requires a verifier.

(e) *Punched card input procedure*

A typical procedure in a scientific environment for entering programs into a computer via punched cards is shown in Fig. 5.3. The programmer writes his program on coding sheets (Fig. 5.4) with one symbol in one square on the sheets. The coding sheets are divided into 80 columns corresponding to the 80 columns of the punched card. Typically there are 25 rows on the sheet giving information for a maximum of 25 cards. Certain programming languages, FORTRAN in particular, allocate specific meaning to symbols in certain columns, and naturally the entering of the program onto the coding sheets must reflect this in these cases.

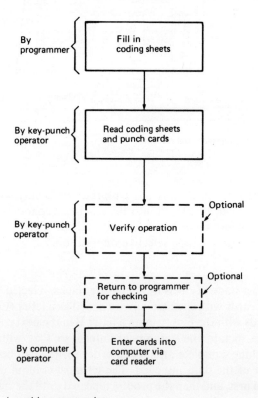

Figure 5.3 Punched-card input procedure.

To distinguish between similar symbols, the following convention is often used in completing the coding sheets: number 0 is distinguished from the letter O by writing it as Ø, the letter Z is distinguished from the number 2 by writing as Z̶, and

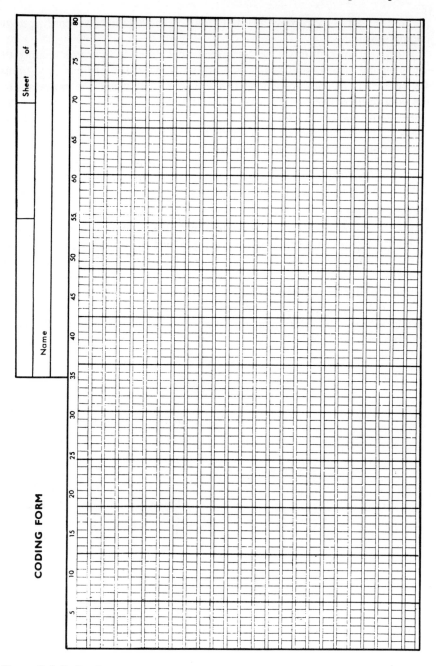

Figure 5.4 Coding form.

the letter I is distinguished from the number 1 by the top and bottom horizontal lines, though to add to confusion the letter O is sometimes written as Ø with the number 0 as O.

The completed coding sheets are handed to key-punch operators, normally part of the staff of the computer installation. Cards are punched according to the coding sheets.

The verify operation can be performed by a different operator reading the same coding sheets, but this is not normally done for ordinary programs. Verifying may be considered worthwhile occasionally when it is important for the data to be correct.

The cards and coding sheets can be returned to the programmer for manual verification. Finally, the cards are entered into the computer by placing in a card reader (done by the computer operator).

5.2.4   Card readers

(a) *Mechanism*

Cards are usually read column by column so that the computer is presented with 12-bit words, though it is of course possible to read by row or by card complete.

The reading mechanism is usually photoelectric, using infra-red light-emitting diodes as light sources and phototransistors as light detectors (Fig. 5.5). With column reading there will be 12 sources and 12 detectors. The cards are fed from a hopper holding around 400–1200 cards and driven between the sources and detectors (the reading station) as shown in Fig. 5.6, and 80 sets of 12 bits of data are obtained in sequence.

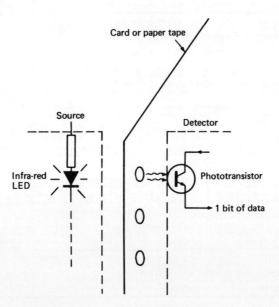

Figure 5.5 Photo-electric sensing.

Punched cards are susceptible to damage whilst being handled (card-users always fear the possibility of dropping the stack, as then the order of the cards can be lost). Cards are usually handled and used many times, and this leads to the likelihood of dog-eared edges. Whilst damaged cards cannot be expected to be

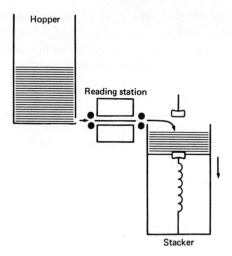

Figure 5.6 Card reader.

read properly, card readers are designed to be jam-resistant and give long life. Typically for this reason only one card is in the reading track at any one time and the track distance is made as short as possible.

To separate cards that might stick together in the hopper due to electrostatic attraction or other reasons, the cards about to be picked up can be subjected to a blast of air to slacken them. Alternatively, a knife separator can be employed. Picking up a card can be by vacuum or by a friction picker. Card-reading speed is typically in the range 100–2000 cards/min.

(b) *Electrical interface*

A card reader is not generally connected to a computer via the ubiquitous asynchronous serial lines (i.e. RS–232/V24). Rather a parallel data connection is made with 12 data lines. Typically there are two modes of operation; the single card-reading operation and the operation of continuously reading the cards in the hopper sequentially. A signal needs to be presented to the reader to initiate a read operation and a typical design will be such so that a read card signal in the form of a pulse will cause a signal card to be picked and read, whilst a continuous '1' signal will cause cards to read one after the other until the signal returns to a '0'. Coupled with the data lines will be an index signals used for strobing the data into the interface unit and various status-type signals such as READY, errors such as HOPPER CHECK, READ CHECK, MOTION CHECK, and BUSY. One input to the card reader will be the READ CARD signal.

The READY signal will have a similar meaning as the ready on a printer; meaning that the peripheral is in a general state of readiness, being switched on and in this case loaded with cards. The BUSY signal will become true when a card has been picked (caused by a read card command), and remain true until the end of the read cycle. If the READ CARD signal is still present, then a second card will be picked.

The error signal, HOPPER CHECK, indicates whether there are any more cards to read. READ CHECK indicates whether certain illumination checks tally such as there is darkness around the card (except where holes can be) and lightness in other places. (This requires additional light sensors and detectors.) An error of this type could indicate a torn or otherwise damaged card. The MOTION CHECK indicates whether a card has been correctly located in the read station within a specified time after a read command (say, after 300 ms). Normally electrical faults such as a faulty light source (indicated by not passing the correct current) are detected in the READ CHECK.

(c) *Programmed input instructions*

Programmed transfer is the normal method of controlling a card reader on a small computer system. On a 16-bit accumulator machine an INA 'card reader' will load the lesser significant bits of the accumulator with the 12 bits presented to the interface by the card reader. Hence to read the whole card 80 INA instructions need to be executed, each preceded by a test busy or status instruction, and followed by instructions to store the contents of the accumulator.

On more sophisticated systems a DMA channel can be used.

5.2.5   Card punches

Manual card punches have been described in the preparation equipment section. A card punch that is controlled directly by the computer is a peripheral in the normal sense. The arrangement is similar to the card reader with a hopper and a stacker, with the reading station replaced by a punching station. This generally punches one row at a time. A feature of these punches is auto verification. Once a card is punched, it is read in a subsequent reading station and a comparison made to check for errors. A card punch of this sort with a separate reading station often can be operated as a card reader or a card punch.

The card punching rate is typically in the range 100–300 cards per minute, often achieving greater speed if there are fewer columns to punch.

On-line punches (i.e. those directly connected and controlled by a computer) find application in data-processing systems rather than scientific applications, and allow computer files to be produced on cards for permanent storage or for subsequent input.

5.2.6   Optical mark cards

Rather than punch holes to represent binary coded data, another method is to use pencil marks which can be sensed optically. Such cards are known as optical mark cards and can be of the same size as standard 80 column cards. The card readers employed need to be able to accept such cards. Some card readers can be operated in one of two modes, punched card and optical mark card, thus giving greater flexibility. Areas on the card are allocated for markings. These areas may be larger than the areas of punched holes on 80 column cards. An arrangement is shown in Fig. 5.7. There are many possibilities which can be tailored to

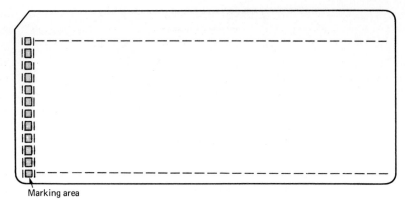

Marking area

Figure 5.7 Optical mark card.

individual applications, with distinct areas labelled for specific data. These can be filled in by non-specialist personnel at the location of the source of input data (a warehouse in a 'computerized' warehouse system, for example).

A typical specification for an optical mark card calls for a soft pencil and a maximum of 25% reflection of a mark over the surrounding area, and 75% reflection of unmarked area over the surrounding area (this later specification defines how much erasure is necessary before a mark becomes not a mark).

The subject of optical mark systems is continued in Chapter 8.

5.3   Paper tape

5.3.1   History

Paper tape was used in telegraphic systems long before the advent of electronic computers. The work of Morse and others from the 1830s on electromagnetic telegraphy (transmisssion of coded information using electrical pulses along wires) eventually led to the vast network of information and telephone channels between cities and countries we have today. Telephony (transmission of sound by conversion into electrical signals which pass along wires, i.e. the telephone system) was developed after telegraphy, though today the two co-exist, with the telephone system also used for transmission of coded information including communication between computers.

The original telegraph system used a key switch to type out the information in Morse code. The electrical pulses pass along a single wire to a destination and cause the original information to be reproduced in sound. This system required skilled operators at both the transmitter and receiver for coding and de-coding the information.

The next step was to mechanize the production of the coded information using distributors (see Section 4.6.1) for both transmitter and receiver rotating in synchronism. Morse code was not convenient, so 5-bit Baudot code was used. To eliminate the problem of keeping the distributors rotating in synchronism, the

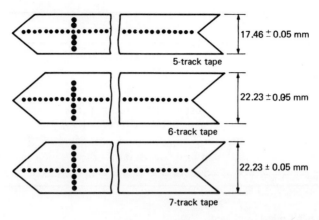

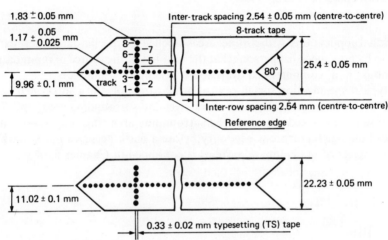

Figure 5.8 Paper-tape dimensions.

start–stop format (see Section 2.4.5) was introduced. The operation of the system involved producing a paper-tape copy of the required information using a key-punch. This tape was then fed into the transmitter unit for generating the serial information. The receiver could produce either a similar paper tape or directly print the information.

The first teletypewriter service of this kind came into general operation around 1931 and has persisted to the present day.

5.3.2   Physical details and coding

The width of the tape can be 17.46, 22.23 or 25.4 mm with 5, 6, 7 or 8 holes (tracks) across the tape. The 25.4 mm width, 8-track tape is almost universal in computer usage.

The general dimensions of these tapes are shown in Fig. 5.8. Between two of the inside tracks on the tape are sprocket holes, holes smaller than the data holes, which were originally used to mechanically propel the tape in the reading and punching equipment. Though this is still an acceptable means of driving the tape, especially in a punch, an alternative is often used of having a friction drive and capstan rollers. The sprocket holes can be used for generating timing pulses.

(a) *8-track tape*
The 8 tracks of this tape provides 256 combinations of holes/no holes. For recording alpha-numeric data, 7-bit ASCII code (see Section 2.3) is very widely used, the 8th hole providing an appended parity bit. Notice that the sprocket holes are between the third and fourth data holes, which allows easy identification of the reference edge of the tape and enables correct loading into reading/punching equipment.

(b) *5-track tape*
Five-track tape is worthy of mention, being the tape used on telegraphic equipment and brought over to be used on the first computers. With five tracks, only 32 combinations of holes/no holes are possible and this is inadequate for normal alpha-numeric data, so two 'shift' codes are used to give almost double this number. Before the first character, a 'shift' code is punched which specifies whether the character is a figure or a letter (table 5.2). All subsequent characters are interpreted in the same way until the alternative shift code is punched to re-specify subsequent characters. An example is shown in Fig. 5.9. Unfortunately this system means that if one shift code is missed (due to a transmission or other error) subsequent characters are misinterpreted. Figure 5.9 also shows that pure binary can be punched on tapes (then known as binary tapes).

(c) *Typesetting tape (advanced sprocket hole 6-track tape)*
Paper tape is used in some newspaper and other printing equipment in an intermediate step between typing the information and forming the metal type. After a paper-tape copy of the information is produced, the tape is fed into equipment which then automatically produces the metal type.

Traditional typesetting tape has 6 tracks and a sprocket hole that is slightly in advance of the data holes (see Fig. 5.8). Many paper tape readers and punches can be adapted for typesetting tape so as to be used in this application, which is increasingly being dominated by computer equipment. Of course standard 8-track tape can be employed in computer-assisted typesetting.

(d) *Materials*
The material used is usually paper though there are other materials which give greater resistance to wear. Materials include:

paper/mylar
mylar
aluminium foil
aluminium foil/mylar
mylar/foil/mylar sandwich
paper/mylar/paper sandwich
oiled paper

Hexidecimal	Tape code	Figures	Letter
0	0 0 0 0 0	BLANK	
1	0 0 0 0 1	1	A
2	0 0 0 1 0	2	B
3	0 0 0 1 1	*	C
4	0 0 1 0 0	4	D
5	0 0 1 0 1	$	E
6	0 0 1 1 0	£	F
7	0 0 1 1 1	7	G
8	0 1 0 0 0	8	H
9	0 1 0 0 1	'	I
A	0 1 0 1 0	,	J
B	0 1 0 1 1	+	K
C	0 1 1 0 0	:	L
D	0 1 1 0 1	-	M
E	0 1 1 1 0	.	N
F	0 1 1 1 1	%	O
10	1 0 0 0 0	0	P
11	1 0 0 0 1	(	Q
12	1 0 0 1 0	)	R
13	1 0 0 1 1	3	S
14	1 0 1 0 0	?	T
15	1 0 1 0 1	5	U
16	1 0 1 1 0	6	V
17	1 0 1 1 1	/	W
18	1 1 0 0 0	@	X
19	1 1 0 0 1	9	Y
1A	1 1 0 1 0	=	Z
1B	1 1 0 1 1	Figure Shift	
1C	1 1 1 0 0	Space	
1D	1 1 1 0 1	Carriage return	
1E	1 1 1 1 0	Line feed	
1F	1 1 1 1 1	Letter shift	

Table 5.2 5-hole tape code.

Various colours (e.g. light blue, dark blue, yellow, green, red, pink, white) are used to aid identification. Materials need to have a minimum transparency for subsequent reading, typically in the range 50–80 per cent transparency (50–20 per cent opacity). Thicknesses up to 0.01 cm are usually allowable. Standards for materials (and hole punching) are laid down under various standards including BS 3880.

5.3.3 Readers

(a) *Mechanism*
As with card readers, paper-tape readers commonly employ photoelectric sensing with, in this case, up to eight phototransistors as detectors on one side of

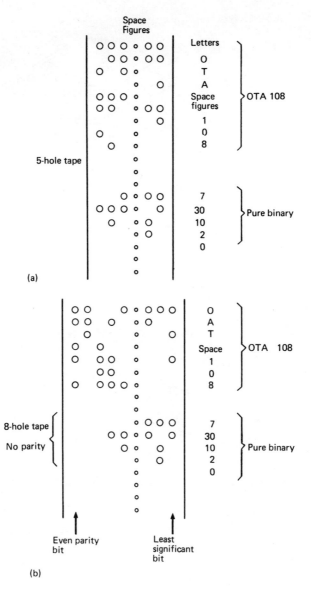

Figure 5.9 5-hole and 8-hole tape.

the tape and a set of infra-red light-emitting diodes (or incandescent lamps) on the other side. A ninth detector may be used for generating a timing signal from the sprocket hole. To obtain a measure of compensation of circuit and material changes, a second set of sources and detectors located $1\frac{1}{2}$ pitch away from the first set can be employed. This second set in normal operation reads a complete blank when the first is reading a frame of holes and the signals obtained used to adjust the operation of the first set of detectors. The end of the tape can be detected by an additional light sensor/detector located before the reading station.

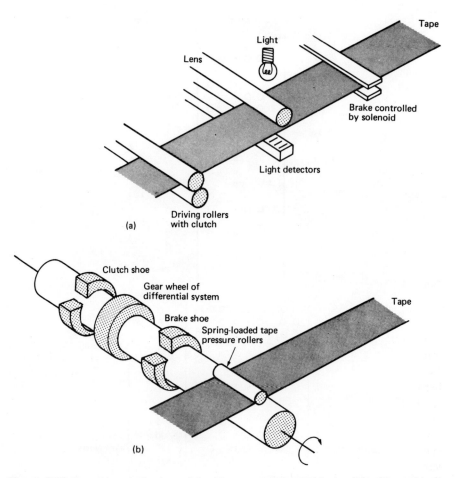

Figure 5.10 Tape drive mechanisms: (a) with separate drive and brake; (b) with combined drive/brake.

Early designs used mechanical sensing with a set of brushes pressed against the tape. When a hole was encountered the corresponding brush would move through the hole causing an electrical contact to be made directly or indirectly. Other methods have been employed including detecting the change in dielectric of the tape in the presence of a hole, and use of air jets which force air through the tape where there are holes. This air can be detected by mechanical means.

The tape can be driven past the reading station by one of two principal ways. In one, shown in Fig. 5.10, the tape is driven by a drive drum with the tape held against the drum by pressure rollers. In Fig. 5.10(b) the tape is halted by stopping the drive drum by means of brake shoes across the drum. When this happens a differential gear causes a second part of the drum to rotate, thus maintaining the drive motor in continuous operation. In Fig. 5.10(a) the tape is stopped by providing the drive rollers with a clutch which disengages the drive when a separate brake acts upon the tape directly. Continuous reading can take place without stopping the tape.

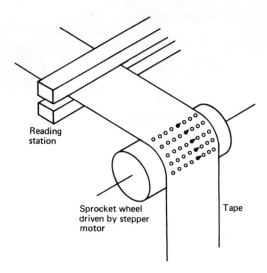

Figure 5.11 Sprocket-feed tape.

The second method of driving the tape is to use a sprocket wheel which locates into the sprocket holes of the tape (Fig. 5.11). The sprocket wheel can be driven by a stepper motor (see Section 7.6.1(c)). In this case, reading can take place between steps and a separate brake is unnecessary.

The two modes of operation, reading with a continuous motion of the tape, and reading with stopping of the tape before each reading, are referred to as synchronous and asynchronous (also called isochronous) respectively. In the synchronous case, the speed of reading may depend upon the control and may vary from 0 to, says 500 character's. In the isochronous case, the reading speed is fixed, typically lower at, say, 300 characters/s.

Figure 5.12 shows the two methods of handling the tape in a tape reader. The commoner method, using reels, is shown in Fig. 5.12(a), and the other, which operates by folding the tape every 19 or 20 cm in a similar fashion to fanfolded printed paper, is shown in Fig. 5.12(b).

(b) *Electrical interface*
As with card readers, paper-tape readers usually connect to the interface unit of the computer via parallel lines. These lines will include eight data output lines and a ninth 'sprocket' line which indicates whether the data are valid. Other output may include conditions such as end-of-tape. One would normally stop the tape before this occurs if possible (of course broken tape is identified by the end-of-tape signal).

Input signals include READ, DRIVE LEFT, DRIVE RIGHT and GENERAL ENABLE. WIND and RE-WIND may be available (for winding and rewinding the tape at higher speed than for normal reading).

Serial RS–232/V24 interface can be employed in a simple reader to give compatibility with other data input devices.

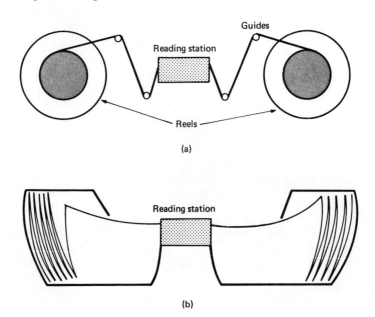

Figure 5.12 Paper-tape readers: (a) with reels; (b) with fan-fold box.

(c) *Programming*

Again programming a paper-tape reader on a small system is usually done using programmed output instructions in conjunction with a BUSY test. Interrupt and DMA mechanisms can, of course, be employed. Both card readers and paper-tape readers are often allocated interrupt lines or interrupt vector addresses.

One consideration is dependent upon the type of reader. If it is the brakeclutch type, the tape is best kept in continuous motion. A typical arrangment is as follows: after the busy signal is reset indicating that data are available, about 100 μs is available to read the data (which will cause the tape to continue in motion). If longer than this is taken, the tape may stop within the space of one character and tape will need to re-start again before reading the next character. Such start–stop operations will cause reader chatter and unreliable operation.

5.3.4 Paper-tape punches

A paper-tape punching mechanism is shown in Fig. 5.13. In this case a drum with an eccentric crank punches the set of punch pins through the tape if the pins have been previously selected by levers. These levers are operated by solenoids and prevent the pins falling back down the driving block as it moves into its highest position. The position of the block is detected by a magnetic pickup and appropriately placed magnets sited on the drum.

The pins and casing are made removable so that different configurations (i.e. 5, 6, 7 or 8 track) can be inserted.

Sometimes a reading station is located after the punching unit, which can be used for checking the punching. Also, there may be a mechanism to check for

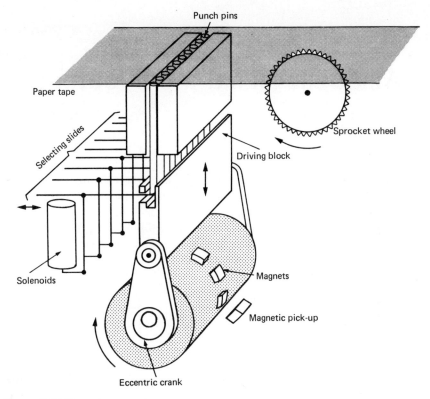

Punch pins

Paper tape

Selecting slides

Sprocket wheel

Driving block

Solenoids

Magnets

Magnetic pick-up

Eccentric crank

Figure 5.13 Paper-tape punch.

'low tape' (less than 30 m, say, left on the reel). Once the punch has been activated (by a machine instruction) the punch motor is usually automatically left running waiting for another command. If one is not received in, say, five seconds, the motor is turned off causing additional delay in re-start (typically, one second). Continuous tape punching is typically in the range 50–300 characters/s.

6

Analogue signal input–output

6.1 Introduction

Analogue signals are continuously variable in amplitude. This contrasts with the digital representation of quantities inside a computer where the finite number of bits to a word means that only discrete values of amplitude can be represented. Hence if analogue signals are to be passed to or from a digital computer, some kind of signal converter is required, as shown conceptually in Fig. 6.1. The terms *data acquisition* or *data conversion* are applied to the process on the analogue input side, and *data distribution* on the output side.

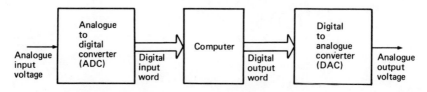

Figure 6.1. Converters are needed for analogue signal I/O.

An analogue signal from the 'real world' outside a computer is shown in Fig. 6.2(a). It is part of a speech waveform. A second example is shown in Fig. 6.2(b), which is from a thermocouple used for temperature measurement. These examples illustrate the wide range of signal amplitude and time scales that are encountered.

Digital processing of analogue signals by computer offers several advantages including accuracy, flexibility, repeatability, and ability to perform complex operations. An exhaustive list of applications would be very long. Moreover, as hardware costs of computers continue to fall such a list would continue to lengthen. A few examples are:

Speech analysis
Artificial speech
Sonar
Seismography
Automatic test equipment
Spectral analysis
Automatic tracking system
Instrumentation
Transducer signal analysis.

Process control of chemical and other
    plants
Simulators
Computer-controlled experiments
Automatic control systems
Pollution monitoring and analysis
Vibration and noise analysis
Graph plotting $X-Y$ recorders

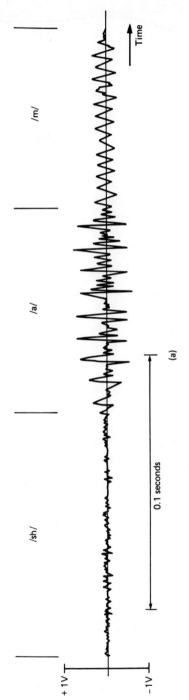

Figure 6.2. Analogue signals: (a) part of a speech waveform.

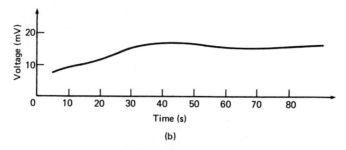

Figure 6.2. Analogue signals: (b) thermocouple signal.

Mini- and micro-computers are usually used for these applications, with mainframes, being reserved for applications which require greater processing power, and where the costs are justified.

One consequence of using a computer is that data can only be input at discrete points in time. Hence only sampled values of an analogue signal can be taken, as is shown in Fig. 6.3, and not the true signal itself. An obvious requirement is that the signal should not change significantly between samples, otherwise information is lost, and a high enough sample rate must be used. The upper limit of sampling rate for a small computer is of the order of 10^5 samples per second. However, it should be kept in mind that the higher the sampling rate, the less time there is available between samples for the computer to do useful processing of the data.

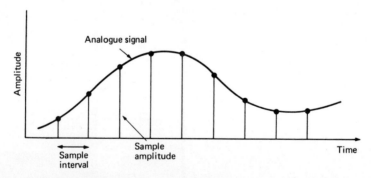

Figure 6.3 Sampled analogue signal.

The computer, likewise, can only output data at discrete points in time and so, for example, the reconstituted form of the analogue signal in Fig. 6.3 would now appear as shown in Fig. 6.4. The horizontal portions of this waveform occur while the next update of output amplitude is awaited. In many cases the staircase effect is not noticeable because the analogue signal is slowly varying, or because the steps are smoothed out by the inertia of the load (as for example when the signal drives a deflection-type meter). Alternatively a smoothing filter can be attached to

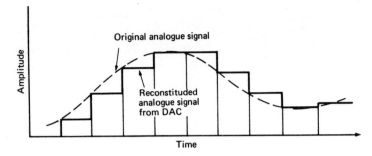

Figure 6.4 Reconstituted analogue signal from samples.

the output of the converter. The optimum response is that of an interpolating filter, details of which can be found in texts on signal processing.[1]

A second consequence of using a computer follows, as was mentioned earlier, because data are represented by words having a finite number of bits. A three-bit data word can assume any of 2^3 (that is 8) different codes: 000,001,010, ... , 110,111. Each code is made to correspond to a fixed level of analogue signal amplitude, and the levels are usually chosen to be equi-spaced. This means that a sampled value of analogue signal is given a code which has the nearest corresponding fixed level, and the signal in Fig. 6.3 now appears as shown in Fig. 6.5. This process of assigning the nearest fixed level to a sample is called quantization and gives rise to a quantization error because the exact value of the original signal cannot be recovered. Quantization errors can have magnitudes up to half the spacing between quantization levels. It is important therefore to choose a sufficient number of data word bits so that uncertainty due to quantization error is kept down to an acceptable amount.

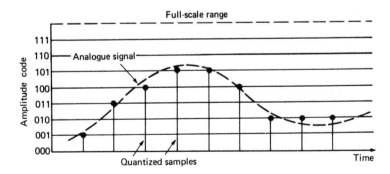

Figure 6.5 Quantization of sample amplitudes.

Figure 6.6 shows a block diagram of a typical form of multichannel analogue I/O system. The hearts of the input and output sides are the analogue-to-digital converter (ADC) and the digital-to-analogue converter (DAC). The sample/hold (S/H) holds the signal sample constant for the ADC. The amplifier is used to condition the analogue signals, which may be small and differential, to take

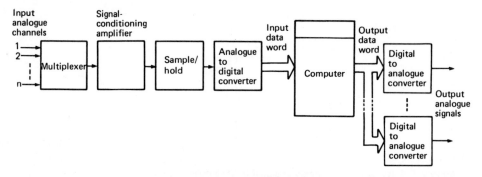

Figure 6.6 Typical form of multichannel analogue I/O system.

advantage of the full-scale range of the ADC. The multiplexer (MUX) enables several analogue channels to be input.

The construction and operation of these blocks are described in the following sections after first dealing with basic features of converters and aliasing errors. Subsequent sections then go on to show the various ways these blocks may be connected to form a complete analogue I/O peripheral unit.

6.2   Basic features of converters

6.2.1   Binary coding

Binary codes, more properly called natural binary codes, are usually used for unipolar analogue signals. Unipolar signals do not change sign: they are always positive or always negative. Positive polarities are often adopted. Using this coding the output voltage from an n-bit DAC is given by

$$V_{\text{out}} = FSR\left(\frac{B_1}{2} + \frac{B_2}{2^2} + \frac{B_3}{2^3} + \ldots + \frac{B_n}{2^n}\right) \qquad (6.1)$$

where the bits B_1 to B_n that make up the data word can each take on a value 1 or 0, and FSR is the full-scale range of the output voltage. Note that in this equation the bits contribute *weights* to V_{out} which decrease by factors of two going from B_1, the most significant bit (*MSB*), to B_n, the least significant bit (*LSB*). Table 6.1 for $n = 3$ illustrates how these weights build up values for V_{out} for different code words. Hence V_{out} may assume values in the range zero to *FSR*, or more exactly zero to $FSR(1 - \frac{1}{8})$. In general, then, the highest value of V_{out} is $FSR(1 - 1/2^n)$, which is 1 *LSB* less than *FSR*.

The smallest increment of voltage that can be obtained is called the *resolution* and corresponds to the weight assigned to the *LSB*. Resolution is usually expressed relative to *FSR*, and therefore has a value of $1/2^n$. The data word lengths encountered in practice in nearly all converters used with computers fall in the range 8 bits to 16 bits. The resolutions obtained are shown in Table 6.2. Values for n of 8, 10, or 12 bits give resolutions which are adequate for many

Code			Binary fraction	V_{out}
B_1 (MSB)	B_2	B_3 (LSB)		(by eq. (6.1))
0	0	0	0.000	$FSR(0+0+0)=0$
0	0	1	0.001	$FSR(0+0+\frac{1}{8})=\frac{1}{8}FSR$
0	1	0	0.010	$FSR(0+\frac{1}{4}+0)=\frac{2}{8}FSR$
0	1	1	0.011	$FSR(0+\frac{1}{4}+\frac{1}{8})=\frac{3}{8}FSR$
1	0	0	0.100	$FSR(\frac{1}{2}+0+0)=\frac{4}{8}FSR$
1	0	1	0.101	$FSR(\frac{1}{2}+0+\frac{1}{8})=\frac{5}{8}FSR$
1	1	0	0.110	$FSR(\frac{1}{2}+\frac{1}{4}+0)=\frac{6}{8}FSR$
1	1	1	0.111	$FSR(\frac{1}{2}+\frac{1}{4}+\frac{1}{8})=\frac{7}{8}FSR$

Table 6.1 Binary coding.

No. of bits (n)	Resolution	
	Fraction	%(approx.)
8	1/256	0.4
9	1/512	0.2
10	1/1 024	0.1
11	1/2 048	0.05
12	1/4 096	0.024
13	1/8 192	0.012
14	1/16 384	0.006
15	1/32 768	0.003
16	1/65 536	0.0015

Table 6.2 Resolutions.

applications. For higher numbers of bits, both the costs and difficulty of handling signals so as to preserve accuracy increase rapidly.

For analogue-to-digital conversion using natural binary coding, the task of the converter is to find that binary code which corresponds most closely to the analogue input signal amplitude. That is, B_1 to B_n are generated so as to satisfy the equation

$$FSR\left(\frac{B_1}{2}+\frac{B_2}{2^2}+\frac{B_3}{2^3}+\cdots+\frac{B_n}{2^n}\right)=V_{\text{IN}}+V_{\text{QE}} \qquad (6.2)$$

The 'slack' variable V_{QE}, which is the quantization error, is included because the left-hand side of this expression assumes discrete values, whereas V_{IN} may assume any value in the continuous range of the converter. Since the resolution is 1 *LSB*, the nearest discrete value of the left-hand side to V_{IN} in this equation is never further than $\frac{1}{2}LSB$, and so

$$|V_{\text{QE}}|\leqslant\tfrac{1}{2}\times 2^{-n}FSR \text{ volts.}$$

Typical of *FSR* voltages for ADCs or DACs are 5 V and 10 V. A value of 10.24 V is sometimes used because it equals $(10 \text{ mV}) \times 2^{10}$ and the binary weights are then convenient multiples and submultiples of 10 mV.

6.2.2   Converter transfer functions and error types

The converter transfer functions, that is eqs (6.1 and 6.2), are shown graphically in Fig. 6.7. The plot for the DAC is a series of dots because there is a unique voltage level for each discrete binary code. On the other hand, for the ADC a band of voltages up to $\frac{1}{2}LSB$ on either side of a quantization level has the same binary code, which gives rise to the 'staircase', as shown.

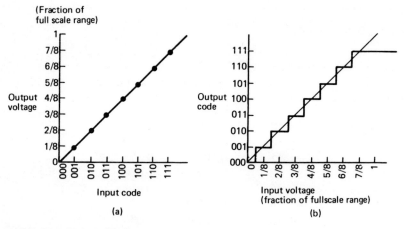

Figure 6.7 Transfer function: (a) DAC; (b) ADC.

In practice, component imperfections within the converter cause deviations from the ideal transfer function, some of which can be adjusted for by the user, and others not. In most applications precision is important and manufacturers' specifications are therefore of interest. Explanations of the terms more commonly used in specifications now follow.

(a) *Offset error*
In a DAC this occurs where the lowest binary input code (all bits 0) produces a non-zero output voltage. For an ADC, conversely, an offset error occurs if the mid-step analogue input voltage which produces the lowest binary output code occurs at a non-zero value (see Fig. 6.8). In practice offset errors in an ADC are more easily determined by adjusting the amplitude of a test input voltage until the transition 00. .00/00 . . 01 occurs. Ideally this should occur at $\frac{1}{2}LSB$, and the deviation from this is the offset error.

In many converters an adjustment facility is provided to null offset errors. Adjustment may not be necessary, especially in low-resolution converters, where manufacturing tolerances guarantee offset errors which are not significant.

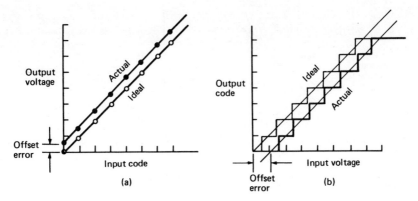

Figure 6.8 Offset errors.

(b) *Scale-factor error* (*also gain error*)
This occurs when the full-scale range differs from the ideal value (see Fig. 6.9).
Again adjustment facilities are usually provided and should be used after offset
errors have been nulled.

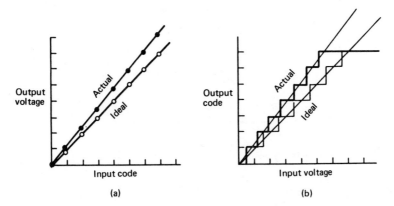

Figure 6.9 Scale-factor errors: (a) DAC; (b) ADC.

(c) *Linearity* (*also called non-linearity*)
This refers to the maximum deviation of the actual converter transfer function
from the best straight line that can be drawn through all points. It is
computationally more convenient to take a straight line between the two end
points, which gives a more conservative measure of linearity. See Fig. 6.10. A
typical figure for linearity is $\pm \frac{1}{2} LSB$.

(d) *Differential non-linearity*
This is a measure of the deviation of individual steps from the ideal size of 1 *LSB*.
For example a maximum differential non-linearity of $\frac{1}{4} LSB$ means that step sizes
for the converter lie in the range $\frac{3}{4} LSB$ to $1\frac{1}{4} LSB$. When differential non-linearity
is specified then linearity as defined above is sometimes called *integral linearity*.

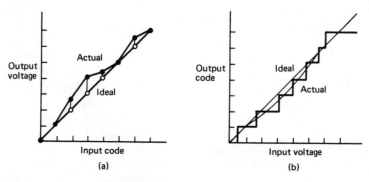

Figure 6.10 Linearity: (a) DAC; (b) ADC.

(e) *Monotonicity*

A converter has a monotic response (see Fig. 6.11) if none of the steps over the whole range are negative. Monotonicity is guaranteed if the differential non-linearity is less than or equal to 1 *LSB*.

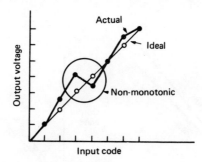

Figure 6.11 Monotonicity.

(f) *Missing codes (Fig. 6.12)*

This occurs in an ADC only, where one or more of the codes are missed out as the input voltage is varied over the whole range. As is shown in later sections some

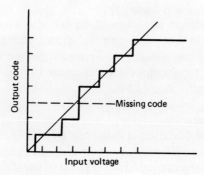

Figure 6.12 Missing code in ADC.

types of ADC use a DAC internally, and where this DAC is non-monotonic then as a detailed analysis shows, missing codes can occur. Missing codes can also be caused by internal electrical noise.

(g) *Absolute accuracy*
This is the difference between the actual analogue voltage that corresponds to any code, compared to the theoretical value of this voltage. When the converter is an ADC the measurement is done at the horizontal mid-point of a step. Usually the maximum difference is specified and the measurement includes errors from all sources except quantization uncertainty.

(h) *Relative accuracy*
This is similar to absolute accuracy, but the difference is now taken between the numerical value of code expressed as a binary fraction, and the corresponding analogue voltage expressed as a fraction of the *FSR*. This measurement does not include scale-factor errors, which can usually be nullified by the user.

Errors are often expressed as fractions of an *LSB*, percentage of *FSR*, or parts per million relative to full scale range.

The above explanations are in terms of errors arising in converters. Where other building blocks are used in analogue I/O (sample/holds, amplifiers, etc.), these will contribute errors which must be taken into account.

In many applications an overall accuracy comparable to the resolution is desirable. However, this need not always be the case. For example, if a DAC is used to generate a small number of voltages for an experiment, say 1, 2, 3, . . . , 9 V (using an *FSR* of 10 V), then only four bits of resolution are needed, but an accuracy corresponding to twelve bits may be required. Conversely for X- and Y-deflection DACs used to generate video display graphics images, a medium accuracy is acceptable, but a higher resolution may be desirable to ensure that the lines displayed have a smooth, rather than a stepped, appearance.

6.2.3   Bipolar codes and conversion

The unipolar coding as discussed so far is inadequate for bipolar signals, such as Fig. 6.2(a). Several coding schemes are in use to represent bipolar quantities, and three of the more common ones are illustrated in Table 6.3. The *FSR*, which spans positive and negative quantities, is taken to be 16 V.

From Table 6.3 it is easy to deduce that if a unipolar scheme of range 0 to $+V$ volts is converted to a bipolar scheme of range $-V$ volts to $+V$ volts, then the magnitude of one *LSB* in volts will be doubled, unless an extra bit of resolution is used in the converter.

In practice bipolar converters are usually obtained using simple modifications to unipolar converters. Figure 6.13 shows schematically how this can be done for DACs. Circuit details are given later in this chapter. For ADCs, similar steps to those in Fig. 6.13 can be used, but in reverse order. Alternatively, for those ADCs which use a DAC internally, a bipolar DAC will produce a bipolar ADC. Many commercial analogue I/O systems allow the user to select either a unipolar or one of several bipolar coding schemes.

Voltage	Offset binary	Twos complement	Sign magnitude
+7	1111	0111	0111
+6	1110	0110	0110
+5	1101	0101	0101
+4	1100	0100	0100
+3	1011	0011	0011
+2	1010	0010	0010
+1	1001	0001	0001
0	1000	0000	$\left(\text{or } \dfrac{0000}{1000} \right)$
−1	0111	1111	1001
−2	0110	1110	1010
−3	0101	1101	1011
−4	0100	1100	1100
−5	0011	1011	1101
−6	0010	1010	1110
−7	0001	1001	1111
−8	0000	1000	

Table 6.3 Bipolar coding.

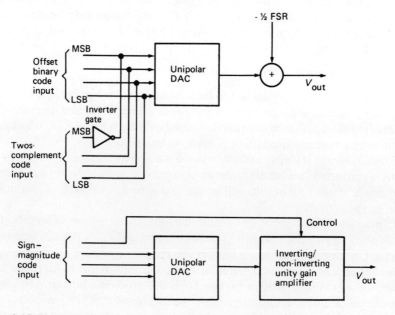

Figure 6.13 Bipolar DACs are obtained my modifying unipolar DAC.

6.3 Aliasing errors and the need for bandlimited signals

It is intuitively obvious that to preserve information during the sampling of an analogue signal, samples have to be taken at a sufficiently high rate that important features of the signal are not missed. From Shannon's sampling theorem,[2, 3] it is known that provided samples are taken more than twice as often as the highest frequency contained in the signal, then there is no loss of information due to the sampling process and it is possible unambiguously to reconstruct the signal from the samples.

It might be tempting to go on from this and conclude that if a signal contains higher-frequency components of no interest (such as noise) then it does not matter if a sampling rate less than twice these frequencies is used since information about these components is lost. However, this would be a wrong conclusion and in fact these components are translated in frequency and contaminate the wanted signal. This can be seen from the example in Fig. 6.14. The unwanted component is presumed to be a 9 kHz sinewave on a zero-frequency component which is presumed to be the wanted component. This composite waveform is sampled at 10^3 samples/s, which is less than twice the unwanted signal frequency. It can be seen that the resulting samples are indistinguishable from those obtained from a low-frequency 1 kHz sinewave sitting on the same zero-frequency component. After taking samples there is no way of knowing if this 1 kHz is genuine or not. The original signal has therefore taken on a new guise and this effect is called *aliasing*. These aliased components add onto the wanted components, thus constituting an error.

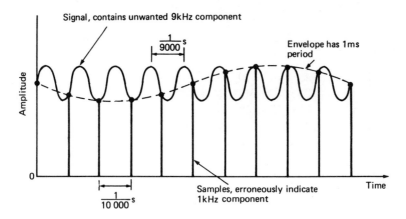

Figure 6.14 Aliasing error.

To avoid these errors the signal has to be 'bandlimited' so that it does not contain components with frequencies greater than half the sampling rate. Fortunately many signals are naturally bandlimited because they originate from physical phenomena which have mechanical inertia (as in many transducer signals) and the sampling rate can be chosen high enough to avoid problems.

Alternatively, a low-pass filter may be inserted in the signal path to cut out the higher-frequency components.

The contribution of aliasing error is generally negligible if the relative magnitude of the residual unwanted components is less than the overall accuracy required of the analogue input channel. A full mathematical analysis of this topic can be found in texts on signal processing and communications theory.[3]

6.4 Digital-to-analogue converters (DACs)

6.4.1 The weighted-resistor method

For the usual natural-binary coded converter, the DAC circuitry must function so that an input number causes an output voltage according to eq. (6.1). The right-hand side of this equation is the sum of binary weighted terms $\frac{1}{2}B_1$, $\frac{1}{4}B_2$, $\frac{1}{8}B_3$, . . . , and a conceptual way to realize this is shown in Fig. 6.15. Each of the current generators is zero or the value shown, depending on the state of the corresponding data bit. The output current is the sum of the currents:

$$I_{out} = I\left(\frac{B_1}{2} + \frac{B_2}{4} + \frac{B_3}{8} + \cdots\right),$$

and is of the same form as eq. (6.1).

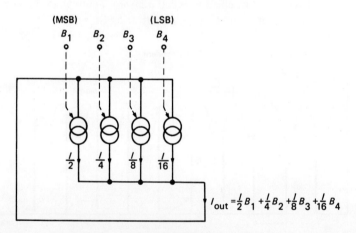

Figure 6.15 DAC concept using current generators.

In the arrangement shown in Fig. 6.16 the function of the current generator has been replaced by a resistor in series with a switch, connected to an accurate reference voltage source. The switch is closed when the corresponding data bit is 1. The high-gain operational amplifier, and feedback resistor, R_{FB}, are added so as to act as a current-to-voltage converter. In most applications a voltage output is preferred.

This is an example of a negative-feedback (NFB) circuit, and one property is that the voltage at the input terminals of an operational amplifier is approximate-

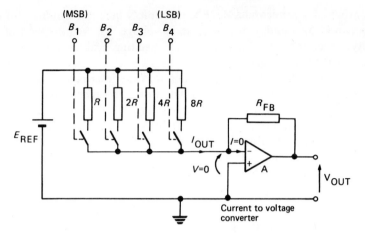

Figure 6.16 Weighted-resistor DAC.

ly zero provided the amplifier approaches the ideal. This property can be seen from the defining relationship $V_{out} = AV$. That is, $V = (1/A)V_{out}$, so taking a typical value for V_{out} of 10 V maximum, and $A = 100\,000$, V has a maximum value of $100\,\mu V$, which is very small compared with other voltages around the circuit. Also operational amplifiers have high input impedances, and therefore, to a first approximation, the terminal input currents can be asssumed to be zero.

That is, for any ideal operational amplifier in an NFB circuit

$$V = 0 \tag{6.3}$$

$$I = 0 \tag{6.4}$$

These conditions enable us to analyse operational amplifier circuits. For Fig. 6.16, all of I_{out} must pass through R_{FB} because of eq. (6.4) above, and causes a voltage drop across R_{FB} which can be equated to the voltage difference between its ends: $I_{out} \cdot R_{FB} = V - V_{out}$. Substituting condition (6.3) gives

$$V_{out} = -I_{out}R_{FB}. \tag{6.5}$$

Further, because of condition (6.3), when any switch is closed the full voltage E_{REF} appears across the resistor, consequently the current sum is given by

$$I_{out} = E_{RFF}\left(\frac{B_1}{R} + \frac{B_2}{2R} + \frac{B_3}{4R} + \cdots\right) \tag{6.6}$$

Combining (6.5) and (6.6),

$$V_{out} = \left(-E_{REF}\frac{2R_{FB}}{R}\right)\left(\frac{B_1}{2} + \frac{B_2}{4} + \frac{B_3}{8} + \cdots + \frac{B_n}{2^n}\right)$$

This is of the form required, with a full-scale range of $-E_{REF}(2R_{FB}/R)$. To obtain a positive value of FSR a negative reference voltage is used. In practice the reference voltage is obtained using the breakdown voltage of a zener diode, or by using a so called 'Band-gap' reference which is based on the logarithmic voltage-current relationship of a semiconductor PN junction, wherein a doubling of current produces a known and stable increase in voltage. The requirement of E_{REF} is stability rather than accuracy, since any resulting scale-factor error is easily compensated by adjusting R_{FB}.

Electronic switches are used in practice, and are described in the next section.

Although the circuit in Fig. 6.16 will work, it suffers from a number of disadvantages. The principal one is the high range of resistor values required: R to 2^nR. Even for a modest resolution of eight bits a range of R to $256R$ is required. It is difficult to manufacture such wide ranges to have adequately matched temperature coefficients and ageing properties when using preferred fabrication techniques such as thin-film, or monolithic-integrated circuits. In practice, then, this technique is limited to DACs with up to four or five bits of accuracy.

6.4.2   R–2R ladder method

The use of an $R-2R$ ladder, shown in Fig. 6.17, overcomes the difficulties mentioned above for the weighted-resistor method because resistor values are now confined to a two-to-one range. Most practical DAC circuits are based on the $R-2R$ ladder.

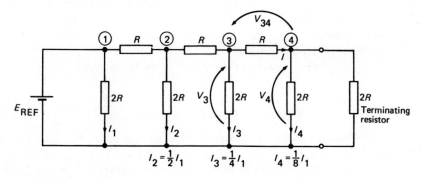

Figure 6.17 *R–2R* Ladder.

One of the useful properties of the ladder is that a reference voltage applied at one end causes the currents I_1 to I_4 to take on values in a decreasing binary weighted sequence. This can be seen by first considering the right-most current I_4. By Ohm's law, the voltage at node 4 is $V_4=(2R)I_4$. Also the current I must split equally down the two identical $(2R)$ resistor, and so $I=2I_4$. From this $V_{34}=R.I=R(2I_4)$. and because $V_3=V_{34}+V_4$; $V_3=R(2I_4)+(2R)I_4=(4R)I_4$. Substituting this result for V_3 in $I_3=V_3(2R)$ for the current down the next element in the ladder gives $I_3=2I_4$. This argument can also be applied to the next stage of the ladder to give $I_2=2I_3$, and once more, $I_1=2I_2$.

Combining these relationships, we have

$$I_1=I_1,\ I_2=I_1(\tfrac{1}{2}),\ I_3=I_1\,(\tfrac{1}{4}),\ I_4=I_1(\tfrac{1}{8}),$$

which is a binary weighted sequence as mentioned. This sequence can be expressed in terms of the reference voltage E_{RFF} by using Ohm's law on the first branch: $I_1 = E_{RFF}$ (2R), and so the nth term in the sequence is given by

$$I_n = \frac{E_{REF}}{R}\left(\frac{1}{2^n}\right).$$

This property leads directly to the $R-2R$ ladder DAC circuit shown in Fig. 6.18, in which the weighted resistors of Fig. 6.16 have been replaced by the $R-2R$ ladder. The switches serve to route each binary weighted current down to the zero-volts line or into the current-to-voltage converter. Using the results above: we obtain

$$V_{out} = \left(-E_{REF}\frac{R_{FB}}{R}\right)\left(\frac{B_1}{2} + \frac{B_2}{4} + \frac{B_3}{8} + \frac{B_4}{16}\right).$$

which is of the form required and provides an *FSR* of $-E_{REF}(R_{FB}R)$ volts.

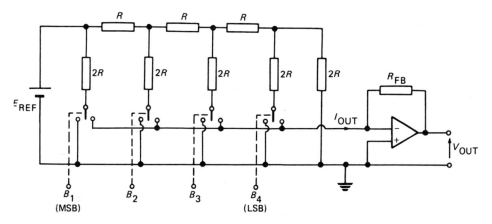

Figure 6.18 *R–2R* ladder DAC.

Most applications require resolutions of eight bits or more, and the extension of the circuit from the four bits shown is obvious.

Speed requirements dictate that electronic switches are used and the principle of operation of the field effect transistor (FET) switch is shown in Fig. 6.19(a). The terminal characteristics, Fig. 6.19(b), indicate that for V_{GS} positive the FET acts as a low resistance (typically $r_{on} = 100\,\Omega$), whereas for V_{GS} negative the FET is switched off and a negligibly small leakage current flows. The action of the two-position switch is then summarized as in Table 6.4.

The finite value of r_{on} increases the effective values of the (2R) resistors which can affect the binary-weighting property. This effect can be minimized by choosing the ladder resistances to be high (say 10 kΩ or more) and also trimming down the (2R) resistors by an amount equal to r_{on}.

Fabrication techniques vary, but typically the FET switches, and associated drive circuitry, are made as an integrated-circuit chip, and the passive $R-2R$ ladder is made in thin-film form on a separate substrate. Both chips are mounted in the same encapsulation. At least one manufacturer is able to put the thin film $R-2R$ circuit directly on the surface of the active-device IC chip.

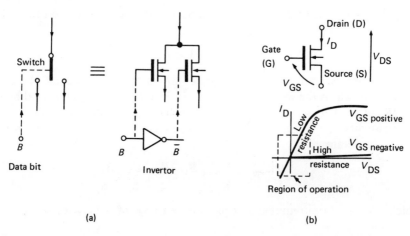

Figure 6.19 FET switch for Fig. 6.18; (a) principle; (b) FET terminal characteristics.

Control B	Q_1	Q_2	Result obtained
1 (positive)	OFF	ON	current passed to volt/current converter
0 (negative)	ON	OFF	current passed to zero volts line

Table 6.4 Action of a two-position switch.

A variety of other DAC circuits are also used in practice, based on the binary-weight property of $R-2R$ ladders.

6.4.3   Bipolar output voltages

As can be seen from Fig. 6.13, to convert a unipolar DAC to provide offset binary-coded bipolar output, the output voltage must be offset negatively by $\frac{1}{2}FSR$. This operation is particularly simple when a current-to-voltage converter is used at the DAC output, see Fig. 6.20. Here R_{OS} is chosen so that an offset current equivalent to $\frac{1}{2}FSR$ is subtracted from the output current of the unipolar converter before conversion to the output voltage.

To obtain twos-complement coding a simple way is to complement the MSB of the input data word before it is applied to the offset-binary DAC just described (see Fig. 6.13).

Sign-magnitude coded data conversion requires that the analogue output signal be inverted, or not, under control of the MSB of the data word. Figure 6.21 shows one way to do this. With MSB at a '0', corresponding to positive V_{out}, the switch is down and the ladder output current is connected to the input of A_2, which with R_3 acts as a normal current-to-voltage converter. With MSB at '1', the switch is up and the current is applied to the current-to-voltage converter, R_1 and A_1. However, in this connection R_2, R_3 and A_2 behave as a voltage-inverting

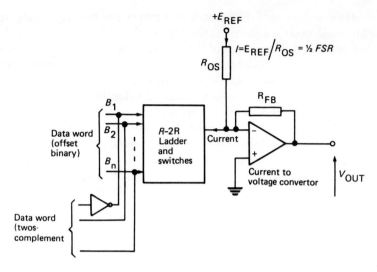

Figure 6.20 Bipolar operation (offset binary and twos-complement codes) of the R–$2R$ DAC.

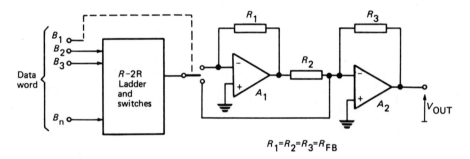

Figure 6.21 Bipolar operation (sign-magnitude) of the R—2R DAC.

amplifier with unity gain, and so the polarity of V_{out} is reversed. Although the sign-magnitude DAC requires another operational amplifier, one point in its favour is that one fewer bit of resolution is required for the unipolar DAC.

6.4.4 Performance limitations

Static imperfections are those arising when all voltage and current transients have settled down, and are principally those outlined in Section 6.2.2. Offset errors can be nullified by adding a small adjustable current to the input of the current-to-voltage converter, in a similar way to the $\frac{1}{2}FSR$ offset mechanism in Fig. 6.20. Scale-factor errors may be nullified by adjusting the feedback resistor R_{FB} in the current-to-voltage converter. Other errors, such as non-linearity etc., are usually under the control of the manufacturer.

Other static performance parameters of interest are the error temperature coefficients, since an error nullified at one temperature will return to some degree at another operating temperature of the circuit.

The principal dynamic performance parameter of interest is the settling time. When the input data code to the DAC is changed it takes a finite time for the circuit to settle down and provide the new output value. Worst-case settling time occurs during the transition from the most negative output level to the most positive output level, or vice versa. The settling time is defined under these worst-case conditions as the time taken for the output to settle to the steady-state value to within some specified band of error (see Fig. 6.22). Often this band of error is taken to be $\pm\frac{1}{2}LSB$. It follows therefore that higher resolution DACs, because of narrower error-bands, tend to have longer settling times. For example, a low-resolution 8-bit converter has a typical settling time of 1 μs, whereas 50 μs is a typical figure for a 16-bit DAC.

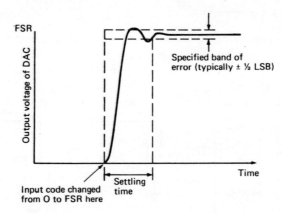

Figure 6.22 Settling time of a DAC.

Another dynamic effect is known as a *glitch*. This occurs because of small differences in the closure times of the switches in the DAC. These differences can effectively cause the DAC to be activated by several intermediate codes as the input code is changed from one to another. For example, suppose the original code to the DAC is $\frac{1}{2}FSR$ (1000), and is changed to a code which is 1 *LSB* less (0111), and assume that the MSB is a little slower to change than the other bits. Then the sequence is

1000   original code
1111   intermediate code (B_2, B_3, B_4 have changed, but not B_1)
0111 B_1 changes to give final code.

The intermediate code in fact corresponds to *FSR* and a large spike, or glitch, may appear at the output (see Fig. 6.23). Fortunately the settling time of the DAC smooths out these effects to some extent and glitches are usually of importance only in high-speed DACs. When necessary a sample hold can be used as a 'deglitcher', see Section 6.6.

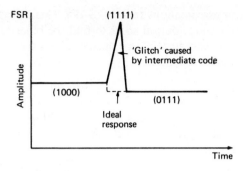

Figure 6.23 Example of a glitch in a DAC.

6.5 Analogue-to-digital converters (ADCs)

6.5.1 Introduction

An ADC 'finds' and outputs the nearest binary code to an applied input analogue voltage. Many techniques to do this are known. The most popular technique applied to computer analogue input is the successive-approximation method, probably followed by the integration method. These are now described.

6.5.2 Successive-approximations methods

As can be seen from Fig. 6.24 this comprises three main parts:

(i) A digital-to-analogue converter.
(ii) A comparator. This compares the incoming analogue voltage, V_{IN} with the output of the DAC, V_{DAC}, and outputs a logic 1 if V_{IN} is greater than V_{DAC}; otherwise logic 0 is output.

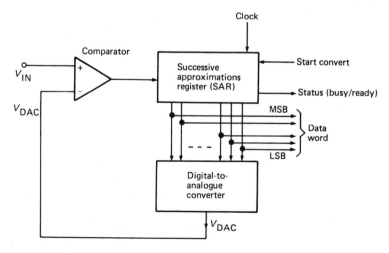

Figure 6.24 Successive-approximations ADC.

(iii)   A successive-approximations register (SAR). This includes necessary logic to use the comparator output so as to find the binary code such that the DAC output is closest to V_{IN}. This binary code is then the required output code of the ADC.

The method is reminiscent of a chemist's scales, in which ever-decreasing weights are tried in the balance pan and left in, or taken out, according to which way the scales are tipped. Consider a simple example using a 4-bit DAC with *FSR* of 16 V. The binary weights corresponding to B_1, B_2, B_3 and B_4 are 8, 4, 2, and 1 V respectively. Suppose the input voltage to be converted is 6.8 V. The timing diagram is shown in Fig. 6.25 and the sequence is as follows.

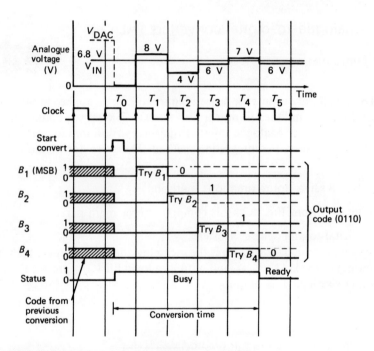

Figure 6.25 Timing of the successive approximations ADC

Before T_0 The data bits B_1 to B_4 are set from the previous conversion.

Period T_0 The arrival of the START command resets all bits to zero, and sets the STATUS signal to BUSY to indicate that conversion is in progress. Subsequent events are in synchronism with the clock.

Period T_1 The MSB (B_1) is tried. The DAC input is *1*000, so $V_{DAC} = 8$ V, which is greater than V_{IN}. The comparator output is 0, which tells the SAR to take out B_1 (i.e. $B_1=0$).

Period T_2 Bit B_2 is tried. The DAC input is 0*1*00, so $V_{DAC}=4$ V, which is less than V_{IN}. The comparator output is 1, which tells the SAR to leave in B_2 (i.e. $B_2=1$).

Period T_3 Bit B_3 is tried. The DAC input is 01*1*0, so $V_{DAC}=6$ V, which is less than V_{IN}. The comparator output is 1, which tells the SAR to leave in B_3 (i.e $B_3=1$).

Period T_4 The LSB (B_4) is tried. The DAC input is 011*1*, so $V_{DAC}=7$ V, which is greater than V_{IN}. The comparator output is 0, which tells the SAR to take out B_4 (i.e. $V_4=0$). The STATUS signal is reset at READY to indicate that conversion is complete.

For this example the output code corresponds to $V_{DAC}=6$ V, whereas the nearest code to $V_{IN}=6.8$ V in fact corresponds to $V_{DAC}=7$ V. A close examination of this strategy shows that the ADC has a transfer function as shown in Fig. 6.26. Comparing this with Fig. 6.8 it is seen that even if the DAC is ideal, an ideal ADC transfer function does not result, and an offset error of $\frac{1}{2}LSB$ is present. This effect occurs in all types of ADC which use a DAC in a feedback connection and is corrected simply by using the offset adjustment in the DAC.

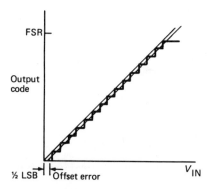

Figure 6.26 Offset error in ADC using an ideal DAC.

The extension of the above for 8 bits and more, as used in practice, is obvious. Also, minor variations in the above timings may be encountered.

6.5.3 Dual-ramp, integration method

This is illustrated in Fig. 6.27. It is widely used in digital voltmeters and panel meters, but is also used for analogue input to computers. The method indirectly converts a voltage to a function of time, and then converts this function to a digital number, using a counter.

The operation of the integrator is as follows. Equations (6.3) and (6.4) once again apply at the input to the operational amplifier, and so

$$I_1 = V_1/R. \tag{6.7}$$

This current must also flow through the capacitor, which is therefore related to the rate of change of capacitor voltage by

$$I_1 = C\frac{dV_c}{dt}. \tag{6.8}$$

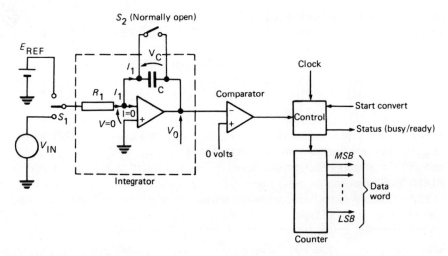

Figure 6.27 Dual-ramp ADC.

But V_c also equals the difference in voltages at the ends of the capacitor: $V_c = V - V_0$; and since $V = 0$ (eq. (6.3)), $V_0 = -V_c$. Combining this with eqs (6.7) and (6.8) gives $V_1 = -RC(dV_0/dt)$. Hence

$$V_0 = -\left(\frac{1}{CR}\right)\int V_1 dt. \tag{6.9}$$

That is, the output of this circuit is proportional to the time integral of the applied voltage V_1.

Passing now to the operation of the converter, the sequence begins with the arrival of the START command, as shown in the timing diagram of Fig. 6.28. Switch S_2 is momentarily closed to discharge the capacitor and reset the integrator output to 0 volts. At the same time

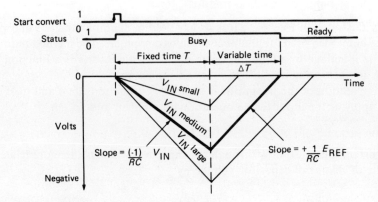

Figure 6.28 Timing diagram of the dual-ramp ADC.

(i)   the counter is set running,
(ii) S_1 is switched to the input voltage V_{IN} (assumed here to be positive unipolar), and
(iii) the STATUS signal is set at BUSY to indicate that conversion is in progress

V_{IN} causes the integrator to produce a negative going ramp, the slope of which is proportional to V_{IN}.

After a fixed period of time, T, as determined by the counter reaching a predetermined value, the switch S_2 is turned to the negative reference voltage, $-E_{REF}$. At the point of changeover the integrator output has a value proportional to V_{IN}; or to be more exact, proportional to the average of V_{IN} over the interval T. At this time, the counter is reset and again set running.

The integrator now produces a positive-going ramp, with constant slope equal to $\left(\dfrac{1}{CR}\right)E_{REF}$. After a period of time ΔT, the integrator output reaches 0 volts. This condition is detected by the comparator, which signals the counter to stop, which then holds a count which is a measure of the time ΔT. The STATUS signal is reset at READY to indicate that conversion is complete.

As is now shown the counter contains a digital number corresponding to the analogue input voltage, V_{IN}. At the end of period T the output of the integrator is given by

$$V_0(T)=\left(-\frac{1}{CR}\right)\int_0^T V_{IN}dt=\left(-\frac{T}{CR}\right)\frac{1}{T}\int_0^T V_{IN}dt=\left(-\frac{T}{CR}\right)\cdot\bar V_{IN}, \quad (6.10)$$

where $\bar V_{IN}$ denotes the average value of V_{IN}. The voltage $V_0(T)$ is reduced to zero over time ΔT. The ratio defines the slope of this portion of the integrator ouput:

$$\frac{-V_0(T)}{\Delta T}=\left(\frac{1}{CR}\right)E_{REF} \quad (6.11)$$

Combining egs (6.10) and (6.11) to eliminate $V_0(T)$ gives

$$\text{Counter contents } (\Delta T)=T\frac{\bar V_{IN}}{E_{REF}}. \quad (6.12)$$

The count representing T is chosen to be fullscale of the counter, and then the final counter output conveniently equals $\bar V_{IN}$ as a proportion of E_{REF}.

This type of converter has two useful properties. Firstly, the accuracy of the conversion, as can be seen from eq. (6.12), does not depend on the accuracy of the passive components C, R or the clock frequency. Stable components and an accurate E_{REF} ensures good accuracy of the converter at a modest cost. Secondly, the average value of V_{IN} is converted. This means that fluctuations in the signal over the period T are averaged out. A common type of unwanted fluctuation is that due to 50 Hz (or 60 Hz in some countries) mains supply. Even a small amount of fluctuation can be troublesome when converter accuracies of 8 bits up to 16 bits are required. By choosing T to be equal to an integral number of periods of the mains supply the average value of any interference voltage in the signal is zero and its effect is therefore eliminated.

6.5.4   Other ADC methods

The two methods described so far are probably the most commonly used (especially the successive-approximations method) for analogue input to computers, but not exclusively so. For example in the counter-method the SAR in Fig. 6.24 is replaced by a simple up-counter which produces a staircase waveform for V_{DAC}. When V_{DAC} exceeds V_{IN} the counter is stopped and then contains the digital number required for output. Although simple, the conversion time is much greater than for the successive-approximations method, and is not suitable for high-performance applications. A further variation is to use an up-down counter in place of the SAR.

Variations on the dual-ramp are used (for example, 'quad-slope') which improve on the performance of the dual-ramp by minimizing small errors due to integrator drift, etc.

6.5.5   Bipolar input signals

Digital conversion of bipolar analogue signals in ADCs using an internal DAC, as in the successive-approximation method, is most easily achieved by using a bipolar DAC. This is not applicable to the dual-ramp type of ADC since an internal DAC is not used. In this case the methods used to produce a bipolar DAC (see Section 6.4.3) can be used in reverse. Offset binary coding is obtained by subtraction of $\frac{1}{2}FSR$ voltage, from V_{IN}. The MSB is then complemented if twos-complement output code is required. For sign-magnitude conversion, the analogue signal is first passed through an 'absolute value' circuit.[4] This circuit converts any negative voltage to a positive one of the same magnitude, and can be arranged to give a logic signal to indicate the original polarity of the signal.

6.5.6   Performance limitations

Accuracy and other static parameters of the successive-approximations type of ADC obviously cannot be better than those of the internal DAC. In fact the parameters will be slightly worse because of offset errors in the comparator. This is caused because the changeover of the comparator output in practice does not occur exactly when the two inputs are equal. Overall offset and scale-factor errors can be nullified, however, by adjustments to the internal DAC.

Offset errors in the dual-ramp converter can be corrected by adding a small voltage to V_{IN}. Scale-factor errors can be nullified by trimming E_{REF}.

The dynamic performance parameter of interest is the conversion time. For an n-bit successive-approximation ADC this is equal to slightly more than n clock periods, as can be seen from Fig. 6.25. To avoid dynamic errors introduced by the DAC, the clock period must not be less than the settling time of the DAC. This means that the increase of conversion time of the ADC accelerates with n because the settling time of the DAC also increases with n. Even so, conversion times are fast enough for most applications, being typically in the range 25 μs down to 1 μs or less.

The conversion time of the dual-ramp method is considerably longer than for a successive-approximations converter because of the long counting sequences. Typical conversion times are in the range 30 ms (low-resolution ADC) to 200 ms (high-resolution ADC). However, for slowly varying analogue signals these times are adequate and the advantages of economy and mains-frequency rejection favour the choice of this method.

6.6 Sample/hold (S/H) circuits

6.6.1 Introduction

A sample/hold circuit is used to overcome a problem that can arise with an ADC. In many types of ADC, such as successive approximations, if the input voltage changes during the conversion process, an erroneous digital output can result. To achieve a conversion uncertainty of less than $\pm\frac{1}{2}LSB$, then the voltage must change by less than this amount over the time it takes to do a conversion, t_{con}. Assuming the signal is smoothly varying then this places a restriction on the gradient of the signal of

$$\left|\frac{dV_{IN}}{dt}\right| \leqslant 2^{-n} FSR \frac{1}{t_{con}}. \tag{6.13}$$

For example, taking typical figures of $t_{con} = 10\ \mu s$, $FSR = 10$ V, $n = 8$, then dV_{IN}/dt must be less than 2000 V/s. This may not appear too restrictive at first glance. However, suppose the signal is a sinewave of maximum amplitude: $V_{IN} = \frac{1}{2}(FSR)$ $\sin(2\pi ft)$. Then simple calculus shows that the greatest rate of change occurs as V_{IN} passes through the origin, and is given by

$$\frac{dV_{IN}}{dt} = \pi f(FSR). \tag{6.14}$$

Using the above figures in this equation shows that a signal frequency, f, in excess of about 120 Hz will give rise to problems. This figure is quite low, especially when compared with the maximum sample rate of the converter of $1/t_{con}$, that is 100 000 samples per second.

Greater signal speeds can be used if the signal is sampled and held constant while digital conversion takes place. The sample/hold circuit performs this function, and the basic idea is shown in Fig. 6.29. With the control at SAMPLE the switch is closed and the capacitor C quickly assumes a voltage equal to V_{IN}. When the control is changed to HOLD, the switch is opened and the capacitor which is across the output terminals holds its voltage constant until the next sample is taken. During the HOLD period the ADC is able to perform a conversion on an unchanging voltage, and the code produced is that of the input voltage at the instant of the SAMPLE to HOLD transition. In practice the START CONVERT command to the ADC is first taken to the SAMPLE/-HOLD control, and then passed onto the ADC, possibly after a small time delay to allow the sample to be taken.

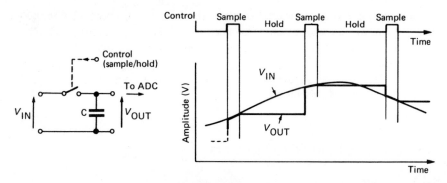

Figure 6.29 Principle of operation of a sample/hold circuit.

Another use of a S/H circuit is as a *de-glitcher* on the output of a DAC. As mentioned in Section 6.4.5, unwanted glitches can occur at the output of a DAC when the input code is undated. Here the glitches are removed by sampling the DAC output in the middle part of one clock period and holding this value past the glitch until the middle of part of the next period. The high speeds involved call for very careful circuit design, and the de-glitcher is often incorporated by the manufacturer within the DAC module.

6.6.2   Practical S/H circuit

The first modification required to the basic circuit in Fig. 6.29 is to attach buffers with unity voltage gain as shown in Fig. 6.30(a). Each operational amplifier has its output connected to one of its input terminals. From eq. (6.3) the voltage between the input terminals of the operational amplifier are constrained to be zero by negative feedback. Hence the output voltage of a buffer is equal to its input voltage; that is, it has unity voltage gain. Unity buffers are used because they are able to deliver a load current while drawing a negligible current at the buffer input. The buffer A_1 provides a high charging current to C when a sample is taken. Without this buffer this current would be taken from the signal source and would probably cause a loading effect. Buffer A_2 conveys the 'hold' voltage on C to the output of the S/H, and protects C from unwanted discharge by load current flowing to the output terminals.

A further modification is shown in Fig. 6.30(b), which is a popular configuration used in practice. Here the feedback signal to A_1 is now taken from the S/H output. With the switch closed in SAMPLE mode there is no basic difference in operation compared with Fig. 6.30(a), since negative feedback ensures that in both circuits V_{IN}, V_{out}, and the capacitor voltage are all at the same voltage. However, there is a practical advantage in the second circuit which is apparent when the switch is open, in the HOLD mode, and about to close to take a sample. If the previous sample voltage stored in C and the present value of V_{IN} are close in value, then in the circuit Fig. 6.30(a), the voltage across the open switch is not large and when the switch is closed a modest charging effort is applied to C. However, with S open in Fig. 6.30(b) the operational amplifier A_1 is in the open-

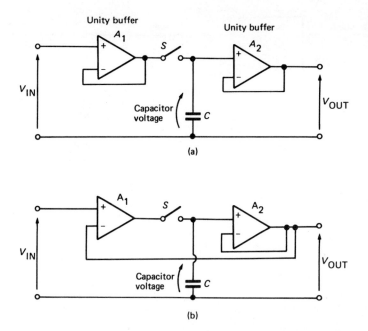

Figure 6.30 Practical sample/hold circuits; (a) buffered input and output; (b) modification for faster sampling.

loop condition, and although the differential input to A_1 is small, it is amplified by a typical gain value of 100 000. The operational amplifier A_1 will saturate at its maximum positive or negative value (typically $\pm$ 15 V) depending on the polarity of the differential input. Hence quite a large voltage exists across the open switch, so that when it is closed C is charged to the sample value at high speed.

6.6.3 Performance limitations

The performance of an actual S/H differs in small ways from the ideal shown in Fig. 6.29. However, these differences contribute to the overall accuracy of the system and can be significant. The more important effects are shown in Fig. 6.31 and are now discussed.

(i) *Acquisition time* (typically 1–10 μs). This is the time taken from the start of the SAMPLE condition for the output voltage to equal the input voltage to within a specified band of error. A large component of acquisition time is due to the charging time of the capacitor. A low capacitor value should therefore be used.

(ii) *Aperture time* (typically 0.01–0.2 μs). This is the time between the HOLD instruction being given and the actual time the switch is opened.

(iii) *Aperture uncertainty* or *jitter* (typically 2% to 10% of aperture time). Of itself aperture times is not very important, since if necessary the HOLD instruction can be advanced in time to compensate. However, aperture-time jitter, which is the fluctuation in aperture time from sample to sample, can be important. For a changing signal, uncertainty in sampling time is equivalent to

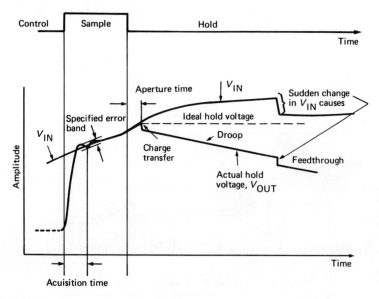

Figure 6.31 Imperfections of a practical sample/hold (effects are exaggerated).

uncertainty in sample amplitude. To ensure an amplitude uncertainty of less than $\pm\frac{1}{2}LSB$, the slope of the signal is restricted by the same relation as eq. (6.13), but with t_{con} replaced by the aperture uncertainty, t_{AU}.

$$\left|\frac{dV_{IN}}{dt}\right| \leqslant (2^{-n})FSR\frac{1}{t_{AU}}. \tag{6.15}$$

As an example, suppose a S/H with a typical $t_{AU}=0.02\ \mu s$ feeds into the same ADC as in the example in Section 6.6.1. Then from eqs (6.14) and (6.15) the maximum frequency of a full-size sinewave signal is about 60 kHz before jitter errors become significant. This figure is probably acceptable in this case, since it is consistent with the maximum ADC conversion rate of 100K samples/s (that is $1/t_{con}$).

(iv) *Droop* (typically 0.1–100 m V/s)   Ideally the output voltage of the S/H in the HOLD condition should stay constant. However, in practice V_{OUT} drifts from this value with time. This is called *droop* and is caused by discharge of the S/H capacitor due to (a) leakage current of the open switch, (b) self-discharge of the capacitor through its own dielectric, and (c) input current to the buffer A_2. Droop is specified as the maximum rate of change of output voltage, and is undesirable since the reason for using the S/H is to obtain a constant sample amplitude. Droop can be reduced by using a large capacitor value. This conflicts with requirements to minimize aquisition time. An adequate compromise can usually be obtained.

(v) *Feedthrough and charge transfer*   Feedthrough occurs during the HOLD condition when a change in input voltage causes a small unwanted change in output voltage even though the S/H switch is open. It is caused by stray coupling between input and storage capacitor C.

Also charge transfer can take place when the switch is opened and a small charge is dumped in the storage capacitor. This causes an offset in the output hold voltage.

Both these effects contribute small errors and are significant only in high-accuracy analogue-input channels.

6.7   Signal conditioning

6.7.1   Introduction

Best accuracy is obtained from the S/H and ADC if they are driven by signal amplitudes which approach the *FSR*, (typically 10 V). In this way the offset errors and quantization errors are relatively small compared to the signal.

However, many signals have low amplitudes at source, so amplification is desirable. Moreover, when the signal source is some distance from the computer, the signal wire is susceptible to electrical interference. It is then necessary to use a second wire connected to ground at the signal source, as shown in Fig. 6.32. The two wires are placed close together (preferably twisted) and pick up essentially the same interference noise signal E_n.

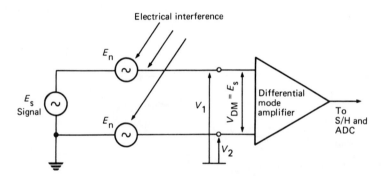

Figure 6.32 Amplification of differential mode voltage eliminates effect of electrical interference.

Two frequently used terms are now defined.

(i) *Differential-mode voltage* (V_{DM}) This is defined as $V_{DM} = V_1 - V_2$. Substituting for V_1 and V_2 using Fig. 6.32, we obtain $V_{DM} = (E_s + E_n) - (E_n) = E_s$. Note that the noise terms cancel, and V_{DM} equals the original signal source e.m.f.

(ii) *Common-mode voltage* (V_{CM}) This is defined as $V_{CM} = \frac{1}{2}(V_1 + V_2)$. Substituting for V_1 and V_2, we obtain

$$V_{CM} = \frac{1}{2}(E_s + E_n) + (E_n) = E_n + \frac{1}{2}E_s.$$

For small signals it is seen that V_{CM} is dominated by the noise component.

Hence a differential-input type of amplifier is required which has the required differential mode gain. A_{DM}, to raise the differential mode voltage V_{DM}, to a level comparable to (but not greater than) the *FSR* of the S/H and ADC. The differential amplifier should have low common-mode gain, A_{CM}, (ideally zero) to common mode voltage, V_{CM}, to avoid corruption due to electrical interference.

6.7.2   Instrumentation amplifier

This name is given to a differential-mode amplifier with the desired characteristics of precise A_{DM}, small A_{CM}, low-signal input currents, and the ability to supply a sufficient output current to a load.

An operational amplifier on its own meets all these requirements except one. This is that A_{DM} (typically 100 000) is imprecise and varies markedly with temperature, power-supply voltage, and from device to device. A more complicated circuit is necessary and a popular instrumentation amplifier circuit is shown in Fig. 6.33. The first stage amplifies V_{DM}, while taking very little input current from the signal. The output of the first stage contains a common-mode component and the second stage eliminates this component while further amplifying the differential mode component. The full analysis is found in texts on operational amplifiers[5]. The output voltage is given by the formula

$$V_0 = A_{DM} V_{DM} = -\left(1 + 2\frac{R_2}{R_1}\right)\left(\frac{R_4}{R_3}\right) V_{DM} \qquad (6.16)$$

The negative sign indicates that the output is inverted with respect to V_{DM}. A non-inverted output is easily obtained by interchanging the amplifier input terminals.

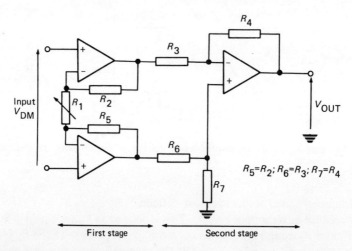

Figure 6.33 Instrumentation amplifier.

Resistor values are chosen to give A_{DM} typically in the range 1 to 10 000. It is convenient to vary R_1 to set the required gain, since other resistors are in pairs which have to retain accurate matching. In many cases the instrumentation amplifier is supplied without R_1 to enable the user to easily set the required gain.

A programmable instrumentation amplifier is obtained by using digitally controlled electronic switches to connect different combinations of resistors inside the circuit module to achieve a range of discrete differential mode gains. Typically A_{DM} can be set at values in range of 1 to 1024 in steps of 1. Although more expensive than fixed A_{DM} instrumentation amplifiers, programmable gain has the advantages of greater flexibility and the convenience of being able to change the gain under the control of the computer.

6.7.3 Isolation amplifier

Although the instrumentation amplifier eliminates the effect of V_{CM}, this common-mode voltage does have to stay within the working range of the circuit. Typically this range is ± 10 V.

In some applications the V_{CM} component may be much higher than this. Other applications, notably in medical instrumentation, require for safety reasons very high isolation between the signal source (often a patient's body) and the main part of the instrumentation system. In these cases an isolation amplifier is used in place of the instrumentation amplifier.

The main approach in the isolation amplifier (see Fig. 6.34), is to allow direct connection of the amplifier to the signal inputs, but other connections are via transformer coupling. One transformer, T_1, supplies alternating current to the AC/DC converter which supplies DC power to the rest of the circuit. Since the output of the differential amplifier may contain zero frequency components, it is not possible to transfer this directly via a transformer, and it is first converted to an alternating signal by the high-frequency modulator, as indicated. Outside the isolated area the demodulator recovers the amplifier output voltage. As an alternative to transformer coupling of the modulator output, optical couplers are popularly used.

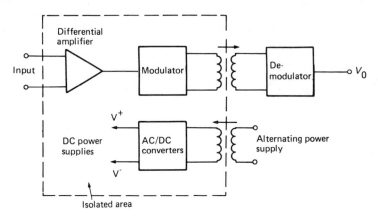

Figure 6.34 Isolation amplifier.

6.7.4 Performance limitations

Some of the principal parameters are:

(i) *Gain error* (typically $\pm 0.25\%$) This is the difference between the measured gain and that predicted by eq. (6.16).

(ii) *Non-linearity* (typically $\pm 0.002\%$ to $\pm 0.2\%$) Ideally the graph of V_0 versus V_{DM} should be a straight line. Non-linearity is a measure of the maximum deviation of the actual graph from the best straight line. It is expressed as a % of full-scale output.

(iii) *Voltage-offset*   In practice the graph of V_0 versus V_{DM} does not precisely pass through the origin. This means that the output voltage will contain a small unwanted offset voltage. The intercept of the line on the V_{DM} axis is called the voltage-offset. A typical value is 0.4 mV. This effect is not too troublesome since it can be nullified on most amplifiers. However, changes in temperature can cause offset voltage to return, and the voltage-offset temperature coefficient is of interest. Values for this are typically in the range 2–100 $\mu V/°C$.

(iv) *Common-mode rejection* (CMR) (typically 60–120 dB)   This is the ratio of the differential mode gain to the unwanted common-mode gain, and is usually expressed in decibels, $CMR = 20 \log_{10} A_{DM}/A_{CM}$, dB. It is a measure of the ability of the amplifier to reject the unwanted V_{CM} while amplifying V_{DM}.

(v) *Full-power band width*   This is the maximum sinewave frequency at which the amplifier can supply a full output amplitude without significant distortion. Typical values are in the range of 10 kHz to 100 kHz, for instrumentation amplifiers. For the isolation amplifier, use of modulators constrains the usable frequency range to typically 10 kHz or less.

6.8   Multiplexers and multiple analogue I/O channels

6.8.1   Introduction

Consider the problem of inputting 64 analogue channels to a computer using the circuits described this far. A separate chain of amplifier, S/H and ADC would be required for each channel. This would be a highly expensive solution to the problem.

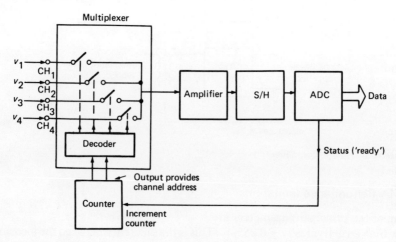

Figure 6.35 Multiplexer (MUX) used for a four-channel analogue input system.

A multiplexer (contracted to MUX), allows a single amplifier, S/H and ADC to be 'time-shared' over several analogue channels, thus saving on costs. The operation of the MUX can be understood from the simple four-channel system shown in Fig. 6.35. The associated waveforms are shown in Fig. 6.36. Each channel is coupled to the output of the MUX via a digitally controlled electronic switch. Channel addresses are input to the decoder, which closes the appropriate switch for a sufficient period to allow the S/H and ADC to perform a data conversion. In the arrangement shown the channel addresses are generated in cyclic sequence by a counter. The counter is incremented to address the next channel by the ADC READY condition which signifies that data conversion of the current channel is completed.

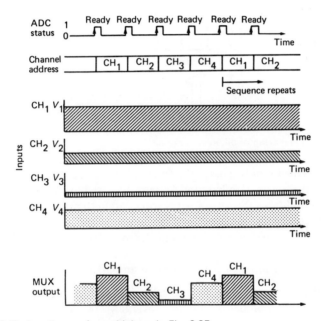

Figure 6.36 Timing diagram for multiplexer in Fig. 6.35.

Channel addresses may also be provided by a register which is loaded by the computer. This allows channels to be accessed in any desired sequence.

6.8.2   Types of multiplexer

Three types of multiplexer input connection are used:

(i) *Single-ended inputs*   This is as shown for the MUX in Fig. 6.35. A single-ended voltage requires one wire for connection, the zero-volts point of the signal being also that of the converter circuitry.

(ii) *Differential inputs*   Here each channel requires two wires, to overcome common-mode interference problems, as mentioned in Section 6.7.1. The MUX now has two output connections which pass to a differential amplifier, as shown in Fig. 6.37.

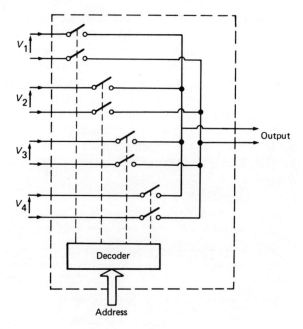

Figure 6.37 Multiplexing of differential signals.

(iii) *Quasi-differential inputs* A differential signal contains a signal wire and a return wire. If a cluster of differential signals is exposed to interference, then under favourable conditions the return wires will contain the same interference signal, and can therefore be replaced by one return wire. In the quasi-differential connection the signal wires are multiplexed to one terminal of differential amplifier using a single-ended MUX, and the one return wire is taken directly to the other input terminal of the differential amplifier.

In practice, 8–16 switches are typically enclosed in one MUX module. To multiplex a greater number of channels, several MUX modules can be connected using the two-tier technique shown in Fig. 6.38, which is sometimes called 'sub multiplexing'.

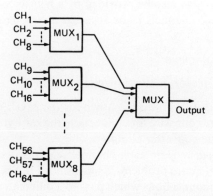

Figure 6.38 Increasing the number of input channels by sub-multiplexing.

6.8.3 Multiple analogue-input channels

The straightforward way is to connect the MUX before the amplifier as shown in Fig. 6.35. However, conditions sometimes require the MUX to be placed at other points in the chain.

In many applications the signal amplitude levels vary from one channel to another. Consequently a fixed-gain signal-conditioning amplifier is unable to scale all channels. To overcome this a more expensive programmable-gain amplifier can be used. Alternatively the MUX can be put between the amplifier and S/H. This requires an amplifier per channel, which is not necessarily uneconomic since medium specification integrated-circuit instrumentation amplifiers are not very expensive. Where isolation amplifiers are needed it is also necessary to place the MUX after the amplifier to preserve the isolation of the signal.

In the arrangements considered this far, the channel samples are taken in sequence. Sometimes it is necessary to sample and convert all channel signals at the same point in time: for example, in measuring the simultaneous responses to a stimulus in an experiment. In these cases a S/H is used for each channel and the MUX is placed after the S/Hs. All channels are sampled at the same instant and then held while the ADC converts each channel voltage in turn.

Occasionally, a MUX may not be used at all. This can be the case where the number of channels is low and the costs and complications of the MUX are not warranted. This is especially so where conditions are favourable, and each channel requires only an ADC and not an S/H and amplifier. In other cases the sampling rate of each channel needs to be high and the conversion time of the ADC is not low enough to allow it to be time-shared, and hence one ADC is used per channel.

6.8.4 Multiple analogue-output channels

The multiplexer can be used in reverse to time-share one DAC over several output channels, as shown in Fig. 6.39. It is often, then called a *demultiplexer* (DEMUX). The DEMUX provides an output to each channel for only one part of the channel sequence. When the MUX is serving other output channels the output on a channel falls to zero. A S/H is therefore usually required on each

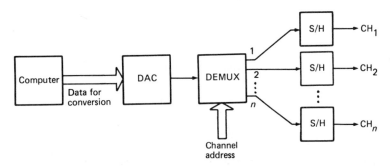

Figure 6.39 Multiple output channels using a demultiplexer (DEMUX).

channel to hold up the voltage until replenished by the DEMUX on the next cycle.

The added costs of the S/H make the advantages of using a DEMUX on analogue output less certain. In many applications, only a few analogue outputs may be needed, and one DAC per channel may then be preferred.

6.9   Complete analogue I/O systems

6.9.1   A full facility system

Complete systems use circuits described in the previous sections together with control logic. A moderately high-performance system is illustrated in Fig. 6.40. Although not an actual product, it illustrates the performance and facilities found on a typical mini-computer analogue I/O system.

It is made up of three sections:

(i)   multichannel analogue inputs, similar to Fig. 6.35;
(ii)   multichannel analogue output;
(iii)   control and computer interface logic.

Specification of the analogue input section:

Input channels	16 (differential) or 32 (single-ended), extendable to 128 (differential) or 256 (single-ended) channels by sub-multiplexing
Input voltage ranges	$+5$ V, $+10$ V, ±5 V, or ±10 V *FSR*.
Digital coding	natural binary, offset-binary, or twos-complement.
Resolution	14 bits. The ADC can be 'short cycled' to 8, 10, or 12 bits resolution to reduce conversion time.
Conversion rate	100K samples/s (on 8 bits) down to 20K samples/s (on 14 bits).
Overall accuracy	$\pm0.02\%$ of *FSR* $\pm\frac{1}{2}LSB$.

Specifications of the analogue output section:

Output channels	16, expandable to 32 channels. DEMUX not used; one DAC per channel.
Output voltage ranges Digital coding Resolution	as for analogue input.
Output rate	500K conversions per second.
Overall accuracy	$\pm0.01\%$ (better than analogue input because no errors due to MUX, amplifier, S/H).

The analogue input and output sections are coupled to the CPU data buses by several registers, each of which is accessible by means of the CPU address bus,

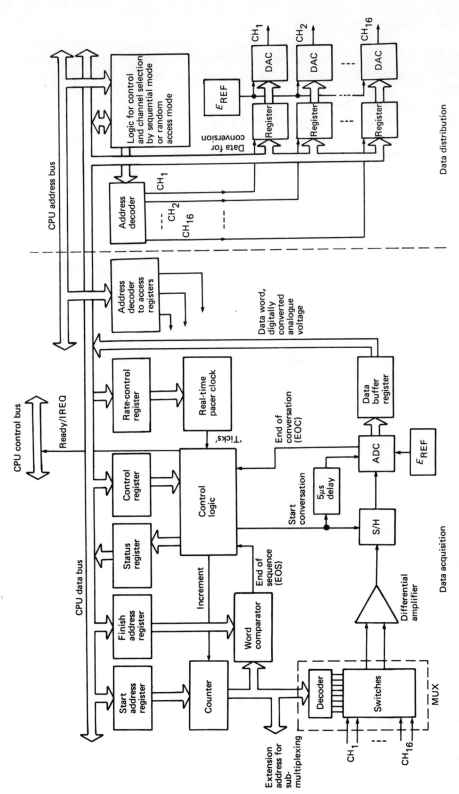

Figure 6.40 A full facility complete analogue I/O system.

and address decoders. These can be built into the Analogue I/O system, as shown. Alternatively, use can be made of one or more general-purpose interface unit I/O ports on the computer.

Analogue input basically requires a channel address to be provided and decoded, together with the initiation of a START CONVERSION command. This command activates the S/H and following a short time delay (5 μs, in Fig. 6.40), to allow the S/H to acquire the sample, this causes the ADC to perform a conversion. At the end of conversion (EOC) the ADC output data word is placed in a buffer register and the CPU is flagged. This data word is transferred to the CPU using normal interrupt or programmed I/O.

There are two ways in which channel addresses are set up; sequential mode or random-access mode. In sequential mode a group of input channels is stepped through and a data conversion occurs at each step. This can be useful where not all channels have signals connected, or when only a subset of them needs to be converted. Before beginning the sequence, the start and finishing channel addresses of the sequence are loaded into registers. At the beginning of the sequence, the start address is loaded into the current-address counter whose output is decoded. The corresponding channel is selected by the MUX and converted by the ADC. At the end of the conversion EOC notifies the CPU and also causes the current-address counter to increment by one count, thus selecting the next channel in the sequence, which is then converted by the ADC. This is repeated until the final channel address is reached. The output code of the current-address counter is continually compared with the contents of the finish address register and when a match occurs an end-of-sequence (EOS) condition is raised. The sequence is then terminated, and awaits the next instruction to start the sequence.

Rather than raise an interrupt, or use programmed I/O, at the end of each channel conversion, a direct memory access facility can be used, where provided, to allow data from the sequence to be passed to the computer memory in one burst.

The sequence may be initiated under CPU control, or perhaps more conveniently by a real-time pacer clock. This clock issues 'ticks' at rates typically in the range 100 μs to 1 s, which can be set by a rate-control word placed in a pacer clock register by the CPU. The control logic then uses these 'ticks' to issue a START SEQUENCE command. Some real-time pacer clocks may not be CPU controllable and instead are set by switches or knobs on the front panel of the I/O system. The pacer clock may not be necessary when the computer is equipped with a real-time clock as a central facility. A 'tick' from this clock then raises an interrupt on the CPU, and the appropriate service routine then instructs the analogue I/O system to begin the conversion sequence.

In random-access mode, the sequence control does not operate and only the particular channel address entered by the CPU is converted. Each address is entered via the start-address register to the current-address counter, which is now frozen, and the channel-address decoder selects the corresponding analogue-input channel. After conversion, EOC is flagged to the CPU but the current-address counter is not incremented. New channel addresses can then be entered, or not if the same channel is to be repeatedly converted.

Analogue output is performed using separate DACs, one to each channel. Each DAC is fed by a data register, which is loaded by the CPU. Similar logic to that in the analogue-input section is provided to store and decode channel addresses, and to perform random-access or sequential mode operation under the control of a real-time clock. The operation of these modes is also similar to that of the analogue-input section.

Typically the analogue I/O system would be housed in a standard 19 in (48 cm) wide rack-mountable cabinet for insertion in the mini-computer frame. The front panel would contain controls to ease the setting up and checking of the analogue I/O channels. Individual channels can be selected by means of switches and conversion performed under manual control. For an analogue input channel the resulting data word is shown on a row of lights; whilst for an analogue output channel a data word for conversion can be set up on switches.

Many computer manufacturers support real-time high-level languages which contain easily understood and used commands and statements. For example 'X = ADC(125):' would mean 'set variable x equal to the voltage on channel 125'. When these languages are not available, it is necessary to use assembly-code languages.

6.9.2 Smaller systems

There is no sharp division between large and small systems. The smaller analogue I/O systems tend to have less accuracy, lower conversion rates and fewer channels. They are usually associated with micro-computers and smaller mini-computers. Often they are made as a single unenclosed printed-circuit-board assembly, and are mounted in the computer cardcage alongside the CPU, memory, and other cards. Small analogue input and output systems are now available in integrated-circuit form or encapsulated in small modules. These are inserted in the circuit board as a single component.

Many micro-computers have an 8-bit databus and where twelve-bit resolution ADCs are used, the ADC output is split into 'high' and 'low' bytes (say 4 bits plus 8 bits) and entered to the CPU in two operations. The converse is applied to the DAC. However, if one of the bytes is applied directly to the DAC it will start to produce an erroneous analogue output before the second byte arrives. The procedure usually adopted, therefore, is to assemble the two bytes in a full-width buffer register before passing this to the DAC.

6.10   Input transducers

6.10.1   General

In this section, we will briefly review some input devices known as transducers which are used to measure quantities such as length, force, pressure or temperature depending upon the type, by converting input energy into an electrical (analogue) signal. The analogue signal can then be converted into a digital quantity for a computer system if required using an ADC. Hence transducers can be computer peripheral devices. Such peripheral devices find application in control applications.

An input transducer converts one form of energy, typically mechanical energy, thermal energy or electromagnetic radiation, into electrical energy. Transducers with a mechanical input are used to measure, for example, distance or rotation force or pressure. Transducers with thermal input are used to measure temperature. Transducers with radiation input are used, for example, to detect or measure visible light. Transducers can also be designed for electrical input, for example to convert from current to voltage.

A sensor is an input device which detects the presence of a form of energy or a change in the energy level or other physical stimulus. For example, light can be detected by a photodetector type of sensor. We shall consider sensors and transducer together as normally sensors are part of transducers and are coupled to circuits to form complete transducers.

6.10.2   Mechanical input transducers

(a) *Displacement transducers*

Displacement transducers are used to measure a change in length. Relatively low-precision displacement transducers can use a resistive potentiometer, as shown in Fig. 6.41. The movement of the wiper of the potentiometer produces a change of resistance between the wiper and each fixed terminal, and hence with the application of a constant voltage across the fixed terminals, a change in the wiper terminal voltage occurs. The potentiometer can be designed for linear movement of the wiper or rotational movement of the wiper. Accuracy can be about 0.1%. These forms of displacement transducers suffer from wear of the wiper and resistive track.

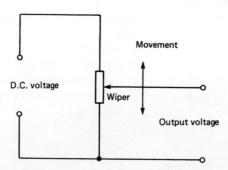

Figure 6.41 Resistive displacement transducer.

Capacitive displacement transducers avoid wiper and track wear by using the movement of a plate of a capacitor to cause a change of capacitance which is directly related to the movement. Normally three plates are used to obtain a linear relationship or approximately linear relationship between the movement and the capacitance or measured signal. Two plates are fixed and one can move.

The movement can alter the area of the movable plate exposed to the fixed plates, or alter the separation of the movable plate relative to the fixed plates depending upon the configuration, as shown in Fig. 6.42.

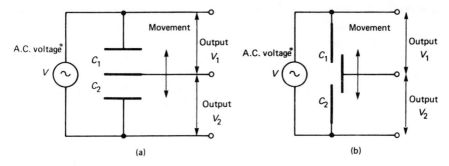

Figure 6.42 Capacitive displacement transducers. (a) variable separation type; (b) variable area type. *Sometimes from a centre-tapped transformer.

The capacitance of a capacitor is given by:

$$C = \varepsilon a/d$$

where ε is the permittivity constant $\times$ relative permittivity, a is the cross-sectional area and d the separation of the plates. For the configuration in Fig. 6.42(a), we can derive the two capacitances as:

$$C_1 = \varepsilon a/(d+x) \qquad \text{and} \qquad C_2 = \varepsilon a/(d-x),$$

where d is the separation of the movable plate and the two fixed plates in the central position, and x is the movement of the movable plate from the central position. The output voltages are given by:

$$V_1 = VC_2/(C_1+C_2) \qquad \text{and} \qquad V_2 = VC_1/(C_1+C_2).$$

Hence by substitution we get the voltage difference between V_1 and V_2 directly proportional to the movement:

$$V_1 - V_2 = Vx/d$$

with the permittivity and area eliminated.

As with many other transducers, a Wheatstone bridge circuit is often employed to measure the change in the parameters of a particular capacitive transducer. For the capacitive transducer C_1 and C_2 form two arms of the bridge, and the ratio C_2/C_1 is measured. This ratio is given by

$$C_2/C_1 = (d-x)/(d+x) = 1 + 2x/d \text{ for } d \text{ much greater than } x.$$

For the configuration shown in Fig. 6.42(b), we have:

$$C_1 = \varepsilon w(l/2+x)/d \quad \text{and} \quad C_2 = \varepsilon w(l/2-x)/d,$$

where w is the width of each plate, $l/2$ is the length of the movable plate over each fixed plate is the central position and the gap between the fixed plates is sufficiently small to be neglected. Fringe effects are also neglected. Hence we have a capacitive ratio in a similar form to previously.

Inductive displacement transducers, as shown in Fig. 6.43, typically employ a movable non-magnetic shaft with a ferromagnetic plunger within an inductor or transformer. Moving the shaft alters the output voltage measured. In the transducer shown in Fig. 6.43(b), an a.c. voltage is applied to one coil and a signal obtained from two coils wound in opposite directions on either side of the input coil, such that when the plunger is in the central position no output signal is measured. When the plunger is moved, the voltage induced in one coil increases and the voltage in the other coil decreases but adds to the change output voltage, to produce an output voltage.

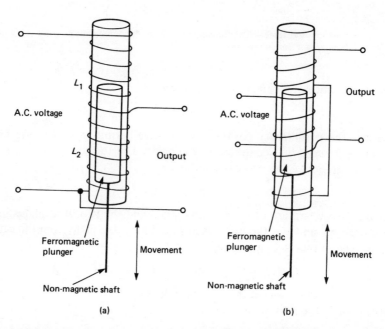

Figure 6.43 Inductive displacement transducers: (a) variable coupling type; (b) linear variable differential transformer

The optical displacement transducer shown in Fig. 6.44 measures rotational movement of a disc by sensing markings on the disc. The markings on the disc have traditionally been in the form of Gray code to limit errors at the change from one number to the next to one position. Alternatively, the markings can represent a single binary pattern of 010101 . . . and the markings counted as the disc is rotated.

Optical displacement transducers can be used for linear movement, and in this case the markings can be in the form of a grating, that is, a large number of parallel finely spaced lines. Typically there are two sets of gratings, one on a movable member and one on an adjacent fixed member. As the movable grating passes over the fixed grating, light from a light source is transmitted through the

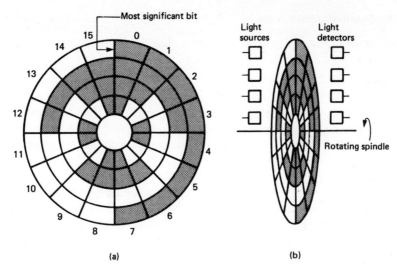

Figure 6.44 Angular encoder: (a) markings; (b) shaft with sensors.

gratings to a detector only when the two gratings are in line. Each occurrence of light passing through the gratings is counted.

(b) *Strain gauges*

The principal element of a strain gauge consists of a material whose resistance changes when stretched or compressed (strained). The substrate of the gauge is typically about 1 cm × 1 cm. Displacements in the region of 0.05 mm can be measured with appropriate circuitry. Strain gauges can be used to measure force by mounting the strain gauge with suitable adhesive on a cantilever beam as shown in Fig. 6.45(b). In this scheme, four gauges in various possible positions can be mounted to form the arms of a Wheatstone bridge.

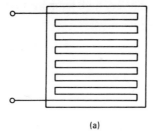

(a)

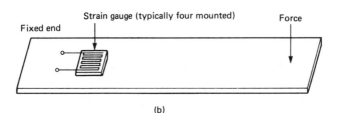

(b)

Figure 6.45 Strain gauge: (a) typical pattern; (b) strain gauge mounted on cantilever beam.

6.10.3   Thermal transducers

Thermal transducers are used to measure a change in temperature. There are several types.

(a) *Resistive*
Resistive thermal transducers use a change in resistance in wire when the temperature changes. These transducers can consist of coil of a wire wound on a former. Metals such as platinum, copper or nickel are used which change in the region of $+0.5\Omega/°C$, depending upon the metal, and the change is almost linear.

(b) *Thermistor*
A thermistor uses mixtures of materials such as nickel oxide, cobalt oxide and manganese oxide whose overall resistance changes significantly with temperature, though the change is quite non-linear. Whereas resistive thermal transducers can cope with very high temperatures, depending upon the metal, and the resistance change is almost linear, thermistors typically cope with temperatures between 0°C and 200°C (again depending upon the materials used) and the change is quite non-linear. However, the resistance change can be several orders of magnitude larger, typically $-1\ k\Omega/°C$.

(c) *Thermocouple (thermo-electric transducer)*
A thermocouple uses two different types of metal joined at the point that the temperature is to be measured. The junction creates a very small voltage which is proportional to temperature. Different combinations of metals create different voltages. The voltage is in the range 3–80 $\mu V/°C$. The general scheme is shown in Fig. 6.46. To obtain a voltage, the junctions with the connecting leads need to be at a different temperature to that of the sensing junction. An error occurs if this reference temperature changes, though special integrated circuits (cold junction compensators or thermocouple conditioners) can be used to compensate for changes. Thermocouples can handle very high temperatures—perhaps as high as 2000°C, depending upon the metals.

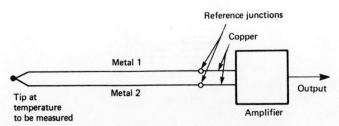

Figure 6.46. Thermocouple.

(d) P–N *junction*
The voltage across semiconductor diodes when forward-biased varies by about $-2\ mV/°C$ and this phenomenon can be used in a thermal transducer. Though the voltage change varies between devices, it is very linear and the basic devices are inexpensive. Integrated circuits can be manufactured containing the sensing

element calibrated for the user. Normally the base–emitter junction of a transistor is used with the base and collector connected together.

References

1. Schwartz, M. and Shaw, L., *Signal Processing*, McGraw-Hill, New York. 1975.
2. Carlson, A. B., *Communications Systems*, McGraw-Hill, New York, 1975.
3. Stremler, F. G., *Introduction to Communications Systems*, Addison-Wesley, Reading, Massachusetts, 1977.
4. Wait, J. V., Huelsman, L. P., and Korn, G. A., *Introduction to Operational Amplifer Theory and Applications*, McGraw-Hill, New York, 1975.
5. Graeme, J. G., Tobey, G. E., and Huelsman, L. P., *Operational Amplifiers, Design and Applications*, McGraw-Hill, New York, 1971.
6. User, M. J., *Sensors and Transducers*, Macmillan, Basingstoke, 1985.
7. Diefenderfer, A. J., *Principles of Electronic Instrumentation*, 2nd edition, Saunders College Publishing, Philadelphia, 1979.

Further reading

1. Clayton, G. B., *Data Convertors*, Macmillan, London, 1982.
2. Sheingold, D. H. (Ed), *Analogue-Digital Conversion Handbook*, Prentice Hall, 1985.

7

Graphic systems

7.1 Introduction

In Chapter 3, the basic requirements for man–machine communication were set out; an alpha-numeric display and a keyboard. This will satisfy the basic communication problem. However, there are computer applications that need more than simple alpha-numeric input/output; they need output in the form of graphs and a means of entering information related to graphs. At one extreme, it may simply be a convenience. For example, a mathematician may be solving equations which might be illustrative if output in graphical form on a display (a graphic display). However, given graphical form, many new applications of computers can be developed – for example in architecture, planning, and numerous engineering fields to aid the design phases, collectively known as computer-aided design (CAD). In these cases, the operator is intrinsically involved in the generation of the graphic output. He can observe the output and cause it to be modified as desired to optimize the design. Special input devices are necessary to communicate with the graphic display. The term *Interactive graphics* has been coined to cover a graphic system which enables this close interaction between the operator and the graphic output.

In the first example, that of a mathematician simply wishing to have illustrative output, the system is non-interactive. The operation performed is only picture or graph drawing, and in this case it may be adequate to use a graphic device which produces drawings on paper.

Graphical output from graphic plotters are described in Section 7.6. The graphic display and ancillary equipment is given in Sections 7.2–5. Presently, the cathode-ray tube (CRT) is the basic display device of graphic displays. The reader is referred to Section 3.3.2 for the description of the operation of a cathode-ray tube.

Graphic displays can be divided into two types:

(i)   random-scan graphic displays;
(ii) raster-scan graphic displays.

The random-scan display has been largely superseded by the raster-scan display due primarily to advances in semiconductor memory used in raster-scan displays, but firstly let us briefly outline the random-scan graphic display.

7.2 Random-scan graphic displays

A random-scan graphic display is one that utilizes the X- and Y-deflection system of the CRT to deflect the electron beam across the screen in a 'random' or unordered way to draw images. The simplest random-scan graphic display is the point-plotting display. In this type of display, the image is made from a number of spots, each of which is specified on the screen by an X-co-ordinate and a Y-co-ordinate. Commonly there are 1024 X-positions and 1024 Y-positions, that is a $2^{10} \times 2^{10}$ matrix size. Each pair of co-ordinates is transferred from the host computer through DACs to the deflection amplifiers of the display, as shown in Fig. 7.1. A further item is required to control the Z modulation (the brightness control connecting to the control grid), and this may take the form of a single binary digit indicating the presence or otherwise of the spot. More usefully, a three or four bit number can be transferred indicating a level of brightness, this requiring a third DAC.

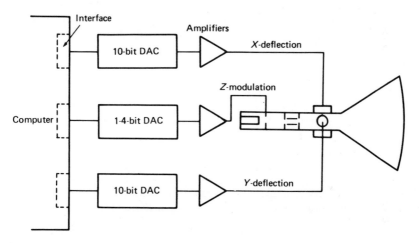

Figure 7.1 Point-plotting display.

To maintain a steady shape requires the information to be repeatedly transferred to the display, sufficiently quickly to avoid flicker, that is sufficiently quickly for the eye not to notice. The persistence of vision coupled with the persistence of the phosphor will determine the required rates. Generally, with normal short-persistence phosphors, this means that there must be at least 20 frames/s: often 50 frames/s is used. Normally it is not satisfactory to allow the host computer to provide the *refresh* data to the screen, for it would be too time-consuming. So there is usually a *display processor* between the host computer and the CRT circuitry, dedicated to the control of the display.

A random-scan graphic display will normally incorporate point plotting, using absolute x- and y-co-ordinates, vector generation with incremental x- and y-co-ordinates, and possibly hardware character generation. Characters can be dot-matrix formed with a *mini-raster*, a raster that is contained in the area of one character. The character position can be specified with DACs used for point plotting. There is no fundamental reason for the scan to be horizontal; it can be vertical (assuming the CRT has no performance differences between the x- and y-direction which might affect the operation). If a vertical mini-scan is employed, italics (that is sloping characters) can be produced by applying appropriate ramp signals to both the horizontal and vertical deflection systems.

A system with hardware vector generation and hardware character generation is shown in Fig 7.2, employing line drawing for the vectors and mini-raster scan dot-matrix for characters.

The speed that a vector can be drawn will limit the number of vectors that can be displayed. Given a 20 ms refresh rate (50 frames/s), if the vector speed is 20 μs, then 1000 vectors can be drawn. This speed would represent a very high quality random-scan display. Lower performance displays draw vectors in around 200 μs.

The display processor generates x- and y-co-ordinates for point plotting, x- and y- or Δx- and Δy-co-ordinates for vector generation, brightness settings, and possibly character codes if there is hardware character generation. The display processor, by DMA transfers, accepts instructions from a store for execution. A program of display instructions will define the picture to be displayed. A typical display processor will have the following classes of instructions:

(a) positioning/point plotting;
(b) vectors;
(c) character generation;
(d) brightness;
(e) control.

There may be a 'bright-up' bit to specify whether the point/vector/text is to be displayed immediately, or after subsequent instruction(s). This is essential if more than one instruction is necessary to complete a particular operation.

Display processor instructions

(a) *Positioning/point plotting*
In this case there are two co-ordinates: x and y for absolute point plotting, or Δx and Δy for point plotting relative to the last point plotted. Both modes are usually provided. The two co-ordinates may be compacted into one location in the case of Δx, Δy, or there may be separate instructions for each of Δx, Δy, x and y.

(b) *Vectors*
As with positioning/point-plotting instructions, vector generating instructions have two co-ordinates, in this case being Δx and Δy, the incremental values of the vector (see Fig. 7.2). The starting co-ordinates need to be firstly specified with a positioning instruction. The co-ordinates may, as with the positioning instruction, be compacted into one instruction for small vectors, or provided in a subsequent location (the next or indirectly addressed) with separate instructions for Δx and Δy. If there are separate instructions for Δx and Δy, the bright-up bit mechanism needs to be invoked in the second instruction.

An alternative approach to using incremental values is to use absolute co-ordinates. In the case of vectors, this would require four co-ordinates, the two starting co-ordinates and the two finishing co-ordinates.

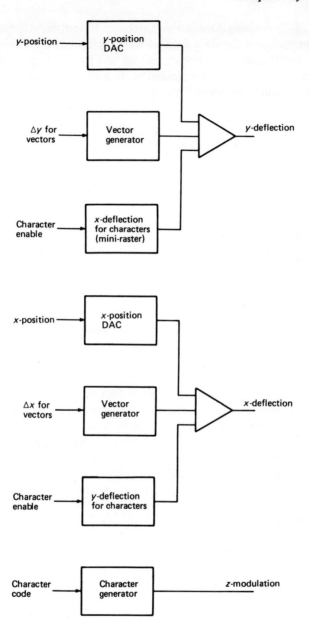

Figure 7.2 Hardware vector and character generation.

An auto-increment vector instruction, whereby the Δx-co-ordinate is always taken to be unity, may be provided. This is useful for graph plotting.

(c) *Character generation*
Characters can be drawn from a sequence of vectors, and this sequence can be held as a sub-routine. Alternatively, there may be special character-generator

circuitry usually producing dot-matrix characters. If so, there will be character-generation instructions, the data field of which will hold the character to be displayed in ASCII code (say). For display of text the characters will often be packed two to a word in locations specified by the instruction (may be subsequent locations), with a suitable symbol for termination, for example a null character.

(d) *Brightness*
This may be incorporated into other instructions or be separate instructions. Generally, there will be 3 (or 4) bits to specify 2^3 (or 2^4) levels of brightness.

Other brightness-associated operations may be included such as 'blink', short and long broken lines.

(e) *Control*
There can be several types of jump instructions in this category:

(i)   absolute unconditional jump, with direct and indirect addressing;
(ii)   relative unconditional jump;
(iii) sub-routine jump and return from sub-routine jump.

These are necessary in order to produce efficient code, especially the sub-routine jump. The sub-routine jump enables sections of program to be called several times, as in the conventional sense, and, for example, enables frequently used symbols and diagrams to be written in sub-routine form.

If a subroutine calls another subroutine (nested subroutines), the return address of the calling subroutine can be held on a hardware stack. This is a number of consecutive storage locations with a top location and a bottom location, each specified by pointers (in two additional locations). The return address is placed on the top of the stack, that is, in the next location after the existing top location, and the top location pointer modified accordingly. This mechanism is referred to as pushing information onto (the top of) the stack. When each new subroutine is called, a new return address is created, and this is pushed onto the stack.

At any point in time the top location of the stack holds the last return address, and when this is retrieved for use, the top location becomes the next one lower down the stack (by modifying the top location pointer). This mechanism is known as pulling information off the stack and always maintains the current return address at the top of the stack.

For the above, push and pull stack operations need to be in the instruction repertoire, and these may be included especially in a display processor.

There may be instructions to control special graphic equipment such as a light pen (see next section).

Finally, there will be a Halt instruction to stop the computer operation, and may be a Null instruction to aid program modification (for example).

Once a list of instructions (the display file, or program), which will produce the desired image, has been assembled, the program can be executed. To maintain the image without flicker, the display program needs to be repeatedly executed typically 30–50 times a second. To effect this, a timer is required. An interrupt timer is convenient. This produces an interrupt at fixed intervals, say every $\frac{1}{30}$ or $\frac{1}{50}$ s. Each interrupt can cause the display program to be re-executed.

7.3 Raster-scan graphic displays

7.3.1 High-definition raster-scan graphic displays

A raster-scan display is one in which the picture or *frame* is composed of a large number of raster lines, which are sub-divided into a large number of dots or *picture elements* (*pixels*). The standard television picture is a raster-scan picture with 625 lines (*interlaced*, that is adjacent frames consisting of alternate 313 lines). The picture element in the case of a monochrome television can be any shade of grey (from black to white) that is various levels of brightness. In the case of colour, apart from brightness, there is an infinite variation in hue (colour). When adapted for digital usage, the picture element or pixel is defined, in terms of brightness and/or colour, by a number of binary digits (bits). For example, in monochrome 8 levels of brightness could be specified in 3 bits. The pixel would comprise 3 bits. Three bits could specify one of 8 colours, with a colour display.

A comprehensive graphic raster-scan display stores every pixel in a random access or serial store (Fig. 7.3). Each pixel is accessed in sequence until the complete picture is formed and this is repeated continually. Early displays employed a disc store because of vast amounts of data (at least half a million bits). The disc speed was synchronized to that of the frame rate, thus obtaining a simple means of continually refreshing the display. The surface of the disc could hold one frame. Current displays employ, typically, MOS (metal-oxide-silicon) store. The store requirment is a major item. A 625-line system using 512 lines with 1024 pixels on each line with a dual intensity (on/off) requires 512×1024 bits or 512K bits. Providing 8 levels of brightness (3 bits), or alternatively 8 colours, increases the store requirement to 1.5 million bits.

With a fixed store size, say 1.5 million bits, and a fixed number of lines, say 512, various combinations of a number of pixels per line and colour/brightness can be specified in some displays. For example:

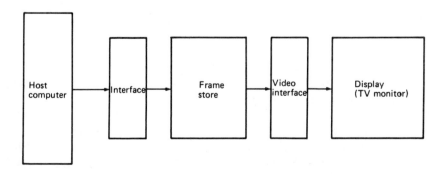

Figure 7.3 Raster-scan graphic display.

1024 pixels/line   3 bits/pixel (8 levels of brightness or 8 colours)
 512 pixels/line   6 bits/pixel (64 colours)
 256 pixels/line   12 bits/pixel (4096 colour/brightness combinations)
 128 pixels/line   24 bits/pixel (16 million colour/brightness combinations)

Additional flexibility can be provided by holding the actual colour/brightness combinations in a hardware look-up table (a mapping store) addressed by the pixel word.

High-capacity, low-cost semiconductor memory, particularly dynamic semiconductor memory, has led to the practical development of high resolution raster-scan bit-mapped graphics. *Dynamic semiconductor memory devices* employ integrated circuit capacitors to store charge representing one binary state (the other state being represented by no charge). Dynamic semiconductor memory requires a recharging operation known as *refresh* to maintain the stored information. The refresh operation is applied to a dynamic memory device typically every 2–4 ms. A memory read operation also refreshes the memory location and hence refresh can be achieved during the normal display refresh operation. However, this is not necessarily done. A graphic controller is normally incorporated into the system for generating the required control signals and this controller may provide memory refresh at the required rate and the display refresh separately, for greatest flexibility.

Domestic televisions use the raster-scan approach with nominally 625 (in UK) or 525 (in USA) raster lines, though some are lost during frame flyback time (the time required to move the electron beam from the bottom of one frame to the top of the next frame). Televisions also use a technique known as *interlacing*, whereby on alternate frames, alternate lines are sent, so that two frames are necessary to produce the complete image. Every frame is produced at the 50 Hz (UK) or 60 Hz (USA) rate. The two-frame rate is half this, at 25/30 Hz, but flicker is hardly noticeable because television images have alternate frames which do not differ much. Interlacing is used to reduce the rate of transmitting information which is often specified as horizontal line frequency (horizontal raster lines/sec). With an interlaced 625 line/50 Hz system, the line frequency is $625 \times 25 = 15\,625$ Hz. With an interlaced 525/60 Hz system, the line frequency is $525 \times 30 = 15\,750$ Hz. Most CRTs can operate at this frequency and above (very high-quality CRTs achieving greater than 36 kHz). Non-interlaced systems with the same number of lines and frame rates have doubled line frequencies. Most display systems, alpha-numeric or graphic, use non-interlacing, because interlace flicker would be noticeable for character and graphic images.

In a raster-scan graphics system, the bit map can be manipulated directly to alter the image. For example, pixels can be shifted to move the image, or duplicated to enlarge images. Alternatively, and with greater scope, a description of the objects to be displayed can be first formed within the host processor memory. These descriptions are altered as required using mathematical transformations. The graphics processor takes the final descriptions and fills the pixel bit-map memory from which the CRT display is formed. This approach is known as *geometric graphics.*

A colour bit-mapped system with direct manipulation of the bit map and using a graphics controller is shown in Fig. 7.4. Each pixel stored in the bit-mapped memory contains several bits and specifies a colour. The pixels are read from the memory in sequence. Because of the speed of refreshing the display is usually required to be much faster than the time to read a single data word from (dynamic) memory; often the memory is arranged so that several words of memory can be read simultaneously and the pixels extracted in series using shift registers. Each pixel word needs to be translated into three values, one to specify the red intensity, one to specify the green intensity and one to specify the blue intensity. Finally the values are converted into voltages for the colour CRT (Chapter 3) using DACs (Chapter 6). The graphic controller also generates the line and frame synchronization pulses as required by a CRT monitor. A microprocessor is shown for overall control. The microprocessor is often a 32-bit type because the mathematical manipulations of the bit map directly, or indirectly using descriptors, normally requires high accuracy and great speed.

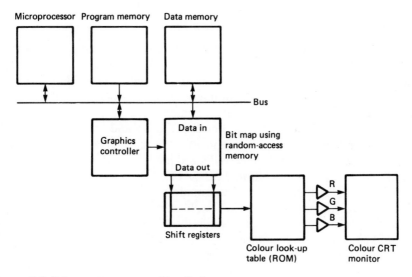

Figure 7.4 Colour raster-scan graphics display system.

The number of displayed pixels provided in a system and the number of colours depends upon the application. High-quality computer-aided design (CAD) applications might need in the region of 1280×1024 with 16–256 colours (4–8–bit pixels) Resolutions of 1152×1536 are necessary for high-quality portrait page make-up displays in the printing industry. High-resolution colour displays are also used by architects dealing with, for example, urban developments or motorway interchanges, and fabric designers, where aesthetic considerations are important.

7.3.2   Raster-scan graphic display terminals

For less demanding applications, monochrome raster-scan graphic terminals have been developed with on/off intensity requiring a 1-bit pixel and a definition of 360 lines each of 720 pixels (360×720 displayable points). This requires a $16K \times 16$-bit frame store. Dot-matrix alpha-numerics can be incorporated into the system with separate character-store and character-generator circuitry. The terminals are often microprocessor controlled and various extra features may be included. The inclusion of hardware zoom facilities enables the display to be magnified (typically up to 16 times). Planning enables the parts of the magnified picture not currently on the display screen to be viewed: this is useful for examination of fine detail.

The *rubber-band line* facility enables a line to be drawn from a specified position on the screen to the current cursor position. As the cursor moves, the line automatically stretches or contracts. When finally positioned, the line can be fixed: this is a possible aid to architectural design.

7.3.3   Limited graphics raster-scan display

An alpha-numeric raster-scan display can easily be modified to provide limited graphics, by having a number of additional symbols which can be used to make graphs and pictures. Teletext systems are such systems, available in the UK. These are news and general information services using the medium of television. The information is presented in alpha-numeric and graphical form on the television screen using the patterns shown in Fig. 7.5 and are decoded directly from the input code. The graphic symbol area (the same area as for a character plus the space around the character) is divided into six areas, which are specified to be intensified or not by six bits in the input character code. Additional control codes are used to firstly set up the graphic mode or alpha-numeric mode, together with a specified colour (red, green, yellow, blue, magenta, cyan or white). There are also flash/steady control codes. Naturally, there are many variations in the patterns. The particular advantage of the Teletext patterns is that a ROM (read-only memory) to hold the patterns is not necessary. Other graphic character symbol sets requiring pattern stores are used in graphic displays.

7.4   Input devices

7.4.1   Using the display cursor

A cursor has been met in alpha-numerical visual display units. The cursor is used to mark the next character position, and moves horizontally across the screen. With a graphic display, a cursor can be used in a similar way as a positioning device for input of new graphical data, or it can be used to point to existing specific graphical data on the screen. In both cases it is necessary to be able to steer the cursor around the screen. The editing controls of an alpha-numeric display, such as ↑, ↓, ← and →, could be incorporated into a graphic display, though the steering operations would be time consuming. Alternatively, the type

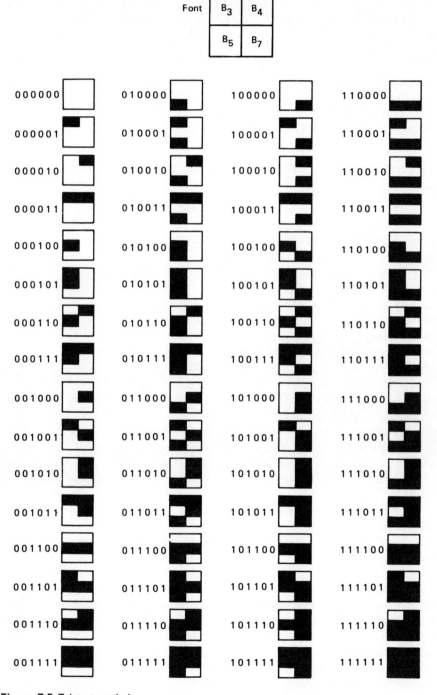

Figure 7.5 Teletext symbols.

of controls traditionally found in radar display equipment, the joystick or the tracker ball, could be used. Both these two devices are controlled by hand and produce voltages for the x- and y-movement, generally using two potentiometers, one linked to the movement of the hand in the x-direction, and the other the movement of the hand in the y-direction. The voltages are converted into digital form using ADCs. High precision in the generation and conversion of these voltages is unnecessary, since the operator positions the cursor visually, thereby completing a feedback system. Additionally, a switch is necessary which is activated once the cursor has been positioned correctly.

More recently, other devices have been used to control the cursor or select information and these methods are described in the following sections.

7.4.2   Pointing to a display object

CRTs (and other displays) can incorporate a *touch screen* device which enables the user to point on the screen with a finger and the corresponding co-ordinates to be detected. Various mechanisms have been developed to find the pointed position, including the membrane (resistive) method, the capacitive method, infra-red method and ultrasonic method.

In one membrane method, a thin sheet with a transparent conductive inner surface placed in front of the screen makes contact with a transparent resistive coating on the screen when the sheet is depressed. The point of contact is measured electrically. The capacitive method uses a single conductive surface and necessitates the use of a finger or conductive stylus to form a capacitive effect (thus gloves cannot generally be worn). Both the membrane and capacitive methods cover the surface of the screen with a thin layer which degrades the image slightly. In contrast, the infra-red and ultrasonic methods leave the screen clear. In the infra-red method, infra-red transmitters are placed along two orthogonal edges to generate infra-red beams across the surface. Sensors are placed on opposite edges of the screen to detect when the beams are broken by a pointing finger (or stylus). The ultrasonic method uses ultrasonic transmitters and sensors. In these methods the screen needs to be flat. Also dirt or flying insects may trigger the mechanism accidentally. However there is no degradation of the image.

The basic hardware of a touch screen enables the display co-ordinates of a selected item to be input, which can be used to cause displayed data to be input or to activate displayed functions. In a point mode, each time the finger touches the screen the co-ordinates are input. In a continuous mode, while the finger is touching the screen the corresponding co-ordinates are input continually whether the finger is moving or stationary. Visual feedback can be utilized, in which the pointed object is highlighted but not selected until the finger or stylus is taken away from the screen and an opportunity is given to change the selection.

An early form of pointing device is the *light pen*, now generally superseded by touch screens or alternative selection mechanisms (see later). The light pen is constructed in the shape of a pen and held close to the screen over an item of interest. When the item is 'lit' up (once per refresh cycle), a light sensor within the pen detects this and a signal generated. This signal sets a flip-flop which either produces an interrupt or can be read under program control of the display processor. Since the display processor controls the refreshing of the screen, it is possible to identify the item pointed at.

The light sensor is either a photo-cell or a photo-diode or a photo-transistor, which can be in the pen body as in Fig. 7.6, or contained separately and the light transmitted from the pen body to the sensor via a fibre-optic cable. A photo-multiplier could be used but is rather slow in operation.

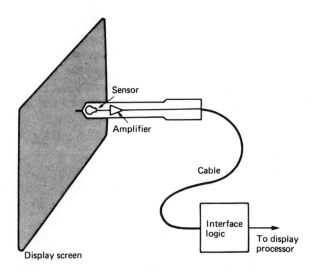

Figure 7.6 Light pen.

Naturally, the light pen must only respond to the light of the screen, and this may mean that the phosphor of the tube needs to be matched with the light sensor. Also, the sensor needs to respond very quickly for correct operation.

7.4.3   The mouse

The mouse is a device which is moved across a flat surface by hand and the movement encoded and transmitted to the display system. The mouse can be used to trace drawings, or to steer the display cursor. For steering the cursor, the absolute co-ordinates of the mouse need not be known as visual feedback enables the cursor to be positioned correctly. The mouse, in conjunction with a cursor, has largely replaced the light pen for selection of display items because the mouse is less tiring in use.

An early form of mouse had two wheels orthogonally mounted. The amount of rotation of each wheel is translated into x- and y-co-ordinates. For absolute co-ordinates, the mouse is placed initially in one corner and the circuitry reset. Then the mouse is wheeled around as required. A more recent form of mouse for steering the cursor is shown in Fig. 7.7. This mouse must be placed on a special table which has a fine matrix of lines imprinted. Lines in one direction are used for the vertical movement of the cursor, and lines in the other direction are used for

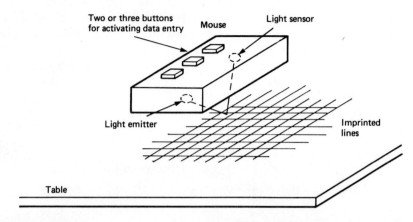

Figure 7.7 Mouse.

the horizontal movement of the cursor. Underneath the mouse, there is a semiconductor light source (an LED) and light detector. Each line crossed over as the mouse is moved on the table is detected by the reflected light reaching the light detector from the light source. It is not necessary to set the mouse down perfectly aligned to the lines.

Other forms of mouse do not need special tables. For example, in the *ball-type mouse*, a sphere is mounted underneath the device and rotated by moving the mouse on a table. The movement is translated into electrical signals. The *foot mouse* is placed on the floor and movement of a foot on the device in different directions is sensed. Tactile and audio feedback is incorporated. The foot mouse frees the hands for other uses. Simple foot controls containing on–off switches also can be useful to free the hands.

7.4.4   Writing tablets

A writing tablet or digitizer tablet (Fig. 7.8) is a flat, square or rectangular slab of material onto which a stylus is placed and held. The position of the stylus is detected in one of various ways, and this information in terms of x- and y-co-ordinates is transmitted to the system. Such a device can be used in conjunction with a cursor. It is a means of steering the cursor.

Tablets can also be used for tracing a drawing or parts of a drawing. These tablets are generally large (typically 35 cm × 35 cm) and have very high resolution (0.01 cm). The drawing to be copied is placed on the tablet, and a stylus used to trace the parts required, which can then be shown on the graphic display. The stylus may be pen-like or a cursor device with cross-wires used to position the stylus over a drawing accurately.

Some cursors are held on the surface by a vacuum which allows the surface to be at various angles and the cursor left in position. When the cursor has been positioned correctly, a push button is used to load the co-ordinates into the computer. For certain applications (e.g. in engineering) very large digitizers with areas of several square metres are used.

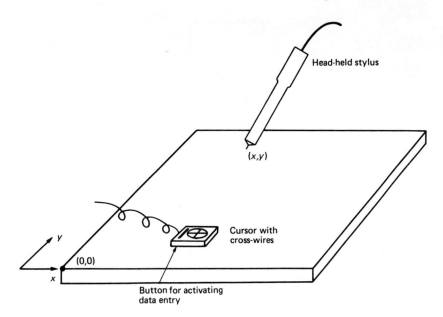

Figure 7.8 Writing tablet.

Another mode of operation of the writing tablet is the 'menu' technique. A number of legends, symbols or a representation of a keyboard is printed on material mounted on the tablet. The stylus is positioned on the item of interest in much the same way as the light pen. If the writing tablet is transparent, then there is the possibility of mounting the tablet over the display screen, and using the display to show the captions.

A complete CAD graphic system may include a graphic display with a mouse, a writing tablet and a graph plotter (Fig. 7.9).

Methods

(a) *Wire mesh (electromagnetic induction)*
The position of the stylus is detected in this case by a matrix of wires embedded in the surface of the tablet, so that when pulse trains are applied to individual x- and y-wires, the stylus can sense the pulses due to capacitive linkage to those x, y wires closest to the stylus. Pulses can be applied to groups of wires using Gray code (Table 7.1) so that adjacent wires receive a unique sequence of pulses that differ by only one digit.

With a 25 cm square tablet, with $2^{10} \times 2^{10}$ matrix (1024 x wires and 1024 y wires), the wires are 0.25 mm apart. The x- and y-planes need to be separated by a sheet of Mylar.

The electromagnetic induction technique is commonly employed in digitizers. In a variation, a current is passed through a wire in the cursor and induced voltages sensed in the embedded wires. In another variation, the interference

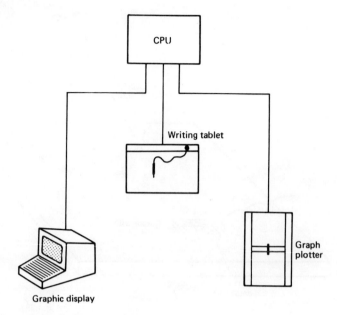

Figure 7.9 Interactive CAD graphic system.

Decimal	'Gray' code
0	0 0 0 0
1	0 0 0 1
2	0 0 1 1
3	0 0 1 0
4	0 1 1 0
5	0 1 1 1
6	0 1 0 1
7	0 1 0 0
8	1 1 0 0
9	1 1 0 1
10	1 1 1 1
11	1 1 1 0
12	1 0 1 0
13	1 0 1 1
14	1 0 0 1
15	1 0 0 0

Table 7.1 Gray code (one form).

between four electromagnetic waves generated from signals in the embedded wires is used, which enables the wires to be spaced further apart.

(b) *Voltage gradient*
This tablet is made of a resistive (partially conducting) material such as Teledeltos paper. A voltage potential is developed across the tablet in the *x*-direction, and

the *x*-co-ordinate of the stylus position obtained from the voltage measured at the stylus tip. Similarly, the *y*-co-ordinate is obtained from a voltage potential developed across the tablet in the *y*-direction. The *x*- and *y*-voltage potentials are applied at different time intervals. Linear equipotentials need to be formed and this can be achieved by connecting the voltage signals to the sides of the tablet at several points through diodes. The diodes provide a means of connecting the voltage source to the edges of the tablet whilst not affecting the linear resistance between opposite edges.

The voltage-gradient method is not suitable for tracing drawings because the stylus needs to be in contact with the tablet to operate.

(c) *Sylvania tablet*
The Sylvania tablet is the name given to a commercial tablet based on using a conducting material. A modulated high-frequency signal is applied across the tablet in the *x*-direction and another modulated signal of different frequency applied to the *y*-direction. The stylus picks up the signals. The modulating signals are derived and the phase shift of each in relation to master signals give the *x*- and *y*-co-ordinates. The stylus need not actually be in contact with the conducting surface due to the use of high frequencies (approximately 100 kHz).

(d) *Acoustic tablet*
This tablet employs an ultrasonic sound source in the stylus and two sound sensors (strip microphones) along two adjacent ends of the tablet (Fig. 7.10), which pick up the sound emitted in the *x*- and *y*-directions. Measurement of the time delay from emitting the sound and receiving the sound gives the co-ordinates. Earlier tablets of this type used an ultrasonic transmitter and four separate sensors at the corners of the tablet.

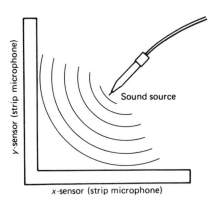

Figure 7.10 Acoustic writing tablet.

An acoustic writing tablet designed for digitizing drawings is typically 35 cm × 35 cm with a resolution of 0.25 mm, reproducibility of 0.1% of full scale, and a data transfer rate of 140 points/s.

(e) *Pressure-sensitive tablet*
In this tablet pressure is applied at the required co-ordinates on the top surface of the tablet. This causes an electrical contact to be made between a particular *x*-wire and *y*-wire of a matrix of *x*-wires (parallel to the *x*-axis) and *y*-wires (parallel to the *y*-axis) embedded in the tablet. The electrical contact thus identifies the location of the pressure point.

7.5   Graphic display software

As one would expect, the subject of graphics software, which encompasses interactive graphics, is very large. Below is a very brief over-view.

7.5.1   Transformations

Transformations are mathematical operations on the stored display data which alter the image in a defined manner. For example, an image may be rotated about an axis using a *rotation* transformation. We shall describe the transformations as mathematical operations on the co-ordinates of each pixel.

(a) *Shifting*
The co-ordinates of a (two-dimensional) object shifted by Δx in the *x*-direction and Δy in the *y*-direction are given by:

$$x' = x + \Delta x,$$
$$y' = y + \Delta y,$$

where *x* and *y* are the original co-ordinates, and x' and y' are the new co-ordinates.

(b) *Scaling*
The co-ordinates of an object magnified by a factor S_x in the *x*-direction and S_y in the *y*-direction are given by:

$$x' = xS_x,$$
$$y' = yS_y,$$

where S_x and S_y are greater than 1.
   The object is reduced in size if S_x and S_y are between 0 and 1. Note the magnification (or reduction) need not be the same in both *x*- and *y*-directions.

(c) *Rotation*
The co-ordinates of an object rotated through an angle θ *about the origin of the co-ordinate system* are given by:

$$x' = x \cos \theta + y \sin \theta$$
$$y' = -x \sin \theta + y \cos \theta$$

(d) *Clipping*

This transformation applies defined rectangular boundaries to a diagram and deletes from the picture those points outside the defined area. This may be useful after rotation has been applied to eliminate co-ordinates outside the field of view of the display.

If the lowest values of x, y in the area to be displayed are x_1, y_1, and the highest values of x, y are x_h, y_h, then:

$$x_1 \leqslant x \leqslant x_h$$

$$y_1 \leqslant y \leqslant y_h$$

needs to be true for the point (x, y) to be displayed; otherwise (x, y) is not displayed.

(e) *Windowing*

This transformation involves selecting a rectangular region of interest in an undisplayed picture and transplanting the view obtained onto the display in a specific position. Consider Fig. 7.11: a rectangular area is selected measuring ΔX by ΔY, with the lower left-hand corner having the co-ordinates (X, Y), in the undisplayed picture co-ordinate system. The points within this rectangle are transformed into a rectangle measuring $\Delta X'$ by $\Delta Y'$, with the lower left-hand corner having the co-ordinates (X', Y'), by the transformation:

$$x' = \frac{\Delta X'}{\Delta X}(x - X) + X'$$

$$y' = \frac{\Delta Y'}{\Delta Y}(y - Y) + Y'$$

Scaling is involved if $\Delta X'$ is not equal to ΔX and $\Delta Y'$ is not equal to ΔY.

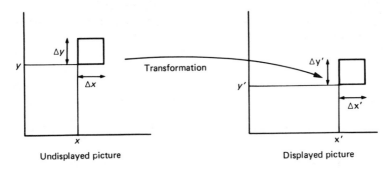

Undisplayed picture   Displayed picture

Figure 7.11 Windowing.

Performing the windowing transformation before other transformations where possible may reduce the amount of computation on the subsequent transformations.

(f) *Three-dimensional transformations*

A three-dimensional drawing, represented with co-ordinates of the form (x, y, z), can be projected onto a two-dimensional surface by a *perspective* transformation. In doing this, hidden lines need to be removed. Beforehand, three-dimensional shifting, scaling and rotation transformations can be performed.

Rotating a three-dimensional object θ degrees about the x-axis requires the transformation:

$$x' = x,$$
$$y' = y \cos \theta + z \sin \theta,$$
$$z' = z \cos \theta - y \sin \theta.$$

Similar transformations give rotation about the y- and z-axes.

(g) *Display of solid objects*

When objects are drawn partly in front of other objects, it is necessary to remove hidden parts. Hidden surface removal can be accomplished by a technique known as *z-buffering*, in which so-called z-values are stored with each pixel to indicate the distance from the front of the image (depth). As pixels of objects are added, the z-values are compared with existing z-values. If the new z-value is less than the existing z-value, i.e. the pixel is nearer to the viewer, the new pixel is included in the image, otherwise the pixel is not included.

Shading is necessary to display a realistic solid object. A slightly different colour or shade can be chosen for each pixel, dependent upon the angle to the light source. To obtain a good sense of depth, pixels nearer to the viewer can be made slightly brighter (*depth cueing*).

7.5.2   View windows

The display screen can be divided into a number of arbitrarily sized rectangular areas known as *windows*. Each window can then be used to display independent information. For example, one window might be formed to display a list of components in an electronic system and another window the circuit diagram, and another window an expanded portion of the circuit diagram under close scrutiny. Windows can be designed to overlap so that some windows partly hide others. The user can operate on a particular window by moving the cursor using a mouse. The software to set up and control windows is known as a *window manager*. Functions exist in the window manager to create windows and to manipulate them.

A portion of display commonly illustrates the commands that can be entered. Such displays are known as *pop-up* menus and often display *icons*. An icon is a small shape representing the function. The function is selected by placing the cursor or other movable symbol over the icon (and say pressing a key on the mouse) which removes the need to operate keyboard command sequences. Windows not in use can be removed from the screen and might become selectable items in a menu.

7.6 Graph plotters

A graph plotter produces drawings on paper. This enables a hard copy of graphical information displayed on a graphical display to be obtained. However, a graph plotter is a recognized peripheral in its own right for producing graphs and graphical diagrams.

Graph plotters find applications in many areas and are not limited to producing graphs on paper. Other media can be used, such as translucent and tracing paper and polyester film. There are plotters for producing scribings on metals (scribing plotters) and plotters for producing images on photographic films (photo artwork plotters). These have rather specialized applications and are not considered.

Three techniques will be described: the electrostatic, the pen-on-paper and microfilming. Thermal printing has also been applied to graph plotting.

7.6.1 Pen-on-paper graph plotter

In this type, drawings are produced by the motion of a pen (liquid ink pen, felt-tip pen etc.) placed on paper relative to the paper, in two orthogonal directions. The pen can be raised or lowered onto the paper as required. It is common to mount three or four pens of different colours or characteristics which can be individually selected. The pen-on-paper class of plotter can be sub-divided into two types, the drum and the flat-bed, distinguished by the mechanical details of the pen and paper movement.

(a) *Flat-bed plotter*
A flat-bed plotter is shown in Fig. 7.12. The paper is mounted on a stationary table (the bed) and the pen is mounted on a carriage that moves on a track. The

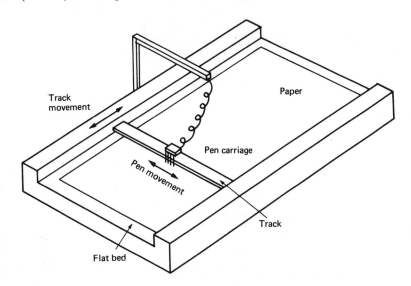

Figure 7.12 Flat-bed plotter.

track moves over the surface of the paper. The pen moves back and forth along the track, thus allowing the pen to be positioned in the desired place over the paper.

(b) *Drum plotter*

A drum plotter is shown in Fig. 7.13. In this case the paper is mounted around a drum. The paper interlocks with sprocket pins on the drum and there may be a vacuum chamber to hold the paper in place. The drum drives the paper backwards and forwards past a pen that is mounted on a stationary track. The pen is driven along the track on a carriage to complete the positioning mechanism. This type of plotter has the particular merit of allowing long lengths of paper to be used. The rolls of paper are often 50 m long. Sometimes there is a maximum practical length of a single drawing of, say, 10 m. Widths vary from 0.3 m to 1 m. The complete unit is quite compact. There may be a paper cutter available to cut the paper.

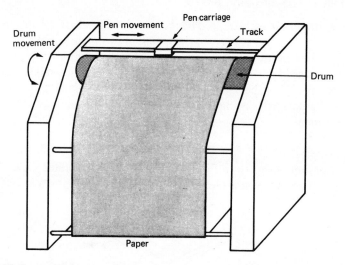

Figure 7.13 Drum plotter.

(c) *Drive mechanism*

The drive mechanism of both types of plotter is usually such that continuous lines are formed in steps or increments, hence the title *incremental plotter*. The increment is typically 0.05 mm in traditional incremental plotters (but see below). The drive can be stepper motor or a d.c. servo motor. Both these motors find application in other peripherals.

The basic components of a permanent-magnet stepper motor is shown in Fig. 7.14. The shaft of the motor, which is to rotate in steps (the rotor), has a permanent magnet embedded. This rotor is in the centre of a fixed stator comprising a metal structure with coils wound around the interior as shown. The rotor is stationary until a coil is energized. With the rotor in the position shown, coil *A* is energized with a d.c. current which causes the rotor to rotate until the

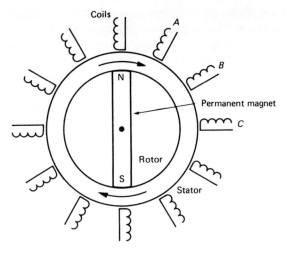

Figure 7.14 Stepper motor (permanent magnet type).

permanent magnet is directly beneath coil *A*, due to magnetic attraction, and then stops. The movement corresponds to one step or increment. The coil is then de-energized. When another step is required, the adjacent coil, coil *B*, is energized, causing the rotor to rotate until the permanent magnet is directly beneath coil *B*. Thus with *N* coils situated around the inside periphery of the stator, there will be *N* individual stepping actions to complete one revolution of the rotor. Motion can be and is necessarily bi-directional. The positioning of the rotor is very accurate, typically to $\pm 3\%$ of the angular displacement of one step. The error does not accumulate with steps and is independent of the number of steps. Speeds of up to 10 000 steps/s can be achieved.

The permanent magnet stepper motor is normally only manufactured in small sizes and has rather poor torque. Two other common types of stepper (or stepping) motors exist which can be manufactured with greater torque, called the variable-reluctance stepper motor and the hybrid stepper motor. The variable-reluctance stepper motor has a toothed iron rotor rather than a permanent magnet rotor, and a toothed stator (the fixed section holding the coils around the rotor). When a current is applied to stator coils, the rotor moves to align the rotor teeth with the stator teeth, which produces the least, magnetic reluctance ('resistance') for the circulating magnetic flux. Continual stepping action is obtained either by having a different number of teeth on the stator and rotor and only activating pairs of opposite coils simultaneously, or by having more than one stator/rotor assembly with a common shaft and a different orientation for each assembly. In the hybrid stepper motor, a permanent magnet is introduced in the body of the rotor. Further information on stepper motors can be found in Acarnley (further reading).

An alternative is to use a d.c. shunt-fed motor with feedback control, obtained using a photo-electric shaft encoder mounted on the motor to provide high resolution.

The incremental plotter as described requires many commands to complete even a single line, due to the fact that each incremental step needs to be specified. A superior approach is to specify absolute x, y co-ordinates and arrange for the pen to move directly from the previous x, y co-ordinate to the new x, y co-ordinate in a straight line. A stepper motor could be used in conjunction with interpolation hardware that generates the required number of stepper pulses. Alternatively a d.c. servo motor can be used which is allowed to rotate for a fixed number or fixed fraction of a revolution. This may be done by suitable digital and analogue circuitry. Additionally control of the speed of operation can be incorporated.

(d) *Control*

The basic incremental plotter accepts commands in the form of a binary code which is loaded into the graph plotter 'command' register, the bits typically having the following meaning:

command register

raise pen	lower pen	$-Y$	$+Y$	$-X$	$+X$	----

This gives rise to six modes of operation:

1. movement in $+X$-direction–drum rotation or pen carriage movement;
2. movement in $-X$-direction–drum rotation or pen carriage movement;
3. movement in $+Y$-direction–pen carriage movement;
4. movement in $-Y$-direction–pen carriage movement;
5. pen-up–allowing pen to be moved without drawing on paper;
6. pen-down–positions pen for drawing.

Naturally contradictory movements either cause an error or are ignored. Raising or lowering the pen is not done at the same time as drawing. To obtain steps at 45° to the X- and Y-axes, both X- and Y-movements are specified together.

There may be other operations that can be specified by command in more sophisticated plotters. These may include:

1. Selection of increment size, say, 0.01, 0.05, 0.1 mm. This can reduce the number of instructions necessary to complete a drawing.
2. Selection of pen. When a new pen is selected the pen moves automatically to the position held by the previous pen.

Operator controls may include:

1. The command operations above.
2. Scale factor adjustment. This follows compensation for expansion and shrinkage of the plotting medium.
3. Y-axis limit switch. This limits the maximum size of the plot.
4. Return to last plotted position/return to origin. This feature allows an operator to change or refill pens, or move plot for inspection and return. It also allows for the use of pre-printed or pre-cut forms.

5. Plot speed control. The drawing speed can be selected as most suitable for the pen and paper used.

(e) *Special features*

Advanced features on a graph plotter include hardware assistance for drawing alpha-numeric characters and arcs of circles. Alpha-numeric characters are usually specified by ASCII code or another code and the size of the characters defined by a programmable scale factor. Slant characters can sometimes be produced, the angle of slant being programmable. Mirror image and rotated plots are featured on the more expensive plotters.

It is common practice to incorporate a microprocessor into the control logic of graph plotters, as it is in all peripherals.

7.6.2 Electrostatic plotters

The electrostatic plotter uses the same technique of printing as the electrostatic line printer, producing rows of dots which can then approximate to continuous lines. Typically there are 1056 or 2112 styli and a dot resolution in both the horizontal and vertical or 40 or 80 dots/cm. Speed of operation is typically specified in the region of 10–100 mm/s vertically.

The paper is stepped in only one direction as in the electrostatic line printer, so that the picture to be plotted needs to be specified row by row rather than vector by vector as in the pen-on-paper plotters. The picture in the form of rows of dots is transmitted to the electrostatic plotter via direct memory access (DMA, see Section 2.2.4) or programmed output. Notice that the picture as described as a number of vectors corresponds directly to pen-carriage movement for a pen-on-paper plotter. The rows of dots as required by the electrostatic plotter require the complete picture before beginning the drawing.

The colour generated by an electrostatic plotter is that of the toner used. Hence colour plotting could be achieved by passing the plot medium through the plotter more than once, each time with a different toner (or by using separate plotters each with different toners). However superposition of colour plots require very good medium registration. Paper and other media are subject to small but significant changes in dimensions due to environmental changes and due to handling. Paper edge sensors can be incorporated into the system to control general skew. For more precise control, registration marks can be printed on the medium but outside the plotting area. These registration marks are sensed prior to each pass through the plotter to correct the plotting. An electrostatic colour plotter incorporating four separate toners is shown in Fig. 7.15. The input serial raster data signal can be taken directly from a colour CRT display.

7.6.3 Computer output microfilming plotters

Computer output microfilming (COM) plotters record images onto photographic film which then can be stored, and read on a special reader. There are two principal methods of forming the images, one by using a CRT to display the image, which is then photographed with a camera (Fig. 7.16) and second, using an

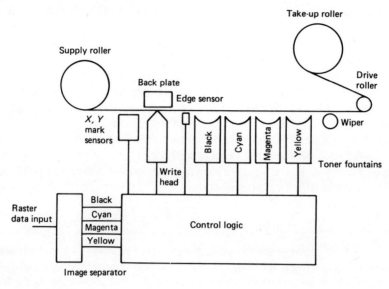

Figure 7.15 Electrostatic colour plotter.

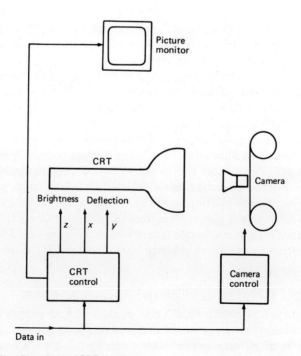

Figure 7.16 Microfilm plotter (CRT type).

electron beam or laser beam to write directly onto special film. The incoming data control the CRT or writing device.

The CRT variety can produce characters and graphic shapes either in the form of dots or vectors as in a graphic CRT display. And as in laser printers preformed information may be overlayed.

The film may be 16 mm, 35 mm or 105 mm rolls or cartridges/cassettes. One roll of 16 mm cartridge film can hold over 3000 pages of fanfolded computer printout. A sheet of 105 mm × 148 mm film can hold typically 220 pages of information on a matrix, this sheet being known as a microfiche. Sheets of film can be held on cards for subsequent selection. The selection can be done automatically using punch holes or optical characters on the cards.

All the microfilm is viewed with a magnifying viewer, the magnification being between 24 and 48.

Computer output microfilming has the advantages of very low bulk of the output which allows easy duplication and distribution to many destinations (each one would have a magnifying viewer). Speed of writing on film is fast, in the order of 200–500 pages per minute (260 000 characters/s).

The COM recorder can be operated on-line or more often off-line (see Section 7.6.4).

7.6.4 On-line and Off-line operation

On-line operation is with the peripheral output device (graph-plotter here) connected directly to the computer and controlled directly by the computer (Fig. 7.17(a)), whilst in off-line operation the device is not directly connected to computer. In this case the output information is first loaded onto an intermediate medium (magnetic or punched tape or punched cards). This is then transferred manually to a reader connected to the output device (Fig. 7.17(b)).

The principal advantage of the off-line mode of operation is that the computer is relieved of the control of the output device, and once the output information is produced on tape or cards the computer may continue with other tasks.

7.6.5 Software for graphic plotters

System software for graphic plotters can consist of sub-routines which enable basic drawing operations and common diagrams and symbols to be produced.

The basic operations of the pen-on-plotter were given previously (Section 7.6.1(d)). These are produced from sub-routine calls which can be embedded into high-level language programs. The following sub-routines are typical of those available on a medium-sized computer system:

$$\text{PLOT } (X, Y, I, N)$$

causing the following actions:

With $N = 0$ moves the pen to the co-ordinates (X, Y)
With $I = 1$ the pen position is unchaged
$\quad I = 2$ the pen is lowered before moving to (X, Y)
$\quad I = 3$ the pen is raised before moving to (X, Y)
With $N = 4$ the current pen position is assigned the co-ordinates (X, Y).

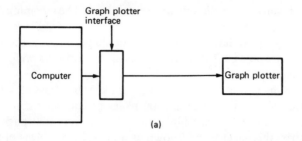

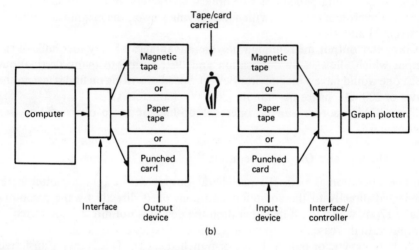

Figure 7.17 (a) On-line and (b) off-line operation.

Typically, the following can be produced:

axis (labelled);
lines, (solid or dashed);
rectangles;
curves (as defined by an equation, name or fixed points);
characters/symbols.

To draw labelled axes, a sub-routine of the form:

$$\text{PAXIS (various parameters)}$$

is likely to be available, producing say:

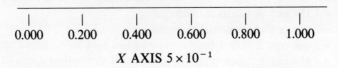

X AXIS 5×10^{-1}

where the parameters would define:

the co-ordinates of the start of the axis;
the values assigned to the first tick mark;
the rotation of the axis from the plotter's X-axis;
the length of the axis;
the scale increment between tick marks;
the label beneath the axis.

Drawing a single line is a composite operation with a basic incremental plotter, requiring each increment to be sent to the plotter. The routine could be of the form:

$$\text{PLINE } (X, Y, N, A)$$

causing lines to be drawn between successive pairs of points whose X-, Y-co-ordinates are stored in the arrays X and Y respectively, with N points. If A is positive the pen moves to $(X(1), Y(1))$ in a raised position. If A is negative the pen moves to $(X(1), Y(1))$ in a lowered position.

Thus with these two routines straight-line graphs can be drawn and annotated. Smooth-curve graphs can be specified in a variety of ways. One, by giving a number of points that the curve needs to pass through, is produced by the routine:

$$\text{PSCURVE } (X, Y, N, L, A, B)$$

where X and Y are arrays holding the x- and y-co-ordinates of the points with N the number of points. The parameters L, A, and B allow the initial and final shapes of the curves to be specified. The method employed to join the points would typically take

$$(x_{i-1}, y_{i-1}), \quad (x_i, y_i), \quad (x_{i+1}, y_{i+1}) \text{ and } (x_{i+2}, y_{i+2})$$

to fit a cubic polynomial between (x_i, y_i) and (x_{i+1}, y_{i+1}). Other methods may be available.

Further reading

1. Acamley, P. P., *Stepping motors: a guide to modern theory and practice*, Peter Peregrinus Ltd./IEE, Stevenage, 1982.

8

Other input–ouput devices

8.1 Introduction

The common manual way to enter data into a computer is by means of a keyboard. Originally this was done via punched paper tape and cards but in recent years direct input from an electronic keyboard has become usual. For computer output, printers have been traditionally used, joined in recent years by visual display devices.

There are applications where these forms of input–output device are not ideal. For example, when large amounts of previously typed documents or data have to be re-keyed into a computer this can be a lengthy and error-prone process. Reading machines can be an answer here. In other cases, where an operator's hands are occupied in controlling some machine, devices which allow voice input or output with a computer can be useful.

Devices which broadly fall into this category are dealt with in this chapter.

8.2 Optical mark readers and optical character readers (OMR and OCR)

8.2.1 Introduction

When large quantities of alpha-numeric data are to be processed, formal procedures are usually adopted to input the data. The main steps are:

(i) collection of source data, often in the form of source documents (e.g. invoices from other organisations);
(ii) transcription of source data onto written or typed coding sheets or suitable forms;
(iii) keying in the data. Originally this was done on paper tape or cards, but the more usual approach now is to key these data at a VDU;
(iv) editing errors which originate in steps (ii) and (iii);
(v) editing errors which subsequent processing reveals occurred at the generation of the source data.

This can be a lengthy process. Modern devices such as VDUs can greatly assist by displaying pre-stored forms for step (ii) or by having built-in text editors for steps (iv) and (v). However, the keying in of the data, step (iii), remains time consuming.

The better solution can be to enter the data at source, by means of a mark or character reading machine. This concept is sometimes called *source-data automation*.

Optical mark readers and optical character readers accept printed or handwritten information directly from documents, and output this information as data in computer-compatible form. The information that is read can be of three kinds:

(i)   marks that are put in predefined areas of the document;
(ii) printed or typewritten characters (alphabetic and/or numeric);
(iii) handprinted characters (alphabetic and/or numeric).

An OMR is used for the first kind, whereas OCRs are used for the second and third kinds (and are often able to read marks as well).

The range of machines is quite large. A simple type of machine can read marks of single-size cards (Fig. 8.1). It could be used for example in a factory where the completion of various production tasks is recorded by pencilling marks in appropriate boxes printed on the card. Machines increase in complexity as the ability to read characters, especially hand-printed characters, is included, and also as automatic handling of documents of various sizes is provided. A large multi-purpose OCR would rank alongside a mainframe computer in both size and capital cost (Fig. 8.2). Such machines tend to be used to process documents in batch mode, and from a variety of sources within an organization—or from outside, where the OCR facility is offered as a bureau service.

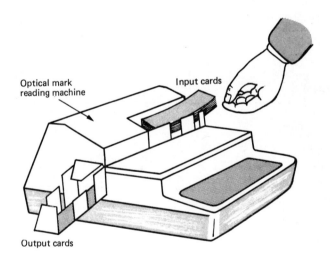

Figure 8.1 A small optical mark reader.

Several techniques are used in optical readers, but the sequence of operation is generally as shown schematically in Fig. 8.3. These operations and other aspects are now described.

8.2.2   Types of marks and characters that can be read

(i) *Location*   Readers are generally designed to read marks or characters positioned in a matrix pattern formed by regularly spaced locations on each of

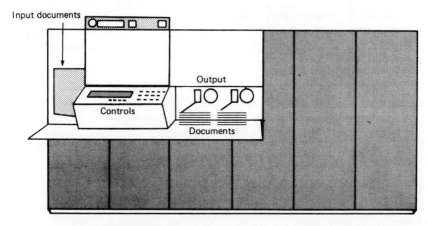

Figure 8.2 A large optical character reader.

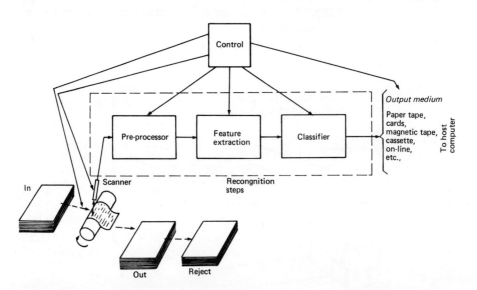

Figure 8.3 Block diagram of OCR/OMR machine.

several rows. This pattern is obtained automatically when a printer or typewriter is used. For hand-printed marks or characters, however, it is necessary to use pre-printed paper or cards on which the required locations are shown (usually as small rectangles).

Often a coloured ink (say pink or pale blue) is used in the pre-printing, and the reading machine is designed to be insensitive to this colour. This avoids the possibility that the mark location rectangle could be misread as a mark. Also the rectangles can be coloured in to improve the layout of the form, or can be printed with characters or short words to indicate the meaning of each mark.

(ii) *Marks* Optical mark readers detect the presence or absence of a mark placed in each permitted location. Some machines will read a wide variety of marks. Figure 8.4(a) shows some examples. Simpler optical mark-reading machines require that the mark is made in a particular way, for example, as shown in Fig. 8.4(b).

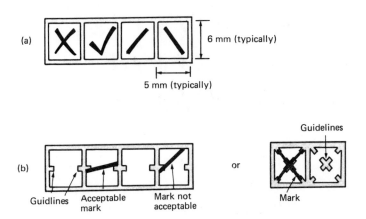

Figure 8.4 Typical marks that may be used: (a) unrestricted; (b) must fit guide lines.

Generally, marks can be made using an ordinary pencil, ballpoint pen, etc., or by a typewriter or printer if desired.

(iii) *Printed or typed characters* Various machine-readable character sets, or fonts, are used. Two standard ones are OCR-A and OCR-B, shown in Fig. 8.5. The A font was the first to be produced and originated from the United States. The stylized appearance of some of the characters is to aid machine recognition. The B font, which originated in Europe, is less stylized and contains a wider range of characters. Both of these fonts are now standards of the International Standards Organization. Printers and typewriters are available with OCR-A and OCR-B fonts.

In addition to fonts designed especially for OCR, character sets of popular office typewriters can be read by some OCR machines.

In some applications it is not necessary to use all of the font. By reducing when possible the character set to numerals and a few special alphabetic characters, the recognition process is made simpler, quicker and more reliable. A large optical reader is able to read several different fonts comprising a total of, say, 360 different characters.

(iv) *Hand-printed characters* Because of the differences in style of individuals, reliable recognition of hand-printed characters is more difficult than for printed or typed characters. Consequently many OCR machines will read hand-printed numerals only, together with a few other characters. Often the pre-printed paper or cards carry an illustration of the preferred hand-printing style, such as shown in Fig. 8.6.

ABCDEFGHIJKLM
NOPQRSTUVWXYZ
0123456789
•,:;=+/$*"&|
'-{}%?♪ΨΗ
ÜÑÄØÖÆÅ£¥

(a)

ABCDEFGH abcdefgh
IJKLMNOP ijklmnop
QRSTUVWX qrstuvwx
YZ*+,-./ yz m åøæ
01234567 £$:;<%>?
89   [@!#&,]
    (=) "´`ˆ ˜ �‚
ÅÖÅÑÜÆØ ↑≤≥×÷°¤

(b)

Figure 8.5 Machine readable fonts: (a) OCR-A; (b) OCR-B.

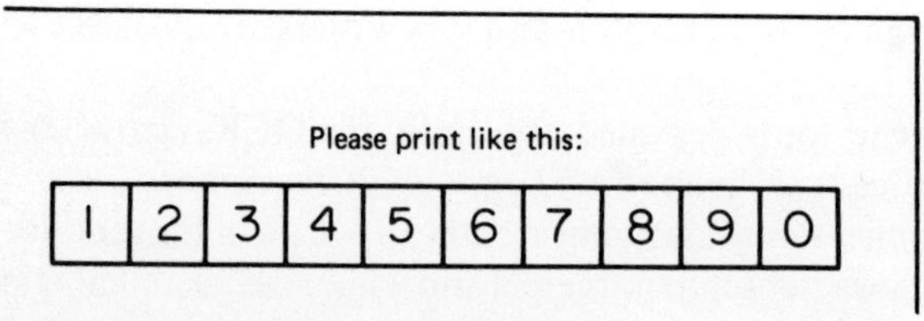

Please print like this:

| l | 2 | 3 | 4 | 5 | 6 | 7 | 8 | 9 | 0 |

Figure 8.6 Pre-printed preferred styles of hand-printing.

8.2.3   Paper or card transport mechanism

At its simplest the item to be read can be pushed by hand along a flat bed and thus passed underneath the optical scanner. In larger machines, which provide greater throughput, a batch of items is placed on an in-tray. A motorized transport then takes these one at a time and conveys them to the optical scanner. The paper or card to be read is often moved past the scanner by means of a drum or can be vacuum held to a flat glass surface. When the reading operation is complete the item is conveyed to the out trays (one tray for successfully read documents, and one for rejects). Some machines have many out trays and are able to perform read-sort operations on input documents.

Various sizes can be handled and OCR machines can be classed on this basis, as follows:

(i) *Journal roll reader* These machines are able to read journal rolls (or tally rolls) that record transactions in cash registers or adding machines.

(ii) *Document readers* These can handle documents up to about 15 by 25 cm. Typical applications include processing of membership subscription forms, bank documents, and bills.

(iii) *Page readers* Typically these can read pages up to about 25 by 35 cm. These machines tend to be larger and more versatile than document readers.

Large machines are able to handle paper of mixed sizes, weights, and conditions. Some machines can automatically re-orientate documents to compensate for skew in the printing of the lines of characters or marks on the document. The transport mechanisms of these machines are very complex and can form a major cost component of the reader.

8.2.4 Scanner

The function of the scanner is to obtain an electronic image of the character to be read, in a form which is suitable for the recognition process. Various scanning techniques are used, and some of these are:

(i) *Raster scan* In one form, the electron beam of a cathode-ray-tube is made to rapidly trace out on the CRT screen a raster consisting of a series of side-by-side strokes. An image of this raster is then projected onto the character. The character is therefore illuminated by a tiny 'flying-spot' which systematically covers the whole area of the character. A photo-electric cell detects the strong or weak reflected light as the spot passes over a part of the character or over the background area, and an electronic image of the character is built up as shown in Fig. 8.7.

In another form a thin horizontal segment of the document is focused onto a light-sensitive charge coupled device linear array. The charge is output serially as a voltage waveform representing the light and data points along the segment. A full raster scan of the document is obtained by mechanically moving the document repeatedly in small vertical increments.

Laser scanners are also used.

(ii) *Artifical retina* This is the converse of the previous technique in that the character to be read is wholly illuminated rather than selectively, and an image of the character is projected onto an array of photo-electric cells. These cells generate signals which are conveyed to the recognizer.

(iii) *Contour tracing* Here the 'flying spot' of a CRT is made to trace out the contour of the character using electronic feedback circuits. The path traced out is recorded.

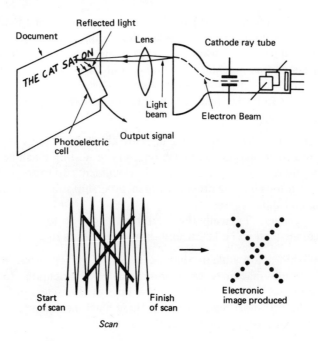

Figure 8.7 Raster scan.

(iv) *Bar scan*   A CRT flying spot is made to scan in a meandering path made up of connected lines, or *bars*. If a bar crosses a part of the character, then this fact is recorded. The route taken by the spot is carefully chosen so that each member of the character set produces a unique set of bar crossings.

(v) *Single photo-electric cell*   This is a simple and cheap method which can only be used to read marks. The mark location is illuminated and the reflected light is detected by a photo-electric cell. The cell output will be less than maximum if a mark is present. To improve the contrast ratio, and therefore also the reliability of detection, the monitored area of the mark location is kept as small as possible. Because of this the mark has to be more accurately placed and to help in this, guidelines can be pre-printed as shown in Fig. 8.4(b).

8.2.5   Recognition

As indicated in Fig. 8.3, the recognition process can be thought of as comprising three stages: pre-processing, feature extraction and classification. There are several recognition techniques in use and these determine the functions performed by each stage.

(i) *Pre-processing*   This stage normalizes the character before feature extraction. Operations that may be performed are: adjusting the width and height to standard size, and also centring of the character. This can be done after scanning or, where CRT scanning is used, a preliminary quick scan can be used to determine the size and location of the character and the parameters of the main scan are then adjusted accordingly. With hand-printed characters it may be desirable to correct for character skew and rotation due to individual hand-printing styles.

(ii) *Feature extraction* This stage identifies a set of characteristics or features in the character which allow it to be distinguished from other characters in the set. The features that are extracted depend on the recognition method adopted. In the matrix matching method, the features are just the matrix pattern of black and white elements obtained from the raster scan or artificial retina image of the character. In stroke analysis the features are the various strokes which make up the character. In contour tracing the contour of the character is used, sometimes approximated to, for convenience, by a closely fitting irregular polygon. In the bar scan method the feature extraction is implicit in the scanning operation itself.

(iii) *Classification* This stage identifies the scanned character. A set of reference features, extracted for each member of the reference character set, is stored in the optical reader machine. The set of features extracted from the scanned character is then compared with those of each of the reference characters until a match is obtained, thus identifying the character. In practice short cuts are taken in this comparison process.

In many cases small distortions in the scanned character may cause the extracted features to differ in detail from the ideal. The procedure then adopted in practice is to find the closest, rather than an exact, match to a character in the reference set. This may lead to substitution errors if larger distortions occur and the features that are extracted actually match closest to those of another character in the reference character set. These errors can be reduced to small proportions by raising a reject condition if the best match obtained is not very close. Some machines automatically repeat the scan and recognition process several times in an attempt to clear the reject condition.

Originally, optical reader machines used logic circuitry to perform the recognition function. This is now giving way to programs executed by an in-built computer.

Many optical character readers are also able to perform as mark readers since this is a relatively simple task compared to character recognition.

8.2.6 Control

This function directs the timing and sequencing of the paper-transport mechanism, scanner and recognition blocks. In addition, control is exercised over data output to a suitable data-storage medium or on-line to a computer.

A further function is that of formating. Very often the document to be read contains printed instructions and other information for the person originally receiving it and which are not intended for the optical reader. The marks or characters to be read are confined to areas on the document called data fields. The sizes, number and locations of the data fields can vary from document to document. The scanner can be controlled to read only from the data fields, in two ways: by means of (i) formating marks on the document, or (ii) formating information about the documents that is stored previously in the controller.

8.2.7   Performance

Typical reading speeds for optical character and mark readers are in the range 300 characters/s to 800 characters/s, but speeds in excess of 2000 characters/s are obtainable. Large, high-speed machines are more suited to batch operation. Smaller machines tend to be slower.

Error performance is very much dependent on the quality of the incoming data and the size of character set. Also error rates are related to flexibility of the reader: machines which can only read marks will have lower error rates than a machine which reads printed characters and hand-printing as well.

Two frequently employed terms are *reject errors* and *substitution errors*. When a source data character is distorted in such a way that the machine cannot reliably recognize it, a reject error is indicated. The data may then be edited and input again. The further, and generally less frequent, occurrence can happen when the distortion may coincidentally give attributes which are close to those of another character. The machine then falsely recognizes data and a substitution error has occurred. Substitution errors can be troublesome since they may go undetected.

Typical reject rates on hand-printed characters are 1%, with typical substitution rates of 0.5%.

Rejected documents are usually stacked in a separate output tray for later correction and re-entry. Some machines can store and replay the scanned image of rejected characters, for correction by an operator.

Several techniques can be used on the document itself to improve the error performance (some of which can be used with other data entry methods, both traditional and modern). Examples are:

(i)   Print important items more than once (for example customers' address)

(ii)   Attach check digits. Commonly, the check digit is set equal to the complement of the modulo-10 sum of the other digits in a numerical piece of data. The modulo-10 sum of a number is obtained by dividing by ten as many times as possible and saving the remainder. The complement is obtained by adding 10 to this remainder and again taking the modulo-10 sum. This procedure causes the modulo-10 sum of the whole data word (including the check digit), to be zero. After the reading operation, the modulo-10 sum of the data is calculated, and if found to be non-zero an error in at least one digit is known to have occurred.

(iii)   With columns of cash figures, and similar data, give totals which are then checked by the computer.

(iv)   Apply 'reasonableness' checks (an entered date of 64/14/78 is obviously in error).

8.2.8   Applications

Optical mark readers and optical character readers can be used for a wide range of applications as an alternative to keying-in data. Optical character reading machines are usually expensive, so tend to be used for applications which generate large quantities of data.

Optical mark readers are more flexible than may at first seem. As well as reading simple choice decisions (as for opinion polls and market surveys), numeric and alphabetic information can be conveyed. For example the format in Fig. 8.8 can be used to enter a three-digit number. By having several rows of 26 boxes with each column corresponding to one letter of the alphabet, alphabetic information can be entered.

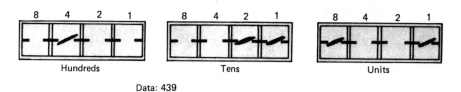

Data: 439

Figure 8.8 Use of marks to enter numerical data.

An important concept that becomes possible with OMR and OCR is that of a *turn-round* document. Here the document contains information printed by computer which is later read in together with data provided by the document recipient. For example, in subscription-renewal forms for a journal, the subscribers' name and address is computer printed on the form and the envelope. The recipient indicates his Yes/No decision as a mark and returns the form. The returned forms are then input for an OCR which identifies the subscriber by reading the name and address printed earlier together with the Yes/No decision. A second example is stock control in a large warehouse, where documents are printed with the assistant's name and a list of items and required stock levels, under that person's control. The assistant then marks the quantity of replacement items needed (possibly using the technique shown in Fig. 8.8).

8.3 Character reader based on writing tablets

This method is used to read hand-printed characters (both numerals and alphabetic).

The general arrangement is shown in Fig. 8.9, and it is seen that a writing tablet replaces the transport mechanism and optical scanner of the optical character reader, Fig. 8.3. Several writing tablets can be used simultaneously.

When the ball-point pen or pencil is placed on the form the writing tablet conveys the X- and Y-co-ordinates of the pen (see Section 7.4.4) to the processor/computer. Thus as the character is printed an electronic image of the character is built up. Unlike OCR machines, the writing tablet also inputs information on the sequence and direction of the various penstrokes that make up the character. This makes the recognition process simpler and more reliable. For example, in an optical-character-reading machine a printed S and 5 are sometimes confused, see Fig. 8.10. However, these characters are normally hand-printed with quite different stroke sequences and are therefore much less likely to be confused using the writing tablet method.

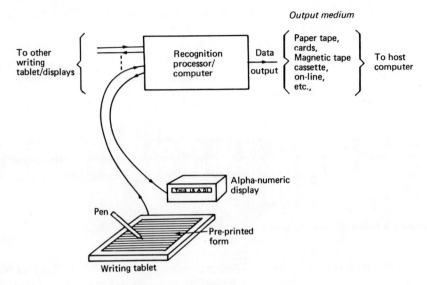

Figure 8.9 Character reader based on a writing tablet.

S   5

Letter 'S'   Figure '5'

Figure 8.10 Symbols which may be confused by OCR.

A further feature is the single-line character display (using LEDs, see Section 3.2.4) which provides visual verification. The name of the current data field and the characters that have been read are displayed. Reject characters are shown with a special symbol. This allows immediate corrections by the originator of the data, unlike OCR, where if the operator is uncertain about the correction, then reference back to the data originator is necessary, which can cause delays. Substitution errors are also reduced because they can be discovered by looking at the display.

This type of character reader is suited to different types of application than those for OCR. For example, it is not suitable for processing journal subscription renewal forms. Rather, data should be originated at a relatively few stations. One reported application is its use by the police for entering data on traffic accidents.

8.4   Bar codes

8.4.1   Introduction

A typical bar-code symbol is illustrated in Fig. 8.11. Numeric data are represented as a series of bars of varying thickness and separations. For convenience, the numeric data are often printed underneath the bar-code symbol, as shown.

Scale: approx. twice full size

Guard bars

Figure 8.11 Typical bar-code symbol.

The codes are easily read by a light pen, or a scanner. The light pen (or *wand*) has a light-sensitive tip and when stroked along the bar-code symbol the light and dark bars produce a corresponding sequence of binary voltage levels. This sequence is then decoded to give the numeric data. With the scanner, the object bearing the bar code is moved across a window. Typically this window is set into a work surface or counter. The window is rapidly scanned from below by a narrow beam of light and the reflected light from the bar code is detected by a light-sensitive device and converted into a binary sequence of voltage levels. The scanning pattern of the light beam is designed so that at least one valid scan along the code is normally obtained, no matter what the orientation of the code as it is moved past the window. With both the light pen and the scanner arrangement a reject condition is given to the operator if an invalid code is read. The operator may then try again.

8.4.2 Applications

One application of bar codes is in article numbering in supermarkets and other retailing operations. This can be useful at the point of sale, stock room or warehouse. The article identity can be quickly conveyed to a computer. Various improvements in efficiency of the retailing operation can thereby be obtained, such as an automatic update of stock levels, automatic re-ordering of new stock, better marketing information, and the ability to carry reduced levels of stock because of quicker replenishment of stock. This book carries a bar code on the rear outside cover.

Bar codes are also used in library systems. Each book is labelled with a unique bar code which is read when the book is issued and returned. This eliminates the form filling and record keeping normally associated with these operations. Book records can now be kept in a computer data base, which permits automatic production of overdue-book notifications, generation of statistics, and other benefits. Other applications of bar codes include control of the dispensing of drugs within a hospital.

8.4.3   Code details

Each data digit in Fig. 8.11 is made up of two black bars and two white bars in alternating sequence. The widths of these black and white bars add up to a fixed width for all characters. This allows the complete code to be scanned at any velocity within reasonable limits, because the timed widths of each bar can be expressed as a fraction of the time to scan a complete digit. These fractions are relatively independent of velocity provided the scan velocity does not change significantly in the course of a scan.

Each digit character can be broken down into seven elements. The individual elements are designated as black or white according to the scheme of Fig. 8.12.

A digit is coded differently depending on whether it is in the right half or left half of the bar-code symbol. All digits on the left half have an odd number of black

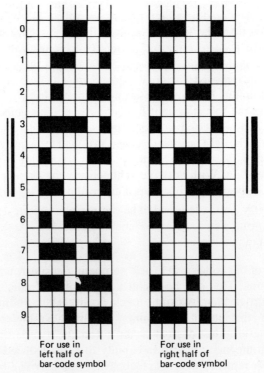

For use in
left half of
bar-code symbol

For use in
right half of
bar-code symbol

Note: The codes are shown shortened, the actual proportions are
illustrated at the sides for digit '4'

Figure 8.12 Coding of bar-code digits.

elements (odd parity) and always begin with a white bar, while those on the right have an even number of black elements (even parity) and always begin with a black bar. This feature allows scanning in either direction because the scanner can determine the direction of scan from the parity of the characters.

The two halves of the symbol are separated by two black guard bars. Two black guard bars also mark the beginning and end of the symbol.

Other coding methods are used.

8.4.4 Formats

An American format, used for article numbering, is that of the universal product code (UPC). One version of the UPC (as shown in Fig. 8.11) is:

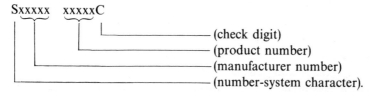

The manufacturer and product numbers occupy respectively the left and right halves of the symbol. They are also printed underneath the symbol.

The number-system character identifies the symbol version and also the type of article. For example, variable price articles such as meat which may require weighing at the point of sale. This character is put at 0 in Fig. 8.11.

The check digit is used to detect errors (see Section 8.2.7).

The check digit and number-system character are not printed underneath the symbol.

An objective of article numbering is to provide unique numbering of articles, with the bar-code symbol. To ensure that codes are not duplicated, articles can be registered at a central article number bank. The bar-code symbol can be machine printed on labels by the article retailer or distributor. The labels are then affixed to the article. A more convenient way is for the symbol to be included at the printing of the article package.

The European article number (EAN) system includes a two-digit code which identifies the country, and is designed to be compatible with the American UPC.

Various other formats are in existence, including 'in-house' codes intended for internal use by organizations.

8.4.5 Errors

Reject and substitution errors are quite low in practice. An invalid scan by a light pen can be caused for example by moving at an acute angle and so not scanning the whole symbol. This is easily detected and a reject indication given, because at least one guard band and possibly some code bars are then absent.

Blemishes on the symbol can cause white elements in a code to be interpreted as black or vice versa. In most cases this will produce an unrecognizable code. If only one digit error is detected it is possible to correct the error by using the check digit to calculate what the original digit must have been. A reject condition has to be given if more than one digit is detected to be in error. It is possible that a blemish will produce a recognizable code of another digit. This error will be detected because the modulo-10 sum will be altered. It is possible, though unlikely, that more than two digits will be in error. In most cases of this the modulo-10 sum is again altered and such errors are also usually detected. However, it is possible that multiple errors will cause the same modulo-10 sum, in which case an undetected substitution error occurs.

Fortunately errors are few and most of these are automatically correctable or will give rise to a reject condition, and the scan can be repeated.

8.5 Magnetic character readers (MCR)

8.5.1 Introduction

Characters are printed using ink loaded with iron oxide. The printed document is passed through the reading machine which first magnetizes the characters and then passes the document under a small coil. The magnetized characters induce a voltage signal in the coil from which the character is decoded.

The term magnetic ink character reader (MICR) is used as well as magnetic character reader.

A special printer is used to print the characters on documents.

This method has found widespread use in banks (for example, on cheques) because of its security and reliability. The method is secure because characters are not easily altered without the special printer. Reliability is obtained because ordinary dirty marks and other blemishes which might cause errors in an optical character reader are less likely to cause errors here because they are generally non-magnetic.

Reliability and simplicity of the recognition process is also enhanced by using stylized fonts. Two MICR fonts in widespread use are E13B and CMC7.

8.5.2 E13B font

This font originated in the United States and is now also used in Britain (see Fig. 8.13). The font includes the ten numerals, four special characters to specify data fields, but no alphabetic characters. The special characters signify: 'dash', 'bank-branch', 'amount', 'on us', respectively.

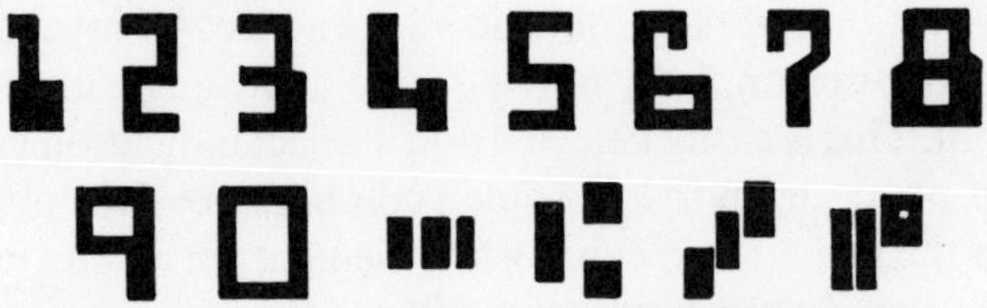

Scale: approximately four times actual size

Figure 8.13 The E13B magnetic character font.

A thin vertical slice of each character is scanned, which produces a signal amplitude that is proportional to the quantity of magnetized ink in the slice, as shown in Fig. 8.14. The signal is unique to each character, which is therefore easily identified.

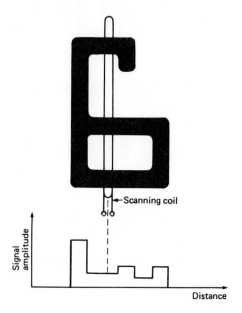

Figure 8.14 Reading of E13B character.

8.5.3 CMC7 font

This font, see Fig. 8.15, is in widespread use on the continent. Numerals, special characters, and also alphabet characters are included. The coding principle is different from that of the E13B font. In this case each character is made up of seven vertical magnetic ink bars. The six spaces between the bars are binary valued: narrow (binary 0) and wide (binary 1). This creates a six-bit code which allows a maximum of 64 possible characters to be represented. CMC7 uses 41 of these. The magnetic character reader again scans a thin vertical slice of the character, but measures the time between the bars and from this the character is decoded. The method is therefore insensitive to the length of each bar, (provided each bar is not too short). This allows pieces to be cut out of the bars to allow the characters to be visually readable as shown.

8.6 Voice input

8.6.1 Speech storage

The digitization and storage of speech finds application in speech synthesis, which is discussed in Section 8.7.1. However, direct applications of speech storage occur. Office computer systems have been demonstrated with speech-storage

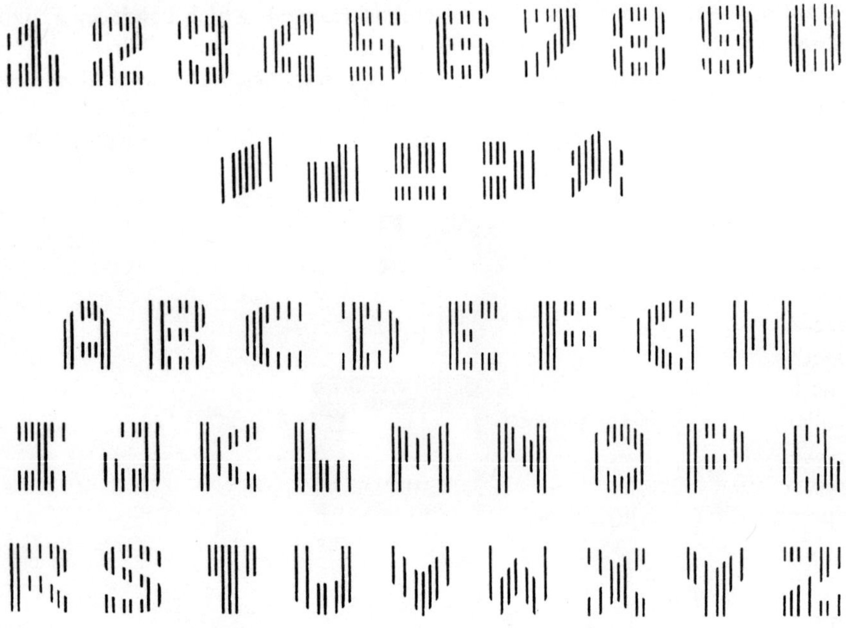

Scale: approximately three times actual size

Figure 8.15 The CMC7 magnetic character font.

capability. Here a document can be displayed on a visual display terminal and particular parts tagged and attached to digitized and stored speech messages. This facility can be used, for example, by persons who do not have the time or skill to operate a keyboard, to specify changes and corrections to the document.

A microphone is used to sense the speech and the analogue waveform produced (see Figure 6.2(a) for a typical segment of speech signal) must be digitized prior to being input to a computer. The direct approach to digitization is to sample the signal and convert each analogue sample into a digital value by means of an analogue-to-digital converter (ADC). Chapter 6 explains the details. The digitized samples can then be stored in computer memory. The original waveform can be reconstructed by putting the digitized sample sequence through a digital-to-analogue converter (DAC) and from there to an amplifier and loudspeaker.

For good quality the waveform should be quantized to at least 11 bits resolution and sampled at 8K samples/s or more. It follows that in using this direct approach to digitization a large amount of data must be stored for even quite short utterances.

A number of ways are used to reduce the amount of data.[1] One way is called *companding*. Here the quantization levels in the ADC are distributed unevenly over the signal amplitude range. They are closely spaced at small amplitudes and allowed to be more widely spaced at high amplitudes. The effect of this is to keep the quantization error relative to the signal amplitude at acceptably low levels while saving on the number of quantization levels and therefore saving on the number of bits required to digitize the sample.

A second approach is to use information from previous samples to help with the digitization of the present sample. An example is the *differential pulse code modulation* (DPCM) method. This relies on the property of analogue speech signals that sample amplitudes do not change rapidly from one sample to the next. Only the amplitude difference between the present sample and the immediately previous sample is passed through the ADC and stored. Since this difference is normally small, a lower-resolution ADC can be used, thus reducing the amount of data to be stored. The original sample sequence is readily reconstructed by adding each difference to the previous digitized sample. Other methods exist. In each case the method to code the samples must be matched by the inverse of the method when samples are reconstructed. Integrated circuits called *codecs* (*coder-decoder*) are available to do these operations.

The use of the above techniques typically halves the amount of data to be stored. This saving is worthwhile, but even so the storage of long passages of speech requires large amounts of digital memory.

8.6.2   Speech recognition

A voice-input system of this type accepts a spoken input, identifies it and converts it to a standard code, such as ASCII, for entry to a host computer. The system therefore does more than digitize speech: it recognizes it. Speech recognition has been the subject of research for some years and some of the features of recognition machines are:

type of utterance:	isolated words,	or continuous speech
size of vocabulary:	limited,	or very large
number of speakers:	one,	or any number
training mode:	required,	or not required,

The right-hand alternatives are the most difficult to achieve and presently all of them are found only in the human listener. Those on the left, while more restrictive, do find application and are available in commercial voice-input systems.

Figure 8.16 shows the system block diagram. The three main steps of preprocessing, feature extraction, and classification are also found in optical character readers (see Fig. 8.3). In fact, this framework applies to the general discipline of pattern recognition, of which speech recognition and OCR are parts.

Spoken sounds can be voiced or unvoiced. Voiced sounds originate from vibrations of the vocal chords and are periodic in character. Unvoiced sounds are obtained by the movement and control of air at certain points of the mouth (lips, teeth, etc.), and are not periodic in character. For example, the waveform in Fig. 6.2(a) is for the utterance 'sham', and the unvoiced 'sh' and voiced 'a' and 'm' can be clearly seen. By changing the shape of the mouth and opening and closing the nasal cavity, the tonal quality (that is, the spectrum) of these sounds is altered sequentially in a wide variety of ways, to create speech.

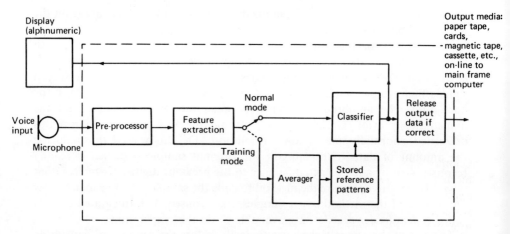

Figure 8.16 Block diagram of a voice-input system.

The word, or short phrase, to be recognized is spoken into the microphone. The signal produced is pre-processed by shaping the frequency spectrum and then splitting the signal into frequency bands using filters (this is called spectral analysis).

The feature-analysis stage examines the shape of, and changes in, the spectrum and extracts typically up to 32 separate features which characterize the utterance. These features include the presence of types of pause, vowel or vowel-like sounds, unvoiced consonant sounds, etc. The distribution of the features that are present varies with time, and the duration of the sound is split into segments (16, for example) and the presence or absence of each feature is noted at every time segment. This provides a pattern for the classifier.

In the classification stage the pattern of features of the utterance is compared with those of the reference set of patterns, and the closest fit is used to identify the word or phrase.

The reference set of patterns is obtained in the training mode. Each word or phrase is spoken several times and the features are extracted in the same way as in the normal mode of operation. The sets of features for each repeated word or phrase are averaged and stored in the reference set. An ASCII coded identifier is also stored with the set of features, which is output to the display and host computer when the word or phrase is recognized.

Typically a few tens to a few hundred words and phrases can be recognized. As the size of the vocabulary is increased, both the time taken to recognize an utterance and the incidence of errors increase.

Recognition reliabilities of 98% have been reported for larger vocabularies. Errors are practically eliminated by the use of the visual character display which shows the words that are recognized to the operator. Errors can be corrected by speaking 'erase' and repeating the utterance. An assembled block of correct progress far without more comprehensive 'artificial intelligence' models of language in which the meaning of the spoken word can be used to assist in the recognition process. Achievement is not limited by the input hardware but by our ability to write algorithms that match that amazing human ability to understand speech delivered in many accents and intonations, and with much extraneous noise.

8.7 Voice output

8.7.1 Speech synthesis

Computers that can talk have been a part of science fiction for many decades. In recent years commercial products have become available to satisfy real applications. Speech synthesis differs from the reconstruction of previously stored speech messages in that there is flexibility to output any desired speech utterance.

Speech is synthesized in effect by joining together segments of generated speech. Sentences are formed of words, and words can be formed by joining up *phonemes*. Phonemes play a similar role in speech as does the alphabet in writing. The utterance 'sham' is formed by the three phonemes /sh/, /a/, /m/.

Speech synthesis methods vary in the size of segments used and the method of generating the segments. The three prominent methods are (i) recorded segment synthesis, (ii) formant synthesis, and (iii) linear predictive coding (LPC).

In the first of these, segments of speech, such as words and short phrases, are uttered by a speaker, recorded and stored in non-volatile memory (such as read-only-memory integrated circuits). To reduce the storage burden, techniques such as DPCM can be used. A dictionary of words and phrases is assembled and each given an identification code number. Speech is then synthesized by supplying the system with the appropriate sequence of code numbers. This method has the restriction that a word or phrase can be spoken only if it is in the dictionary, and there can be no alteration to the prosodic features recorded originally. Nevertheless, it is sufficiently flexible for many applications and has the advantage of being inexpensive and producing sound which is from a recognizable speaker.

In formant synthesis, use is made of the resonances in the vocal tract. Sounds are caused by the vibration of the vocal chords, (for example /O/) and by the fricative action of the controlled release of air by the lips, teeth and tongue (examples are /p/, /th/, and /t/ respectively). To produce the full range of phonetic sounds the movable parts of the mouth take up different shapes, forming cavities which resonate at different frequencies. These frequencies are called *formant* frequencies. Synthesis is achieved by constructing an electronic circuit model of this action with signal generators to act as the vocal chords and fricatives, and adjustable filters to copy the action of the resonant cavities. By updating the parameters of the circuit model at a rate of typically once every 5–20 ms, acceptable quality speech can be synthesized. This rate of updating is considerably slower than for synthesis from pre-recorded speed and hence the data storage to drive the synthesizer is much less.

The linear predictive coding method has proved to be very successful and is widely used. The basis of the method is quite mathematical, but it can be thought of as a form of curve fitting. The parameters of a special function are found which closely predict the sequence of speech samples. Synthesis is achieved by evaluating the function given these parameters. The parameters are updated every 10–20 ms to give acceptable speech quality. Again storage requirements are low. The LPC method is well suited to low-cost digital implementation, and is the basis for example of the educational toy *Speak 'n Spell*.

Formant synthesis and LPC can be used to synthesize phonemes, words, or longer segments of speech.

Synthesis at the phoneme level has the advantage that any message can be synthesized without the restrictions caused by using word dictionaries. However, the speech produced can sound robot-like and unnatural. Speech is a complicated process. One reason for an unnatural sound is that phonemes can depend on adjacent phonemes. For example, the phoneme /k/ in 'kew' differs from that in 'kite' because when speaking /k/ the tongue anticipates the following vowel 'e' in one case and 'i' in the other. These effects are called *allophonic variations*. They can be overcome to some extent by building extra rules into the synthesizer. Even so the speech does not sound completely natural. Natural speakers utter the same word in different ways. The tempo, pitch and emphasis, can all be altered depending on the meaning intended. These effects apply to the utterance as a whole and are called *prosodic features*. For most applications a degree of unnaturalness in the speech quality can be accepted.

Speech synthesis products are manufactured as small stand-alone units or as assemblies for incorporation in the other apparatus such as computers.

Applications are numerous. Instructions to machine operators can be given without the need to look away from the work to read a screen display. Alarms need not merely ring but say what the problem is. A remote plant can be monitored by telephone; speech synthesis is used to say on the telephone what the condition of the plant is. Another application is to voice response systems. These systems have been available for several years and are described in the next section.

8.7.2   Voice-response systems

A voice-response system is able to respond to a user with pre-recorded messages that can guide the user in keying-in data, validate the data entered, and return information to the user. Data may be entered by means of cheap push-button key units and transmitted over telephone lines. A typical voice-response system is shown in block diagram form in Fig. 8.17.

The terminal is a simple 'tough-tone' push-button unit with typically 16 pushbuttons (digits 0–9 and six control keys). The terminal can be plugged into a standard telephone socket, or acoustically coupled to the telephone handset by a small loudspeaker which is attached to the handset mouthpiece. In some countries (notably North America), 'touch-tone' telephone switching systems are installed and the 'touch-tone' telephone instrument is then used as the terminal.

The depression of a button causes a unique combination of tone frequencies to be transmitted for a short period. The frequencies are within the bandwidth of the telephone system.

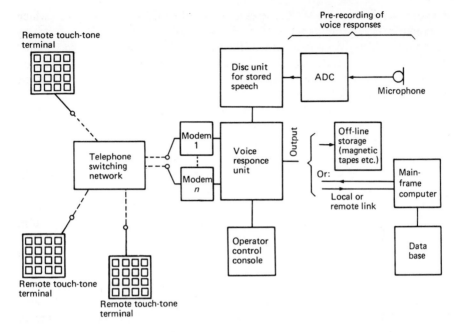

Figure 8.17 Block diagram of a voice-response system.

Voice-response systems are installed frequently for use on the public telephone switching network, but private switching networks or direct connection can be used.

Incoming lines to the voice-response processor are first handled by a modem which accepts the originating call and decodes the tone combination into digital data which are compatible with the voice-response processor. Several simultaneous terminal connections can be handled by the system up to a maximum of typically several dozen. The number of incoming lines and modems provided is determined by a traffic analysis of the intended application.

The responses can be produced from previously stored words or phrases, or by using speech-synthesis techniques.

Voice response systems are used in a number of different applications; examples are remote enquiry of stock position and sales order-entry systems. In a typical sales order-entry system, a salesman, having visited a customer, goes to the nearest telephone and enters the order to his company (say XYZ Ltd) via the central voice-response system. The dialogue (which is designed for each application) may go as follows:

Salesman: Dials the telephone number of the response unit, and places acoustic coupler of the terminal on the telephone handset.

Response: 'This is the XYZ order-entry system. Please enter salesman identifier.'

The salesman continues with the push-button unit:

Salesman: '134', followed by 'send' key.

Response: 'Salesman 134. Please enter security code.'
Salesman: '93', 'send' key.
Response: 'Security code accepted. Please enter item number.'
Salesman: '433', 'send' key. (The salesman has a list of item numbers.)
Response: 'Item 433. Please enter quantity.'
Salesman: '6', 'send' key.
Response: 'Quantity six. Please enter next item number.'

and so on, until terminated by,
Salesman: 'finished' key.

If the salesman dials and the maximum number of terminals is in use, then the response can be 'XYZ order-entry system busy. Pleasy try later.'

By linking the voice-response unit to a data base, the salesman can also be informed: 'out of stock, three weeks delivery' where necessary on a particular item.

8.8   Badge and 'smart' card readers

In their usual form these cards are made from plastic or plasticated material. They are the size of credit cards, that is typically 6.35 × 8.25 cm.

Badge cards contain data which is recorded using optical marks, punched holes or, very commonly, a magnetic strip. In the latter case data are recorded on several parallel tracks using similar techniques to those used for recording on magnetic tapes and discs (see Chapter 9).

The reader includes a small slot into which the card is inserted. The data are read from the card using the same techniques as when marks, punched holes, or magnetic encoding are used in other peripheral devices.

The amount of data that can be stored is limited and in most applications is used principally to identify uniquely the owner of the card. Applications are varied, and include the control of entry to secure buildings, library book borrowing, and *automatic teller mechines* (ATMs). In applications of badge cards it is common to provide further security against forged and stolen cards by requiring the card bearer to key in a few digits which comprise a previously assigned *personal identification number* (PIN).

ATM terminals are now widely used in banks etc. to provide services such as the issuing of cash, the provision of account statements and the transfer of money between accounts. As well as freeing the work of human bank tellers, by mounting the ATM terminal through the wall of the bank, or in the bank entrance, a 24–hour service can be provided for customers. Another application of these cards is to *electronic funds transfer at point of sale* (EFTPOS) terminals in retailing outlets such as supermarkets. The customer uses the card at the checkout point to initiate a funds transfer directly from the customer bank account to the retailer's account. EFTPOS terminals differ from ordinary credit card readers in that the terminals are linked by a data communications network and the checking of the customer status, and the transfer of money is done on-line. This provides both a greater protection against fraud and a quicker way to perform the transaction.

In banking and similar installations, because customers can access ATM machines in different locations it is necessary to network the machines with a central data-base computer to control and vet the transactions requested by the card bearer. The costs of this data communication can be high. One answer to this is seen by some as the 'smart' card. This card has embedded within it one or more integrated circuits containing non-volatile memory and calculating capabilities. The integrated circuits are accessed by the reader by means of electrical contacts on the surface of the card. The main feature of these cards compared with the basic type of card is that more data can be stored on the card and moreover it can be changed by the card reader. This means that data about the cash balance of the owner, for example, can now be stored in the card rather than in some central data base. This reduces the costs of data communication.

In typical applications of smart cards the user is able to buy a card with an initial money value. As the card bearer uses the card to obtain services such as petrol, telephone calls, public transport, and cash delivery, the money value of the card is debited by the appropriate amount by the card reader. The view is held by some that the 'smart' card heralds the arrival of the 'cashless society'.

References

1. Witten, I. H., *Principles of Computer Speech*, Academic Press, London, 1982.
2. Anderson, R. G., *Data Processing and Management Information Systems*, Macdonald and Evans, London, 1975.
3. *Input/Output*, Infotech Information, Maidenhead, England, 1975.
4. Jones, G. T., *Data Capture in the Retail Environment*, National Computing Centre Publications, Manchester, 1977.
5. *Modern Data Entry Techniques*, Online Conferences, Uxbridge, 1976.
6. *Retail Data for Management*, Online Conferences, Uxbridge, 1977.
7. Rosenthal, L. H., Rabiner, L. R., Schafer, R. W., Cumminskey, P., Flanagan, J. L., Automatic voice response: interfacing man with machine, *IEEE Spectrum*, 61–8, July 1974.
8. Savir, D. and Laurer, G. J., The characteristics and decodability of the Universal Product Code symbol, *IBM Systems Journal*, No. 1 16–34, 1975.

9

Backing stores

9.1 Introduction

Almost from the earliest times in the history of computers proper (i.e. the late 1940s), the store has been divided into a main store and a backing store. The first working stored-program computer, reputedly the Manchester University prototype Mark I (in operation from June 1948), used a magnetic drum for backing store and the ingenious Williams tube for main store.[1] Although the Williams tube lost favour in the 1950s upon the introduction of magnetic-core stores, the magnetic-drum store has survived as one type of backing store.

The magnetic-drum store is, as the name suggests, a drum which can be magnetized. Referring to Fig. 9.1, the drum has a magnetic surface (such as iron oxide). The drum revolves and local areas of the surface are magnetized by small electromagnets, known as *write heads*. The magnetization can be in one of two directions (north or south) which can represent 0s and 1s. The direction of magnetization can be detected by electromagnetic transducers known as *read heads* (actually similar to the write heads and the two functions can be combined in one head).

The principle of recording onto a moving magnetic surface has since been employed in the majority of backing stores, though the physical arrangements

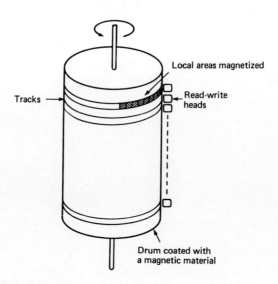

Figure 9.1 Magnetic-drum store.

226

have altered, leaving the drum not very common nowadays. Hence, only the magnetic-disc store and magnetic-tape store will be considered.

Backing stores not employing magnetic surface recording are also described in this chapter.

9.2   Recording on a magnetic surface

9.2.1   Read–write process

Figure 9.2(a) shows a write head in the process of magnetizing the magnetic surface, i.e. writing information. The head consists of a material of high permeability with a coil wound on it, and has a small air gap near the magnetic surface. Magnetic flux is produced by passing a current, I_w, through the coil. The flux passes around the core and some passes through the magnetic surface, thus causing a small area of the surface to be magnetized. Reversing the current, I_w, causes a reversal of the magnetization. The area magnetized can represent one bit of information. The surface is moved and the process repeated for subsequent bits. In practice the surface is not stationary whilst recording each bit.

Figure 9.2(b) shows a read head in the process of detecting magnetization on a magnetic recording surface, i.e. reading information. Here some of the flux in the recording medium is diverted through the high-permeability head. The coil will thus have flux passing through it. As the surface moves, this flux will change and this change will cause an induced emf, v_r, across the coil, proportional to the rate of change of flux (Faraday's law). So the surface must move for the reading operation. Figure 9.2(c) shows read and write waveforms.

The read pulse can be approximated to a Gaussian pulse of general formula

$$v(t) = Ke^{-t^2}.$$

A useful measure of this read pulse is the width of the pulse between the points where the amplitude is 50% of the maximum. This width is known as PW_{50} and is approximately given by the formula:

$$PW_{50} = 2\sqrt{[(g/2)^2 + (a+d+t)\,(a+d)]},$$

where g = head gap,

    $2\pi a$ = transition width (length of surface required to change magnetic state of surface from one direction to opposite),

    d = separation of head from surface (zero for tape),

    t = thickness of magnetic surface.

For the write process, a large air gap in the head is required to minimize the write current, and a few turns are required to give a low inductance and hence high switching speeds. For the read process, a large gap gives high efficiency, but a small gap is required to give a narrow read pulse (and hence a large number of bits per length of track). A large number of turns is required to give an adequate read voltage. For a combined read–write head, there needs to be a compromise. Typically in a conventional read–write head there are 10–1000 coil turns, a gap of

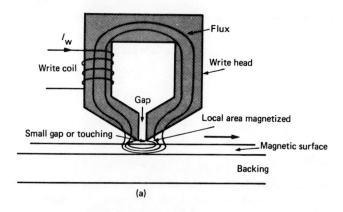

(a)

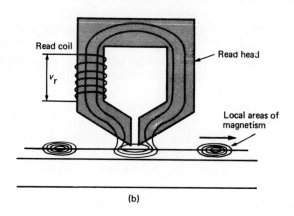

(b)

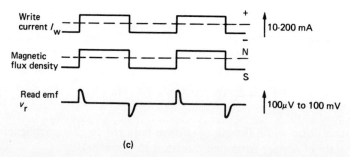

(c)

Figure 9.2 Recording on a magnetic surface: (a) writing; (b) reading; (c) waveforms.

50–600 μm, inductance of 10 μH to 100 mH, a write current of 10–200 mA (peak) and an output voltage of 100 μV to 100 mV.

Read–write heads can be made by thin-film techniques.

The thickness of the recording surface needs to be small to give a narrow pulse, and is typically 500 μm for ferric oxide and 25 μm for Ni–Co.

The magnetic recording process described so far is *horizontal recording*, as the magnetic regions lie with the north and south poles across the surface of the

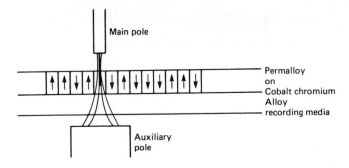

Figure 9.3 Vertical recording.

medium. An alternative process known as *vertical recording* (or *perpendicular recording*) creates magnetic regions through the medium with the north pole on one surface and the south pole at the opposite surface. The magnetized columns are substantially narrower than conventional horizontally magnetized regions and also the magnetic columns have a tendency to reduce in width under the influence of adjacent oppositely magnetized columns. Recording densities of vertical recording are typically 30 times greater than equivalent horizontal recordings. Vertical recording can be achieved with a write head having a main pole on one side of the medium and an auxiliary pole of the oppose side of the medium so that flux passes through the medium from one side to the other as shown in Fig. 9.3. Alternatively, a write head can be designed to operate from one side of the medium only.

9.2.2 Recording codes

This section defines various *codes* for recording digital information on magnetic surfaces, illustrated in Fig. 9.4. The bit cell is an area on the magnetic surface. A discussion of the relative merits of these codes together with circuit implications follows this section.

(a) *Return to zero* (RZ)
A 1 is represented by one state of magnetization for part of the bit cell, the rest of the cell being 'returned' to zero magnetization (i.e. not magnetized). This can be obtained by supplying the write head with a *pulse* of current. A 0 is represented by no magnetization throughout the cell.

(b) *Return to saturation* (RS)
A 1 is represented by one state of magnetization for part of the cell, the rest of the cell being returned to the opposite state of magnetization. A 0 is represented by no change from this latter magnetic state throughout the cell.

(c) *Bipolar return to zero* (BRZ)
A 1 is represented by magnetization in one direction (north, say) for part of the cell, and a 0 is represented by magnetization in the opposite direction (south, say)

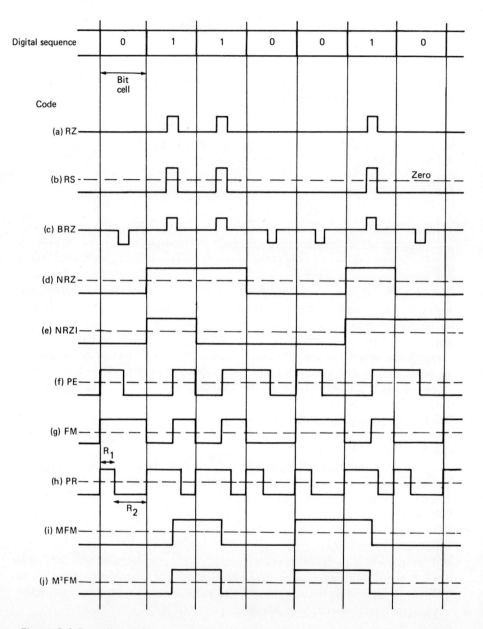

Figure 9.4 Recording codes.

for part of the cell. The surface is returned to an unmagnetized state in each case for the rest of the cell.

Return to saturation has the advantage over the other two methods in that erasure is not necessary before further recording of information. The above three methods are not generally used, as other methods below are superior in terms of the number of bits that can be recorded in a length of track (packing density), and other factors to be discussed.

(d) *Non-return to zero* (NRZ)
Perhaps the most obvious, a 1 is represented by one state of magnetization and a 0 is represented by the other state of magnetization thoughout each bit cell.
Changes of magnetization occur only at the boundaries of these cells.

(e) *Non-return to zero one or non-return to zero invert* (NRZI)
A 1 is represented by a change in magnetic flux (from north to south or south to north) at the beginning of the bit cell, and 0 is represented by no change.

(f) *Phase encoding* (PE)
A 1 is represented by a change in one direction of magnetic flux (say south to north) and a 0 is represented by the opposite change (say north to south) each at the mid-way point of the bit cell. Thus consecutive 1s or consecutive 0s will require another flux change, taken at the beginning of the bit cell.

(g) *Frequency modulation* (FM)
A 1 is represented by a flux change at the mid-way point of the cell and a 0 by no change at this point. There is also always a change in flux at the beginning of the cell.
NRZI, PE and FM find wide application; the next two are occasionally encountered.

(h) *Pulse ratio* (PR)
Referring to Fig. 9.4(h), a 1 is represented by a pulse such that $r_1/r_2 < 1$ and a 0 is represented by a pulse such that $r_1/r_2 > 1$, where r_1 is the width of the pulse and $r_1 + r_2$ the width of the cell.

(i) *Complementary non-return to zero* (CNRZ)
This is not shown in Fig. 9.4; it is an example of two-track recording. A 1 is represented by one state of magnetization (say, north) on one track, together with the opposite state of magnetization (say, south) on the second track. A 0 is represented by the inverse combination, i.e. a 'south' state on the first track, and a 'north' state on the second track. The two remaining combinations of magnetization can be used for timing purposes. In all cases, the magnetization is throughout the bit cell.

The final three codes are examples of advanced codes.

(j) *Modified FM* (MFM) (Fig. 9.4(i))
Similar to FM except the flux transition at the beginning of the cell is included only if both the previous and present data bits are a 0.

(k) *Modified-Modified Frequency Modulation*[2] (M^2FM) (Fig. 2.3(j))
As FM but change of flux at beginning of cell is only included if previous cell does not contain a flux change (at beginning or mid point) and the present cell also does not have a flux change at the mid point (i.e. not a 1).

(l) *Group coded recording* [3, 4] (GCR)

Each word (4 bits, say) to be recorded is converted into a slightly longer but more desirable code, from the point of view of recording/playback. This code is then recorded. One example, called modified NRZI (MNRZI), converts a 4-bit data character into a 5-bit pattern (Table 9.1), which prevents more than two successive 0s being recorded. The converted pattern is recorded in the NRZI method.

4 bit data	5 bit recording
0 0 0 0	1 1 0 0 1
0 0 0 1	1 1 0 1 1
0 0 1 0	1 0 0 1 0
0 0 1 1	1 0 0 1 1
0 1 0 0	1 1 1 0 1
0 1 0 1	1 0 1 0 1
0 1 1 0	1 0 1 1 0
0 1 1 1	1 0 1 1 1
1 0 0 0	1 1 0 1 0
1 0 0 1	0 1 0 0 1
1 0 1 0	0 1 0 1 0
1 0 1 1	0 1 0 1 1
1 1 0 0	1 1 1 1 0
1 1 0 1	0 1 1 0 1
1 1 1 0	0 1 1 1 0
1 1 1 1	0 1 1 1 1

4 bits translates into 5 bits for recording and is re-constituted on playback

Table 9.1 MNRZI pattern.

9.2.3   Circuitry

Figure 9.5 shows a simple read–write circuitry for NRZ recording. The write amplifier provides a current, $+I_w$, whenever a 1 is to be recorded. A positive flux transition produces a positive read pulse from the read head. This is amplified and clipped by one read amplifier, and then used to set the R–S flip-flop, thus indicating a 1. Similarly, a negative read pulse, produced by a negative flux transition, is amplified and clipped by the other read amplifier and the signal used to reset to R–S flip-flop, thus indicating a 0. The read voltages are in the range $100\,\mu V$ to $100\,mV$, and comparators can be used for the read amplifiers in a simple design.

Figure 9.6 shows modifications for NRZI recording. In this case, the presence of a read pulse (either positive-going or negative-going) sets the D-type flip-flop, and the absence of a pulse causes the flip-flop to be reset. A strobe signal is generated which needs to appear around the peak of the read signal.

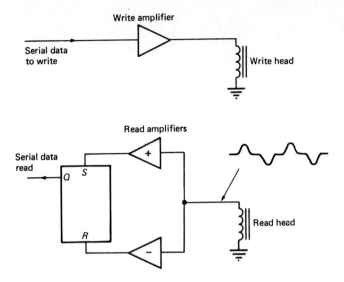

Figure 9.5 NRZ read–write circuitry.

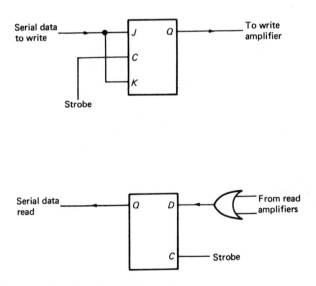

Figure 9.6 Circuit modifications for NRZI recording.

The circuitry of PM and FM is generally a little more complicated. In these codes, there is always a flux transition in each cell, and this can be used to produce a strobe signal directly related to the recording. This 'self-clocking' nature is advantageous.

When the read signal is amplified and clipped, a large original signal will produce a wider pulse (Fig. 9.7). This can cause timing problems. An alternative approach is to detect the peak of the read signal (*peak detection*). This can be done

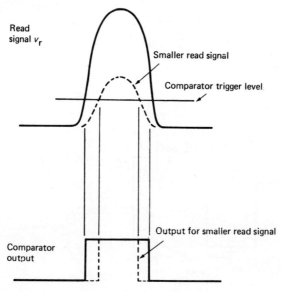

Read signal v_r

Smaller read signal

Comparator trigger level

Output for smaller read signal

Comparator output

Figure 9.7 Effect of using a comparator with read voltages of different amplitudes.

by differentiating the read signal (after full-wave rectification) and then detect the zero crossing using a comparator, as shown in Fig. 9.8. The falling edge appears at the peak of the signal. At lower packing densities, the peak is stable in position. Further stages of rectification and differentiation can be applied.

At high packing densities, a phenomenon known as *peak shift* occurs: that is, a shift in the position of the peak of read signal pulses, due to neighbouring pulses. It depends upon the pattern recorded. For any particular pattern it can be predicted theoretically. Circuitry may need to take this into account. Figure 9.9 shows the effects of neighbouring pulses on the resultant read voltage. This can be obtained by algebraically adding the individual waveforms of isolated pulses. The superposition theorem holds unless the pulses are very close.

A strobe signal can be obtained by recording a single separate clock track which is read simultaneously with the data track. Two heads would be required and this introduces a factor known as *skew*. This is the variation on readback between parallel tracks which were initially recorded using the same timing signal. Thus skew may be significant when reading several data tracks in parallel. If the heads are moveable (see later), the accuracy of re-positioning will contribute to skew, as will variations in the head construction, and component variations in the read circuitry of each head.

De-skewing circuitry may be incorporated. One technique[5] is to measure the skew digitally at the beginning of the data using a prerecorded preamble, and then use the skew measurement to produce a suitable strobe.

9.2.4   Discussion

For the largest capacity of the storage system, the code used should have the least number of flux changes per bit. In this respect, the NRZ and NRZI are the most

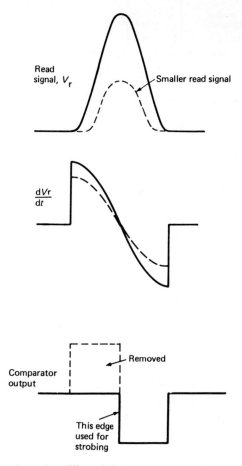

Figure 9.8 Peak detection using differentiation.

efficient of the four major codes ((d), (e), (f) and (g) above), requiring at the most one flux change per bit. In the case of NRZ, a succession of 0s or a succession of 1s cause no flux change at all, and in the case of NRZI a succession of 0s causes no flux change at all. Thus the bandwidth of the signal could conceivably extend down to dc. In practice there will normally be a break from a succession of 0s or 1s. However, it has two major effects; firstly, the read and write amplifiers needs to have a wide bandwidth, and secondly, in consequence, the signal-to-noise ratio will be poor in comparison with PM and FM. With these two latter systems, the maximum number of flux changes per bit is two and the minimum number, one. Thus they are less efficient but require narrow-bandwidth amplifiers and the signal-to-noise ratio is much improved (low-frequency noise can be filtered out).

Another and equally important factor is whether the code used demands that the speed of magnetic surface be accurately fixed. Both NRZ and NRZI require that the read circuitry be able to differentiate between the presence or absence of a read signal at specific times and a clock signal is required for strobing. Using an internally generated clock, any difference between the speed of the surface at

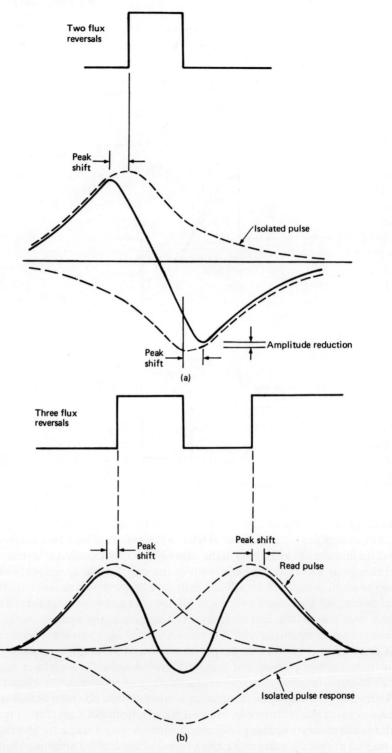

Figure 9.9 Peak shift and pulse crowding: (a) superposition of two close flux reversals; (b) three close flux reversals.

writing and at reading could cause errors. In contrast, PM and FM are *self-clocking* codes: they produce read signals at regular intervals which can be used for synchronization.

In the event of a single bit being misread, the effect on subsequent bits depends upon the code used and the read circuitry. If a transition is missed, this error can always be detected (a positive transition must be followed by a negative transition and vice versa). However, in the case of NRZ, when a transition is missed, all subsequent bits are misinterpreted until the next transition (i.e. a series of 0s will be taken as a series of 1s and vice versa). NRZI has the advantage that this does not happen and thus is preferred over NRZ.

The modified FM (together with other codes) has been employed on high-speed disc drives to obtain self-clocking with the packing densities close to NRZ/NRZI, but the circuitry required is complex. Generally NRZI has been popular for tape drives (capstan driven), and FM/PM popular on all media. Pulse ratio code has on occasion been employed in hub-driven tape drives, being tolerant of slow speed changes. Two-track codes (complementary) are also tolerant of speed changes but have tight skew requirements, though they have found application in data loggers. Capstan driven and hub-driven (reel-to-reel) tape systems will be discussed later.

9.3   Discs

9.3.1   General aspects

The disc of a (rigid) disc store is generally made from aluminium with a coating of a magnetic material such as ferric oxide or chromium oxide. The disc revolves continuously. Read–write heads are positioned very close but not touching the surface of the disc, so that concentric tracks can be recorded or read back. Having the heads touching the surface was abandoned at a very early date, due to the excessive wear on both the surface and the heads. A consequence of non-touching heads is that the read signal will be less.

A method of keeping the read–write head very close to the recording surface is to design the shape of the head so that when the disc is revolving at high speed, air is drawn between the head and the surface to raise the head off the surface (the head being on a suitable mounting). This arrangement is known as a *flying head* and very small fly heights of 0.5–3 μm can be achieved. The head must retract away from the surface when the disc is not revolving at full speed, as in this case the air pressure would decrease and cause the head to crash into the disc surface. An alternative, though less attractive, method to raise the heads is to provide air jets in the head mounting.

The heads can be designed to take off from and land onto the surface. Such systems are generally referred to as *Winchester drives*. The surface is lubricated and the heads designed to land without damaging the surface. This system can achieve closer flying distances and greater precision of alignment than ordinary flying-head systems, and this results in a higher packing density, and a greater number of tracks (typically double that of equivalent ordinary flying-head system). The complete system is hermetically sealed to prevent dust from entering.

The above does not apply to floppy discs, the operation of which will be dealt with separately in Section 9.3.4.

Figure 9.10 shows the layout of the tracks on a disc. Each track is divided into a number of sectors (eight are shown in the figure), and each sector will generally hold a fixed number of words. The central area of the disc is not used for recording because with a fixed number of words per track, the packing density increases towards the centre of the disc and there is a maximum permissible packing density. A typical disc uses the outer 5 cm of a disc of 38 cm diameter. The layout of sectors, tracks and words is known as the *disc format*. The tracks and sectors are given identifying addresses: in Fig. 9.10 the sectors have been numbered consecutively, though for particular applications numbering alternate sectors consecutively may have advantages. Usually the tracks are numbered consecutively from the outermost inwards. The sectors, in particular, can be altered to suit the application. This is known as *sectoring*. The sectors can be specified in the software (*soft sectoring*) by, for example, recording the address of each sector on a header preceding the data on each sector (on every track). Alternatively, a hardware approach can be used with slots around the disc indicating the position of the sectors, and sensors to detect the slots. This is known as *hard sectoring*.

There is an index marker to indicate the first sector. This may take the form of an index track recorded on the disc surface, or index slot in the disc.

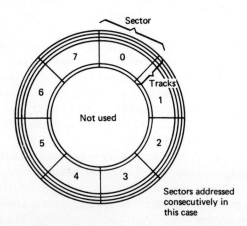

Figure 9.10 Tracks and sectors of a disc.

The smallest unit of data that can be transferred to or from the disc unit is a sector (also referred to as a block in this context). Once a read or write request has been received by the unit, there is a delay until the required sector reaches the read–write heads, known as rotational latency. On average this is one half of the period of revolution (assuming one set of read–write heads; there may be more than one set distributed around the surface of the disc, resulting in a smaller latency time).

The method of recording is often PE, but other codes are used. There is usually error detection employing cyclic redundancy codes (CRC) (see Chapter 11). A CRC word is appended to each block on writing the data and checked upon reading the data. At the beginning of the sector there may be a preamble recorded and at the end a postamble, each of the predefined patterns, which can be used by the circuitry to counter mechanical and electrical variations.

It is normal practice to provide a protection against accidentally writing over essential data/programs. This can be done by hardware which causes the write circuitry to be inhibited for particular tracks or surfaces. This may be activated by *write protect* switches on the front panel of the unit.

9.3.2   Fixed-head discs

A fixed-head disc is one which has a separate read–write head for each track (Fig. 9.11). This head is permanently positioned over each track. Usually, the disc unit is completely enclosed and slightly pressurized to keep dust out. The disc itself is usually spun horizontally and has a diameter about 38 cm (some older units were vertical and had larger diameters). Given a sufficient number of read–write amplifiers, one bit on each track may be recorded or read back simultaneously. Often, however, an individual read–write amplifier is shared amongst several heads, allowing as many bits in parallel to be recorded/read back as there are read–write amplifiers.

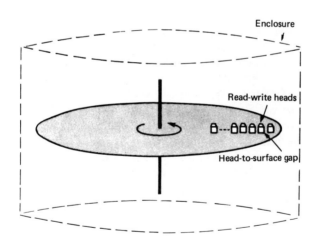

Figure 9.11 Fixed-head disc.

9.3.3   Moving-head discs

A moving-head disc (Fig. 9.12(a)) is one which employs a single read–write head for each surface of the disc. This head moves to the required track by a servo mechanism. The track width is typically 0.05 mm or less. Consequently a precision mechanism is necessary to position the heads correctly over a track. A common method is to use a d.c. servo motor to drive the head assembly across the

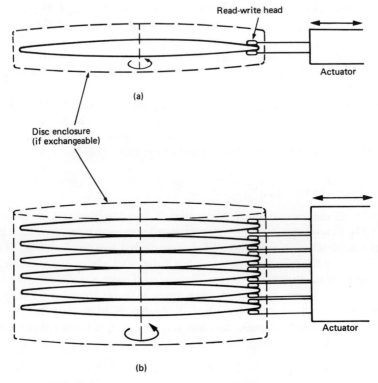

Figure 9.12 Moving head discs: (a) single disc; (b) multiple disc.

disc, coupled with a pair of flat windings, one mounted on the head assembly and the other stationary beneath (Fig. 9.13).

A high-frequency signal (typically 500 kHz) is applied to one winding and the amplitude of the signal obtained on the other will depend upon the degree of primary to secondary coupling between the windings. As the head moves from one track to the next, the amplitude will vary as shown in Fig. 9.13(b). Counting these occurrences gives the number of tracks transversed.

On shutdown the heads are automatically retracted. The head mounting may include erase heads to trim the recording track and prevent spread onto adjacent tracks.

To obtain larger capacity, a stack of discs can be formed as shown in Fig. 9.12(b). One head is required for each surface used for recording. Thus, reading and writing can occur in several tracks in parallel, one on each surface. At any instant, the same track (for example, track 1) on corresponding disc surfaces are selected together. Each such group of tracks is known as a cylinder of tracks and there are as many cylinders as there are tracks on one surface. In the specification of a multi-disc unit, the number of cylinders and tracks per cylinder will be given. For example, a unit with 19 tracks/cylinder may have 10 discs with one (outer) surface not used. Such a unit may hold over 40 million words and a greater transfer rate than a single moving-head disc unit, due to the parallel heads.

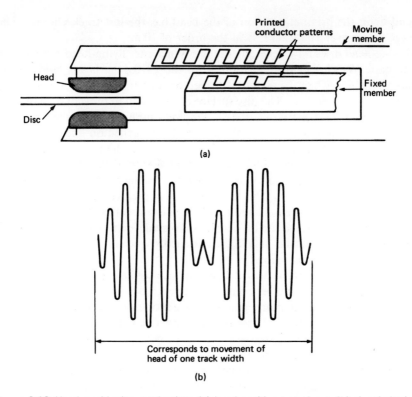

Figure 9.13 Head-positioning mechanism: (a) head position transducer; (b) signal obtained from secondary winding.

The moving-head disc (unit) is associated with the *exchangeable disc*, where the disc itself can be removed from the unit completely and a different disc inserted. A single exchangeable disc, generally known as a cartridge disc, has an enclosed plastic shell. The cartridge can be designed to be inserted into the front of the unit (i.e. *front loading*), and upon insertion, part of the enclosure is exposed automatically to enable the moving heads to enter. Alternatively the cartridge can be designed to be inserted from the top (top loading) in which case the plastic shell is removed upon insertion. Multiple exchangeable *disc packs* exist on larger computer systems, with 6 discs per pack and 10 recording surfaces (outer surfaces not being used). These are usually loaded from the top of the unit (i.e. *top loading*). In all cases, the heads are not allowed to move from their retracted position when the disc is not in place or not revolving at full speed. There will be a *ready* indicator on the unit showing when it is fully operational.

One useful combination is two moving-head disc units, one of which is of the exchangeable-disc type and the other not. The non-exchangeable disc can hold the operating system (for example) and the other the user programs, individual users having separate cartridges.

In addition to rotation latency, the moving-head disc has a delay due to the time required for the head to move to and settle on the required track. This will depend upon the original position of the head (i.e. the last track chosen). The average delay, over 100 tracks, is in the order of 10 ms.

Moving-head discs now generally use the Winchester flying-head mechanism. In the basic Winchester disc, introduced in the 1970s, the heads land on the surface of the disc when the system is turned off, rather than retract completely away from the disc surface. The disc surface is lubricated to prevent damage and also a special outside track is devoted as a landing zone upon which the head rests when the disc is stationary. When the disc motor is turned on, the disc rapidly accelerates and the head experiences a sliding contact with the surface for about 1/3–1/2 of one revolution, taking off at about 400 rpm. When the system is switched off, a brake is applied to the disc spindle and the head lands as the speed reduces below about 400 rpm. This technique allows greater precision in the head actuator and disc assembly and a reduced flying distance of 0.05 μm or less can be achieved, greatly increasing the bit densities. To achieve this low flying distance, the head assembly must be very lightly loaded, typically 8–10 g rather than around 350 g in previous flying-head systems.

The Winchester system is sealed from the atmosphere except for a highly efficient air filter, because it is very important to exclude air borne particles. Some particles are generated internally through the action of the head landing on the surface and dislodging oxide. These particles must be removed from the unit as soon as possible. The whole system should then be very reliable and be able to withstand the occasional head crash.

Though Winchester development began as a replacement technology to earlier large flying-head disc systems using 14 inch (35.6 cm) diameter discs, it soon became apparent that it could be developed as a low-cost mass storage system suitable for microprocessor systems by using 8 inch (20.3 cm), $5\frac{1}{4}$ inch (13.3 cm) and even $3\frac{1}{2}$ inch diameter discs. (Diameters are normally given in inches; 8 inch, $5\frac{1}{4}$ inch and $3\frac{1}{2}$ inch are diameters of floppy discs, see Section 9.3.4.)

Principal figures of merit of Winchester discs are the number of tracks recorded per inch radially, the number of bits recorded per inch of track (linear recording density), capacity and the access time. The access time is generally the time to locate and read the sector or write to the sector and is composed of the time to move the head to the required track, the time for the required sector to appear underneath the track and the time to read/write the data. The number of tracks per inch is typically in the range 300–1000 and the number of bits per inch in the range 7000–12 000. Capacities of 8 inch Winchester discs are typically 25 Mbyte/-disc, $5\frac{1}{4}$ inch discs about 10 Mbyte/disc and $3\frac{1}{2}$ inch discs about 6 Mbytes/disc. Fourteen-inch Winchesters designed for large computer systems can have capacities of 160 Mbytes. Up to eight discs can be driven on the same spindle depending upon the unit. Recording densities quoted are for traditional horizontal recording.

Data access time is typically in the range 15–30 ms for high-performance 14 inch Winchesters. The access time can be longer for smaller units, perhaps as poor as 200 ms for inexpensive models. For very low track densities (less than 300 tracks/inch) the inexpensive *open-loop* stepper motor band mechanism or similar mechanism can be used as on floppy discs (see Section 9.3.4). Here, the positioning relies totally on the mechanical stepping action being sufficiently accurate. However, such mechanisms are generally insufficiently accurate for higher track-density systems (i.e. most systems) and then the heads are moved using the so-called *closed-loop* mechanism. The closed-loop system can use position information recorded on a dedicated surface. First the head is stepped to the approximate position and then the closed loop system homes in on the track using the pre-recorded positional information on one surface. The use of a dedicated surface for positional information means that this surface cannot be used for data. Consequently, the dedicated surface closed-loop technique is better applied to multidisc systems driven by a common spindle.

9.3.4 Floppy discs

The *floppy disc* (Fig. 9.14) was developed by IBM in the late 1960s and was a significant departure from conventional discs. The disc itself is small (originally about 8 inches (20 cm) in diameter) and flexible (made from Mylar coated with ferric oxide). The disc rotates much more slowly than conventional types, at 360 rev/min, and is shown in use with a belt-driven hub. The read–write head touches the surface of the disc when recording or reading, and lifts away otherwise to reduce wear. Originally only one surface was used. The head is the moving-head variety, positioned by a helix drive, driven by a stepper motor as shown (or positioned by a coil actuator). The disc (called a *discette*) is exchangeable, front loaded, and always contained in a plastic sleeve. There is a slot in the sleeve for the read–write to enter and a central hole for the drive shaft. A further small index hole is used in conjunction with a light source and optical sensor for defining the beginning of the tracks. Other sensors may be employed for hard sectoring.

IBM have provided a standard format:

26	sectors/track	
73	data tracks	⎫
1	index track	⎬ 77 tracks
2	spare tracks	⎪
1	reserved track	⎭
128	8-bit bytes/sector	

The total disc capacity is 3 203 128 bits (1 943 552 bits of data with the above format). The packing density is typically 8300 bits/cm (inside track) and the transfer rate 250 000 bits/s (4 μs/bit).

A smaller version of the floppy disc has been developed, known as the *mini-floppy*. The diameter of this disc (mini-discette) is $5\frac{1}{4}$ inches (12.7 cm), revolving at 300 rev/min (slightly slower than the standard floppy disc). The total capacity is about a quarter of the floppy disc, but the unit is appropriately less expensive.

Originally, 8 inch and $5\frac{1}{4}$ inch floppy discs employed FM recording using one surface. Subsequently, MFM (and M^{2}FM) was introduced leading to double recording capacity (the so-called *double-density* discs). Recording on both surfaces of the disc was also introduced (*double-sided* discs). By 1978 double-sided double-density 8 inch and $5\frac{1}{4}$ inch discs were available having four times the capacity of the early single-sided single-density discs.

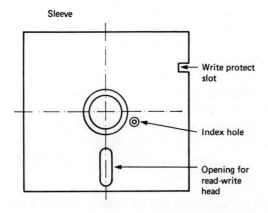

(a)

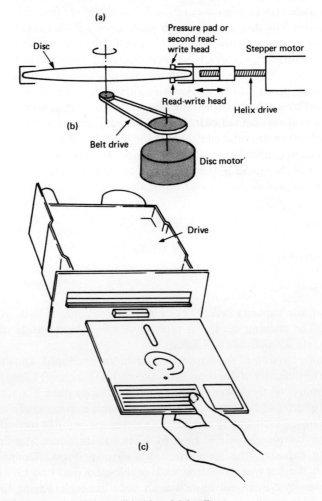

Figure 9.14 Floppy disc: (a) discette; (b) drive; (c) loading.

Increasing the capacity further could be achieved by increasing the number of tracks recorded on the surface. However, a limiting factor is the stability of the medium under thermal and environmental changes and mechanical stress. Double track density (i.e. 96 tracks/inch) has been introduced with the $5\frac{1}{4}$ inch disc resulting in a double bit density, double-sided, double track-density disc. The track density can be increased further (for example doubled to 192 tracks/inch but such systems generally require a track-following system and a manufacturer's pre-recorded track format. The higher-density (above double density) systems also require high coercivity medium which is more resistant to magnetic changes.

The bit rates of standard single-density and double-density $5\frac{1}{4}$ inch discs operating at 300 rpm are 125 000 bits/s and 250 000 bits/s respectively, while the bit rate of standard single-density and double-density 8 inch discs operating at 360 rpm are 250 000 bits/s and 500 000 bits/s respectively. A double density $5\frac{1}{4}$ inch disc operating at 360 rpm results in a bit rate of 300 000 bits/inch.

The rotational speed of the $5\frac{1}{4}$ inch disc has been in some cases increased from 300 rpm to 360 rpm (the same as the 8 inch disc). If the rotational speed is kept constant across all tracks, and the same number of bits is stored on each track, the linear bit density (bits/inch) on tracks towards the outer edge decreases. Occasionally the rotational speed has not been kept constant across all tracks but has been increased for tracks nearer the outer edge, to enable more bits to be stored on outer tracks while still maintaining acceptable bit densities.

Smaller 3 inch (7.6 cm) and $3\frac{1}{2}$ inch (8.9 cm) discs (known as *microfloppy discs*) were introduced in the early 1980s, with high track densities and high recording capacities. The media in these *microfloppies* are enclosed in rigid plastic cases. Shutters are provided which open for the read/write heads when the disc cases are inserted. This mechanism gives improved protection from dust. Both these smaller discs originated in Japan, the 3 inch disc being popular because the cost of posting 3 inch discs in Japan is the same as for letters. The 80 track $3\frac{1}{2}$ inch microfloppy recording at 8000 bits/inch achieves 0.5 M bytes/side, which is the same as a standard 96 track/inch $5\frac{1}{4}$ inch floppy disc recording at 5000 bits/inch.

Vertical recording, mentioned in Section 9.2.1 has also been applied to floppy discs, resulting in greatly increased recording capacities.

Floppy discs have found wide application in small systems, being good partners to the microprocessor.

9.4 Tapes

9.4.1 General aspects

In a tape-storage system the recording medium is tape which is usually between 0.38 cm and 2.54 cm wide, about 0.025 mm thick, and made from polyester coated with magnetic oxide (about 100 μm thick). The tape is wound on reels, the larger variety being 26.7 cm in diameter. Reading and writing is effected by moving the tape past, and in contact with, stationary read–write heads. Across the tape, several tracks are usually read or written simultaneously, requiring one read–write head per track. Separate read and write heads can be used to allow a writing process to be immediately checked by a subsequent reading process.

Figure 9.15 shows the layouts often used in recording on a tape. One data character (or byte), together with an associated (vertical) parity bit, are recorded at a time. A group of characters is recorded or read together and is known as a record (or a block). One record is separated from another record by a blank inter-record gap, often 1.52 cm in length, which allows the tape to be positioned for recording or replay. The number of characters in a record is defined by software. Each record is identified by a header.

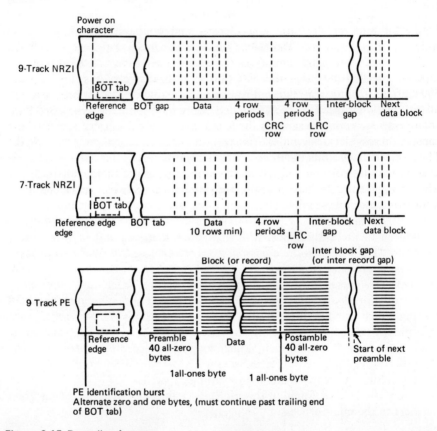

Figure 9.15 Recording formats.

As with disc recording, a CRC word may be appended to each record, separated from the data by blank characters. These blanks may be used to indicate the end of the data characters. Additionally, there may be a parity bit recorded on each track at the end of the record, the nine parity bits (in this case) forming a longitudinal parity word. (See Section 11.3.)

There are physical markers to indicate the ends of the tape, in the form of metallic foil or small holes, that can be sensed, and software markers in the form of EOT (end of tape) and BOT (beginning of tape) characters recorded on the tape.

The method of recording is traditionally NRZI but other codes are used, for example, MNRZI.

Write protection of specific reels of tape can be afforded by having an annular groove in the reel. If a ring is fitted, this can be mechanically detected when the reel is in position, and this serves to indicate that write protection is not to take place. (Similar schemes can be applied to exchangeable discs.)

9.4.2   Larger tape transports

Figure 9.16 shows a large tape transporter system. The tape is often $\frac{1}{2}$ inch (1.27 cm) wide with 9 or 7 tracks (8 and 6 data bits plus parity), held on reels of $10\frac{1}{2}$ inch (26.7 cm) diameter. 1 inch (2.54 cm) wide tape with more tracks have been used. The tape is propelled past separate read and write heads at high speed, perhaps 300 cm/s for reading and writing. The tape is maintained at the correct tension at all times, even during acceleration and deceleration, by employing vacuum chambers which allow some slack in the tape and isolate the heavy reels from the capstan drives. A *capstan* is a roller that is rotated at constant speed by a motor. The tape is pressed against the capstan by a *pinch roller*, causing the tape to move at constant speed. An optical system senses the tape in the chamber and signals when the reels should release or take up more tape. The reels are driven separately from the capstan drives.

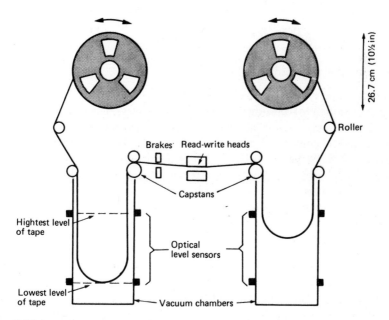

Figure 9.16 Large tape transport using vacuum chambers.

For slower speed systems (less than 100 cm/s), the vacuum chambers can be replaced by tension arms, as shown in Fig. 9.17. The reels of tape with this arrangement often measure 7 inch (17.8 cm) or $8\frac{1}{2}$ inch (21.6 cm).

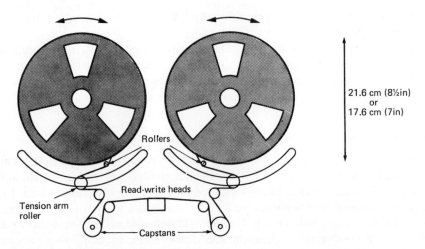

21.6 cm (8½in)
or
17.6 cm (7in)

Rollers

Read-write heads

Tension arm
roller

Capstans

Figure 9.17 Tape transport using tension arms.

In the larger systems, the reels often hold 730 m of tape or more, and packing densities of 4064 bytes/cm are common, using NRZI recording with transfer rates of 320 kilobytes/s. Recent advances in design have enabled packing densities in excess of 15 000 bytes/cm to be achieved, and transfer rates of over 1200 kilobytes/s (with a reduced inter-record gap of 0.76 cm).

9.4.3   Smaller tape drives

In a smaller tape system where the reels of tape are a few centimeters in diameter, vacuum chambers or tension arms are unnecessary. There are two principal methods of transporting the tape past a read–write head. One is to use capstans to drive the tape at constant speed, and the other is to drive the reels only, the so-called reel-to-reel drive. In the latter, there is a tape-speed variation of perhaps 2.5 to 1 between the situation in which one reel is full and that in which the other reel is full, unless there is a servo feedback mechanism, which is frequently incorporated, as shown in Fig. 9.18. Here the speeds of the motors, s_1 and s_2, are measured (by their counter emfs, for example). The instantaneous lineary velocity of the tape is given, as is easily proved, by

$$v = \frac{k s_1 s_2}{\sqrt{(s_1^2 + s_2^2)}}$$

where k is a constant depending upon the empty and full diameters of the reels. The tape velocity is held constant using a high-gain amplifier which produces the difference between the actual tape velocity as calculated from the velocity function and the required tape velocity (a constant) to drive one of the motors (see Fig. 9.18). Reasonably constant velocity (to about 5%) can be obtained by approximating the above function to $v = s_1 + s_2$ (i.e. using a summer rather than a function generator).

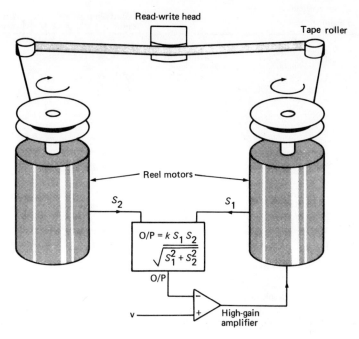

Figure 9.18 Reel-to-reel tape transport with servo mechanism to maintain tape speed constant.

Generally, a capstan drive produces very accurate tape drives (better than $\pm 2\%$ speed variation) but treats the tape more harshly than reel-to-reel drives.

The audio-cassette approach, whereby the reels are permanently enclosed in an easily handled package, has been brought over into the digital environment and is known simply as the (digital) cassette, being similar to the audio-cassette. Indeed, some early cassettes were originally audio-cassettes. Figure 9.19 shows the essentials of a capstan-driven cassette. Cassettes are also available with reel-to-reel drive.

Special *digital cassettes*, known as *cartridges*, have been designed specifically for digital applications. For these, tape tension should be constant, and stopping, starting, forward and reverse directions is under digital control. Figure 9.20 shows the arrangement of a popular cartridge. There are two reels of unequal size. The tape passes in the forward direction from the supply reel (the large reel) to the take-up reel. Tape tension and speed is maintained constant by a unique drive band that passes around the tape on the supply and take-up reels and around a capstan that is driven from outside the package. This scheme does not require pinch rollers.

Cassettes and cartridges can be single, two or four track, traditionally phase encoded and with packing densities of 314–628 bits/cm. Tape read–write speeds are in the region 7–100 cm/s (higher for wind–rewind), data capacity over a million bytes for cassettes and up to 20 million bytes for cartridges. The tape is either 0.38 cm or 0.64 cm wide.

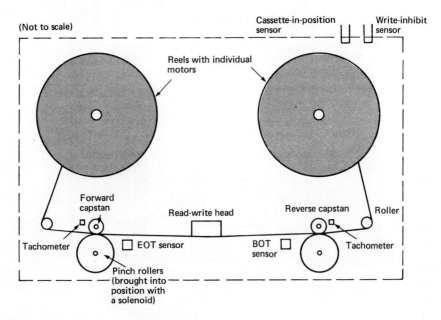

Figure 9.19 Digital cassette (capstan driven).

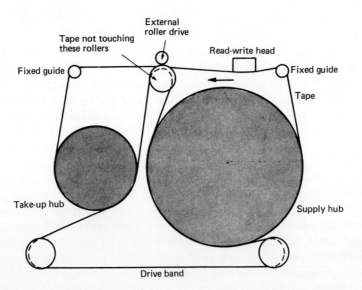

Figure 9.20 A cartridge system.

These systems can be used to replace paper-tape input in addition to normal bulk storage. For increased freedom from environmental effects, two track recordings using complementary codes are used.

9.4.4 Tape standards

There is a natural desire to arrange that the method of recording, tape format, and other relevant factors are the same on all computer systems so that tapes can be interchanged. This also applies to exchangeable discs. Standards have been produced for this end by ANSI (American International Standards Institute) and ECMA (European Computer Manufacturers Association). Such standards specify:

1. dimensions of the tapes and allowable tolerances;
2. tape speed;
3. bit density;
4. recording code;
5. error detection methods (LRC, VRC and CRC);
6. size of block (generally a minimum and maximum set);
7. preamble and postamble where necessary.

Once a standard is set, subsequent improvements in recording design resulting in higher packing density or other factors need to be incorporated in an updated standard produced at a later date. This results in the older standards being incompatible and in a continual change in standards. For example, 9-track 2.54 cm wide ($\frac{1}{2}$ inch) tape is very common, but recently improvements in head design allow 18 tracks in the same width to be recorded. Consequently this may in future be incorporated.

Standards are produced for cassettes, notably the ECMA–34 standard.

9.4.5 Streaming

Tape systems are suited for archival storage and back-up storage. For example, a copy of a Winchester disc can be made on a tape at the end of transactions to afford protection against loss of data due to a disc crash or other fault. A convenient tape mode known as *streaming* can be used. In a traditional tape operation, inter-record gaps (IRGs) are inserted into the recording to enable the tape to be stopped between recordings. In the streaming mode, the tape is not stopped between records (blocks) and the complete contents of a disc (for example) are recorded without stopping the tape. Hence it is not necessary to include IRGs specifically or to use costly tape transport systems. Should it be necessary to stop the tape at the beginning of a block, a process of stopping the tape which causes an overrun, and slow reversing process and forward motion, is necessary to position the tape. This process would be performed infrequently in the streaming mode. The tape format can be the same as the conventional *start-stop* mode to allow the tape to be accessed in a slower start-stop operation.

9.5 Disc and tape Controllers

9.5.1 Configuration

A disc or tape drive is connected to the CPU through a controller. The controller has the task of carrying out read-write requests from the CPU, which are in the form of machine input-output instructions, using direct memory access (DMA). The controller will handle all the CPU-interface requirements and all the drive-interface requirements.

In larger systems, one controller may be shared amongst several discs or amongst several tapes, as shown in Fig. 9.21. The controller–drive interconnection may be in the form of a star (Fig. 9.21(a)) or in the form of a 'daisy chain' (Fig. 9.21(b)), or a combination of both. In the daisy-chain approach signals are passed from one drive to the next. The daisy chain does not establish a priority scheme. The connection is simply a convenient means of coupling drives.

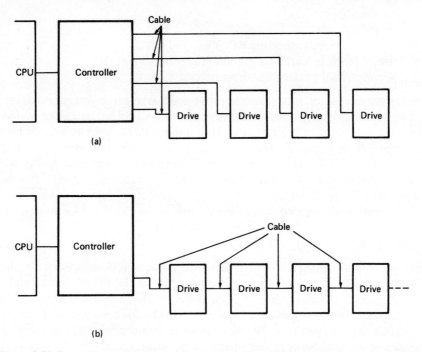

Figure 9.21 Tape-disc configuration: (a) star connection; (b) 'daisy-chain' connection.

The disc or tape drive may contain only the minimum of circuitry, sufficient to drive the control mechanisms, decode read signals, and encode write signals. In the case of larger discs it is convenient to include sector-searching logic, as shown in Fig. 9.22. Referring to Fig. 9.22, each drive can be given a unit number that can be manually set on thumb switches (for example) on the front panel of the unit. To cover the case in which extra logic is incorporated into smaller disc or tape drives (discettes, cassettes and cartridges), the term *formatter* has been coined.

9.5.2   Disc controllers

Given that the disc drive contains the logic shown in Fig. 9.22, further logic is required in the controller to fully implement the following typical operations, which may be individual or combined machine instructions:

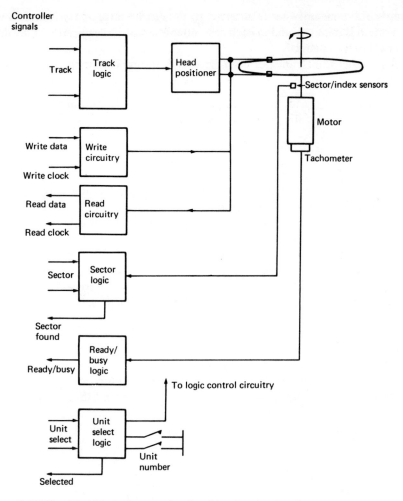

Figure 9.22 Simplified block diagram of a disc drive (moving head).

1. Select unit (drive), sector and track
2. Load memory address register
3. Write to sector
4. Read sector
5. Read status word

Instructions (1)–(3) are machine output instructions, and (4) and (5) are machine input instructions.

Normal DMA transfers take place (see Section 2.2.4). The memory address register is loaded with the address of the first of a set of consecutive locations in main memory. In the case of a read operation, consecutive words of the selected sector are autonomously loaded into the set of memory locations once the read operation is initiated. Similarly, in the case of a write operation, the consecutive words in the memory are transferred to the sector, autonomously once a write operation is initiated, and in each case, after one word is transferred, the address register is incremented.

The status word indicates both error and normal conditions. Typically, this includes:

1. ready (i.e. turned on, disc in place if exchangeable, and disc up to speed);
2. busy/done (in the process of an operation/completed operation);
3. CRC check fault;
4. write to a write-protected sector;
5. data lost.

The controller can be implemented using random logic, but nowadays a preferred approach is to use micro-programmable devices which follow a list of *micro-instructions* (i.e. a micro-program). Figure 9.23 shows a flow chart for a disc-read micro-program. First, the drive is selected. Then it is checked to see that it is ready. This condition is usually also shown on an indicator on the disc unit. In this particular case, the block length is one or more sectors, and this, together with the memory address, the first sector address and the password, are held in specified memory locations. This information is brought into the controller. A password is employed for security reasons, and this is checked before proceeding with a wait for the index pulse to appear. Subsequently, sector pulses are counted until the required one is reached. (Notice that in Fig. 9.22 this has been done in hardware in the drive.) There is a header to each block of data giving the sector address. This is checked against the number of sector pulses, i.e. hardware sectoring is checked by software sectoring. If this is correct, the data are read one bit at a time. When the CRC word is read from the disc, it is checked with the CRC word internally generated. The steps are repeated for each sector required.

9.5.3　Tape controllers

Typical instructions for the tape controller to implement are:

1. select unit;
2. load memory address register and word count register;
3. write;
4. write end of file;
5. erase;
6. read;
7. read status word;
8. space forward/backward;
9. rewind.

The length of a block of data is defined by the user. In all other respects the read and write operations are similar to the disc read and write operations, and are autonomous DMA transfers.

'Write end of file' records a file marker, perhaps 8 cm of blank tape. 'Erase' records a blank length of tape. 'Space forward/backward' is used to jump over a specified number of records.

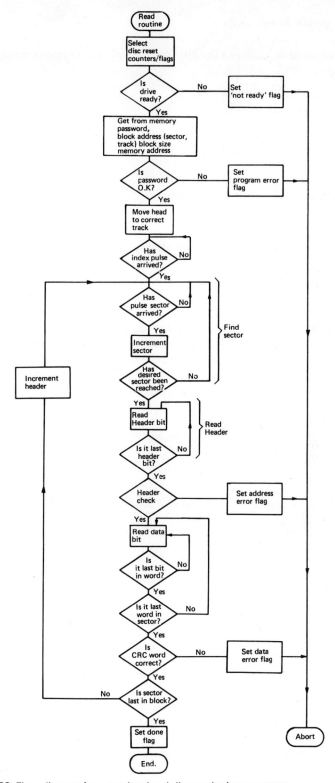

Figure 9.23 Flow diagram for a moving-head disc read micro-program.

The status word is similar to the disc status word. Additional error conditions may include:

1. vertical or horizontal parity error;
2. end of tape encountered;
3. bad tape.

Normal conditions indicated may include:

1. specified density (normal/double, for example);
2. number of tracks (9 or 7, for example) ⎫ if selectable

9.6   Environmental aspects of discs and tapes

Finally, a few comments on the environmental aspects of running disc and tape equipment.

A flying-head disc is particularly vulnerable to dust, grit and airborne particles. The distance between the head and the surface under normal conditions is very small, much less than the width of a human hair or common particles in the air (Fig. 9.24). If any of these manage to find themselves between the head and the surface, a head will crash into the recording surface and considerable damage will occur to both the disc surface and the head.

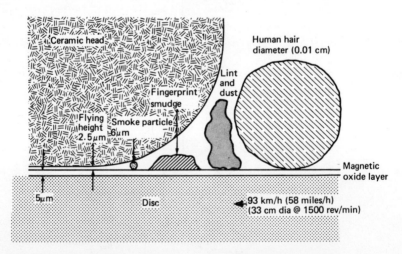

Figure 9.24 Particles that can cause a disc crash in a flying-head system.

So extreme cleanliness is necessary. In the non-exchangeable disc, the unit can be supplied with filtered air and the risks are less than in the case of exchangeable discs. Discs can be cleaned by wiping the surface with isopropyl alcohol or other specialized cleaners as a preventive measure. In a dusty or smoky environment, this might be done once a week. In a cleaner environment, perhaps two times a year.

A tape system is also vulnerable. The tape itself should not be touched (as in the case of a disc, though a disc surface cannot usually be touched). A fingerprint will attract dirt and may subsequently damage both the heads and the transport. Any marks in the back surface will be passed onto the front surface when the reel is wound. Tapes especially should be kept in modest and constant temperature–humidity conditions (70°C/50° to within 10%).

Most magnetic tape and disc coatings have the ability to retain recordings for very long periods of time. Naturally, adverse magnetic conditions will affect the recording. Generally, the magnetization can be degraded by at least 50% before the recording must be rewritten. For long-term storage, periodic rewriting may be necessary.

9.7 Optical disc drives

9.7.1 Basic form

This type of device has been developed from the video-disc player, this being a consumer product for playing previously recorded programmes on a television receiver. The video-disc player has largely been superseded by the video cassette player, but its inherently high information storage capacity and high signal rates make it attractive for large-volume digital storage.

The data are read from the discs using the arrangement outlined in Fig. 9.25. Data are stored along a single spiral path for typically 40 000 revolutions or tracks. The tracks are divided into sectors each of which carries an identifying address. The reflectivity at the active surface of the disc is made to change between high and low values according to the data pattern stored. The low-power laser beam is focused by the lens to a small spot (typically 1 μm in diameter) and

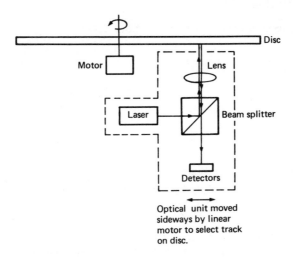

Figure 9.25 Optical-disc memory.

reflected, or otherwise, from the surface. This is sensed by the detector and converted to an electrical data signal.

A two-stage process is usually used to access the required sector. The optical unit is first moved to the vicinity of the track containing the required sector. This is not done exactly because the tracks are very closely spaced. The number of tracks that the desired sector is away from the track under the optical unit is determined by reading the sector addresses passing under the optical unit. Next the second stage of the process is initiated to access the track containing the desired sector. Commonly the second stage is done by having a low-mass adjustable reflecting surface in the optical path (not shown in the figure), which permits rapid selection. The arrangement is also used as part of a feedback system to maintain the alignment over the track as it moves position. Misalignment can happen because of the spiral nature of recording and also because of any wandering due to disc eccentricity etc.

Because of this two-stage process the time to access an adjacent track is quite low, typically 1 ms, whereas a time of typically 150–500 ms is required to seek tracks some distance away.

Discs are exchangeable and manufacturers have produced them in varying sizes, including 12 cm (4.72 inch), 133 cm ($5\frac{1}{4}$ inch), 20 cm (8 inch), and 30 cm (12 inch). Storage capacities typically range from 500 Mbyte to 4 Gbyte. Much higher capacities are obtained from 'jukebox' systems which can automatically load onto one or two drive units discs from a bank of typically a hundred discs.

Optical discs are inherently more robust than magnetic media. The optical unit is placed away from the surface and head crashes do not occur. Also the disc is covered with a transparent protection surface and can tolerate small scratches and dust particles.

Disc media have been progressively developed and can be classified as:

 (i)   read only memory (ROM) discs;
 (ii) write once read many (WORM) discs;
 (iii) re-writable discs.

The following section discusses them in more detail.

9.7.2   Read only memory (ROM) discs

Discs of this type are manufactured in a similar way to conventional audio records. A master disc is created by the producer from which a large number of pressings are taken. In this case the pressings are into a thin metallic layer in which indentations, or the absence of them, represent data. A transparent protection layer is applied.

A popular form of read only unit is derived directly from the 12 cm compact-disc audio player. This consumer product records audio signals digitally using optical disc principles (and is in fact itself a development of the video player technology) and is thus very suited for storage of digital data. It is usually referred to as a compact disc read only memory (CD-ROM) drive.

Large production volumes as an audio player have resulted in low prices and this has spurred computer-related applications.

The ROM disc cannot be written to by the user (strictly it cannot be classed as a backing store) and this has a significant effect on its application. The most important type of application can be classed as electronic publication. Here publishers are able to sell information in the form of an optical disc for many times its volume production cost. The amount of data which can be stored is very large. A 12 cm CD-ROM disc can store the equivalent of 275 000 pages of A4 text. Information published in this way includes an encyclopaedia, company accounts from the New York Stock Exchange, and legal and medical works.

9.7.3 Write once read many (WORM) disc

The writing surface in the WORM disc is usually a thin sheet of an alloy of tellurium. This is sandwiched between two layers of transparent material, usually glass. The writing action is obtained by driving the laser source in Fig. 9.25 at a higher power. This heats the surface and causes pits to be created to represent the data sequence. In an alternative method minute bubbles are created in the surface which has the same effect of reducing the surface reflectivity when data comes to be optically read. This increases the cost of the drive compared with ROM drives but extends its range of application. In particular it can be used as a backing store and competes with hard magnetic-disc drives on capacity (but not data access time) and with magnetic-tape drives on access time.

Because these discs can be written to once only different file control systems have to be used than for magnetic discs. In the latter a directory of files is located at a fixed place on the magnetic disc. The disc operating system accesses this directory to find the location of a particular file on the disc. The directory is continuously updated according to the file transactions taking place. Because of the write once property of WORM discs this approach cannot be taken. The very large capacity of the WORM disc means its directory is usually too large to hold in computer main memory where it could be updated. One approach is to hold the directory on a magnetic-disc drive. The approach preferred by some is to hold the directory on the WORM disc itself. If a directory entry is altered it is deactivated and the new directory entry put elsewhere. Similarly files are changed by copying the new file into an unused part of the disc. (Actually in the usual case where part of a file is changed it is more economical to copy just that part rather than the whole file.)

WORM discs, unlike magnetic backing stores, are write once only and are not re-usable. With use they fill to capacity. This suits them to archiving applications. The write once property means that all earlier versions of a file remain stored, thus facilitating audit trails when the history of, say, engineering drawing modifications or financial transactions can be traced. The write once property can be seen as a positive virtue in the latter case as a deterrent to computer fraud.

It has also been realized that it can be cheaper to record information on a WORM disc and to physically transport it than to send the same data through a data communications service. This could be of benefit to a heavily used central data base which is networked to other stations. Copies of the data base are regularly sent via WORM discs to other stations.

9.7.4   Re-writable discs

Re-writable discs (also called erasable discs) remove the write-once limitation of WORM discs. At the time of this writing products are not yet available. However, development is well advanced. Two approaches hold promise.

One approach uses a material with special magneto-optic effects. The action of the laser in the disc drive when writing is to cause the magnetic orientation of the disc material to reverse in the minute area upon which the focused laser beam lands. A succession of reversals, and non-reversals, is used to store data. The data are optically read using the magneto-optic effect, whereby a magnetic field changes the plane of polarization of light.

A second approach is to use a material in which the local effect of the writing laser beam causes a reversible local phase change in the material surface. Materials are being investigated in which the reflectivity is changed, or where the colour changes.

It is likely that re-writable optical-disc drives will emerge as products in the relatively near future. This should place them in direct competition with magnetic-disc and tape drives.

References

1. Lavington, S. H., *History of Manchester Computers*, NCC Publications, 1975.
2. Franchini, R. C. and Wartner, D. L., A method of high density recording on flexible magnetic discs, *Computer Design*, 106–9, October 1978.
3. Ringkjøb, E. T., Achieving a fast data-transfer rate by optimizing existing technology, *Electronics*, 86–91, May 1975.
4. Tamura, T., Tsutsumi, M., Aoi, H., Matsuishi, N., Nakogoshi, K., Kawano, S. and Makita, M., A coding method in digital magnetic recording, *IEEE Trans. Magnetics*, 612–14, September 1972.
5. Edwards, D. B. G., Whitehouse, D. A. E., Warburton, L. E. M. and Watson, I., The MU5 disc system, *IEE Conference*, Publication No. 121, October 1974.
6. Lamb, L., The evolution of mass storage, *Byte*, **11** (5), 161–72, May 1986. See also other articles on optical discs in the same issue.

Further reading

1. Sebestyen, L. D., *Digital Magnetic Tape Recording for Computer Applications*, Chapman and Hall, London, 1973.

10

Data communications

10.1 Introduction

Various ways are described in Chapter 2 of electrically connecting computers and peripheral devices so that data may be passed between them over quite short distances. When the distances are relatively long other factors come into play and these come within the subject of data communications. Two of these factors are (i) the type of transmission path which can require special circuitry (such as *modems* in the case of telephone lines) to send and receive the data and (ii) the occurrence of errors in the transmission of the data, which can be significant. Another major concern of data communication is that of *Networking*, that is the connecting together of several, possibly many, computers and peripheral devices. The peripheral devices in data neworks are commonly, but not exclusively, VDU terminals. These various communicating devices are collectively referred to as Data Terminal Equipments (DTEs). To communicate successfully they must be electrically compatible with the communication link or network and also be able to perform the necessary protocols.

Early computers operated in batch mode. Users accessed the computer typically by means of card or tape readers for input, and obtained output from a printer. Later developments of more powerful large computers and more versatile operating systems provided multi-user working. Here numbers of terminals ranging typically from a few tens to a few hundreds are connected to the computer via *I/O ports*. This allows the user to access the computer interactively and is a significant improvement in user convenience. Not surprisingly, it was quickly realized that further user convenience to some users and also new applications could be realized if the terminals could be sited remotely from the computer, in the same town, or another town, country or even continent. The most readily accessible medium for this was the telephone system. Large numbers of terminals connected in this way form a *terminal network*. Currently they are the dominant type of data communications network.

In more recent times the continued lowering of costs and increasing computer population has created the need to couple computers to other computers and to other resources. Distributed processing and data bases are then possible to serve applications such as banking and ticket booking systems. A network of this type usually covers a wide geographical area and is termed a *wide-area network* (WAN).

In similar vein network technologies have been developed to couple computers and other devices together which are more locally situated. Such *local area networks* (LANs) are typically installed in suite of offices and readily allow resources to be shared among, and information to be passed between, many users.

Paper-free transactions can take place, such as *electronic mail*, in which messages can be deposited at a terminal and accessed and responded to when convenient.

In most countries the telecommunications facilities are administered by government departments or public corporations. In other countries this is carried out by private companies, called *common carriers*. Collectively they are referred to as PTTs (post, telegraph and telephone administrations). Most PTTs are members of the CCITT (Comité Consultatif International Téléphonique et Télégraphique), which belongs to the ITU (International Telecommunications Union), itself an agency of the United Nations. The CCITT sets standards governing communications. Actually these are not strictly standards but are recommendations since the PTTs are not obliged to follow them. In practice there is generally good conformity with the recommendations. Examples of CCITT recommendations are the V-series which govern the use of the 'analogue' telephone system for data communication (V.24 has already been mentioned in Chapter 2), and the X-series which apply to digital data networks. Other standards bodies such as ISO (International Standards Organization), and the EIA (Electrical Industries Association), of the USA also play a part in governing data communications. In the USA the EIA carries greater influence than in Europe where the CCITT is more prevalent. However, EIA and CCITT standards are frequently identical or very similar, an example being the pair RS-232-C and V.24.

Standards are important because they allow a degree of commonality among and between countries, and perhaps more importantly, because they allow compatible systems to be constructed from different manufacturers.

These, and related aspects, are discussed in the following section.

Use will be made of terms such as half-duplex (HDX), full-duplex (FDX), asynchronous and synchronous which have been defined in Chapter 2.

10.2   Data transmission

10.2.1   Transmission media

A variety of physical media are in use for transmitting data. The simplest is probably a single pair of wires, which can be twisted to reduce the effects of interference. Twisted pairs allow data rates up to about 10 Mbits/s. If the conductors are in co-axial cable form, then higher data rates up to several Mbits/s can be achieved, but at a greater cost. Fibre-optic cables are a more recent addition. Telephone circuits are also used. The drivers and receivers required to send data down these media are described in Chapter 2.

For data transmission over distances of a few kilometres and beyond, by far the most commonly used medium is the telephone circuit provided by the PTT. It can be simply uneconomic for the user to lay a private cable. Moreover, in many countries only the PTT is authorized to provide cable transmision over or under public land.

The conventional 'dial-up' or public switched telephone network (PSTN) is shown in schematic form in Fig. 10.1. Each subscriber is connected by a two-wire circuit to the local exchange which handles dialled calls between subscribers in

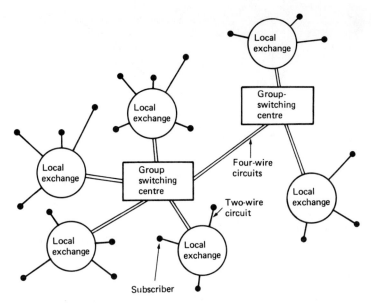

Figure 10.1 The public switched telephone network.

that area. For calls to more distant subscribers, the local exchanges are linked by means of 'four-wire' trunk circuits via group-switching centres. The reason for using four wires is that the greater distances require repeater amplifiers to be used in the signal paths and since they are unidirectional, separate go and return paths are used. In practice wide-bandwidth multichannel media, such as co-axial cable, are used, the four wires are then only conceptual.

The PSTN has the advantage of flexibility in that any destination is easily accessed by dialling the appropriate code. This type of connection is called *switched* or *dial-up*. However, exchange equipment can be electrically noisy and significant numbers of errors can be caused especially at higher data transmission rates. (One cannot really blame the PSTN for this since it was originally designed for the communication of speech and not data.) The noise, and hence error rate, is reduced in so-called *private* lines provided by the PSTN which by-pass the exchange. Thus, private lines, unlike dial-up connections, are unswitched and have a fixed route to the destination. Four-wire private lines can be supplied which allow simultaneous both-way communication, that is FDX, or the private lines can be lower cost two-wire for HDX working.

Switched connections are charged on a time-used basis and so costs increase with the use made, whereas private connections are usually leased at a fixed charge and costs are independent of usage. The economies of this are illustrated in Fig. 10.2. Beyond a certain usage it is cheaper to use private lines. However, the decision on switched or private lines is also affected by other factors such as error rate, cost of terminal equipment, and whether or not the flexibility of dial-up is required.

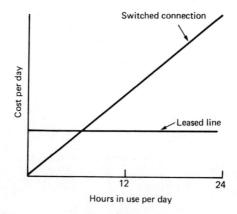

Figure 10.2 The relative costs of switched and leased lines.

10.2.2   Modems

Telephone circuits are intended to carry speech and therefore normally propagate signals in the frequency range of 300–3400 Hz. Data transmission is not straightforward because signal frequencies in the range 0–300 Hz are cut off. If a data sequence is applied directly to a telephone circuit, then difficulties can arise, as illustrated in Fig. 10.3. In this example, the data sequence changes from a few zeros to a sequence of ones. The sequence of ones is equivalent to a constant voltage, that is it has zero frequency, and since this is outside the transmission band the output of the telephone circuit quickly dies away, as shown. Hence later bits in the sequence are lost.

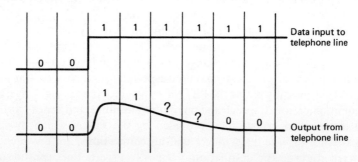

Figure 10.3 Difficulty of transmitting data directly on telephone lines.

One type of signal which does not suffer in this way is a sinusoidal tone, provided it has a frequency in the 300–3400 Hz pass band of the telephone circuit. In practice data are transmitted by modulating such a tone. At the receiving end a demodulator is used to convert the tone signal into a data signal. Usually both-way transmission is required, so a modulator and demodulator are required at each end of the link. The two are usually combined into one unit together with circuitry for control and other purposes, and this unit is called a *modem* (this is a contraction of the words modulator and demodulator). The general arrangement is shown in Fig. 10.4. The computer or peripheral (that is, the data terminal equipment, DTE), is coupled to the modem (that is, the data communication equipment, DCE) using an RS-232-C/V.24 interface, as discussed in Chapter 2.

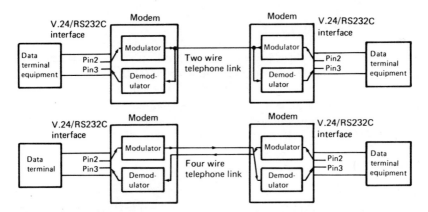

Figure 10.4 General MODEM arrangements for 2-wire and 4-wire telephone link.

Several methods of modulation are in use. The possibilities are to modulate the frequency, amplitude, or phase of the tone, or combinations of these.

(a) *Frequency-shift keying modulation (FSK)*

Here the data ones and zeros are represented by different carrier frequencies (see Fig. 10.5). For a transmission data rate of 1200 bits/s these frequencies are typically 1300 Hz for a data one and 2100 Hz for a data zero. In this case half duplex and not full duplex transmission is possible on a two-wire circuit because simultaneous transmission by both ends using these frequencies confuses the respective demodulators. For full duplex transmission, then, two pairs of frequencies can be used to create two channels. One pair of frequencies is used for transmission in one direction and the other pair is used for transmission in the reverse direction. For example, a two-channel system, allowing 300 bits/s maximum data rate on each channel, may use the following frequencies:

Channel 1: 1850 Hz for a 0; 1650 Hz for a 1
Channel 2: 1180 Hz for a 0;   980 Hz for a 1

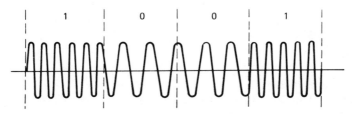

Figure 10.5 Frequency-shift keying modulation.

This is also referred to as frequency multiplexing. With frequency-shift modulation each data bit must be long enough in time to allow a sufficient number of cycles to be transmitted for the demodulator at the receiver to recognize which frequency it is. Since the frequency of the tones must be less than the upper limt of 3400 Hz of the telephone circuit handwidth, this results in data rates limited in practice to about 1200 bits/s.

(b) *Amplitude modulation*
With amplitude modulation a zero may be represented by a small amplitude and a one by a large amplitude, as illustrated in Fig. 10.6. A refinement is to sequentially pair off data bits into the combinations 00, 01, 10 or 11, called *dibits*, and assign each of one of four amplitudes of the sinusoidal signal. This now allows two bits of data to be transmitted per signalling element and provides an increased data transmission rate.

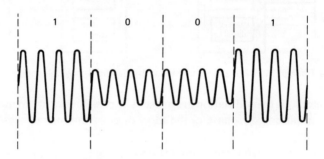

Figure 10.6 Amplitude modulation.

(c) *Phase-shift keying modulation (PSK)*
In a simple form a data zero does not affect the sinusoidal signal but a one causes a phase shift in the signal equal to half a period (that is, 180 electrical degrees). This is shown in Figure 10.7. The dibit idea can be applied here also by including more phase shifts, typically as follows:

Dibit	00	01	01	11
Phase change (°)	0	90	180	270

With phase-shift modulation the receiver has the problem of deciding on the reference phase angle of 0°, since this is located at the distance transmitter. Special methods such as differential phase-shift keying (DPSK) are used to overcome this.

(d) *Combined methods*
Amplitude- and phase-shift modulation are often combined. Here the phase shift and amplitude of the sinusoidal tone are independently modulated. By using the dibit technique, for example, on each type of modulation, four data bits can be

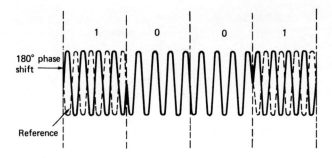

Figure 10.7 Phase-shift keying modulation.

conveyed by one signalling element. Using techniques such as these, high data rates of 4800 bits/s and 9600 bits/s and beyond can be achieved.

Modems can be either asynchronous or synchronous. In asynchronous working the data characters are just a few bits long and the receiver timing clocks can run independently from the transmitter clock. Provided the two clocks are reasonably close in timing, the data bits can be picked off by the receiver without getting out of step over the duration of the data character. In synchronous working, the bit stream is very much longer and it is then necessary to synchronize the receiver clock to that of the transmitter. This is done by hardware in the modems. This type of synchronism is called bit synchronism. When the longer data sequences are byte oriented, byte synchronism needs to be maintained as well. This is usually done by including SYN characters in the data message, as described in Chapter 2, and is handled by the computer or interface unit rather than the modem. Asynchronous modems usually offer the lower data rates, while at higher rates modems are usually synchronous and also much more expensive because of their added complexity.

The attenuation and time-delay characteristics of telephone lines vary with frequency. This has the effect of distorting the shape of the signal and can cause errors at the receiver. The receiver is often therefore compensated by using a filter, called and *equalizer*, which has attenuation and time-delay characteristics that are complementary to those of the telephone line and thus restore the signal shape. This may not be a complete curve, however as line characteristics change with time, and also on switched circuits depend on the actual route taken through the network, which may be different every time a circuit is dialled up. Complex modems are made to meet this problem, using *auto-equalizers* which automatically change the equalizing filter characteristics to match those of the telephone circuit.

One type of modem, the *acoustic coupler*, uses a loudspeaker and microphone for output and input, into which is plugged the handset of an ordinary telephone, as shown in Fig. 10.8. This modem is quite inexpensive, but because the signals are acoustically coupled to the line rather than electrically, it is suitable only for low data rates up to about 300 bits/s. It has the advantage, however, of being easily portable and can operate at any location that has an ordinary telephone.

The connections between the data terminal equipment and the modem are governed by the Standards EIA RS-232-C/V.24. Actually CCITT recommend-

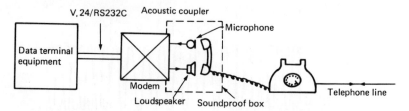

Figure 10.8 Acoustic-coupler modem.

ation V.24 does not cover the electrical aspects of the interface, the latter being covered by recommendation V. 28. On the other side of the modem the various modulation methods are covered by other V-Series recommendations. Table 10.1 gives a list[1,2]. The suffics 'bis' and 'ter' indicate second and third sets of recommendations in the same V-Series numerical group. Recommendations V. 23/26/27 offer an optional 75 bits/s backward channel using FSK techniques. This low-speed channel can be useful, for example, for returning short acknowledgements to longer messages sent in a higher-speed channel in the other direction.

The USA tends to follow its own modulation standards. Two popular ones, the Bell 103 and Bell 202, are equivalent to V.21 and V.23.

As analogue telephone systems are replaced by digital systems and special-purpose digital data networks become universal, the eventual demise of the modem seems certain. In the meantime the pupulation of modems is large and increasing.

10.3   Errors

10.3.1   Causes of errors

Undetected errors in the movement of data within a computer are rare. However, the situation is very much different when computers and peripheral devices are linked over data communications circuits, where errors are a natural feature. The two principal causes of errors are:

(i) *Distortion*   As was mentioned earlier distortion is due to the characteristics of the circuit altering the transmitted signal. Errors caused by this can be minimised by using equalizers. On leased lines special conditioning can be obtained at increased tariff, to further improve performance.

(ii) *Noise*   This can come from a variety of sources such as continuous background thermal noise, *cross talk* from signals on adjacent lines, impulse noise from lightning and switches, and short breaks in the transmission path. Often errors are grouped together in bursts.

Average error rates depend on a number of factors, but on telephone lines are typically of the order of an average of one bit in error for every 10000 bits transmitted. As data rates increase, there is a tendency for error rates to increase

CCITT recommendation	Data rate (bits/s)	Mode	HDX/FDX PSTN	HDX/FDX 2-wire	4-wire	Modulation method
V. 21	300	async	FDX	FDX	—	FSK
V. 22	1200	sync/async	FDX	FDX	—	DPSK
V. 22 bis	2400	sync/async	FDX	FDX	—	Combined AM/PSK
V. 23	1200, (75 opt.)	async	HDX	HDX	FDX	FSK
V. 26	2400, (75 opt.)	sync	—	—	FDX	DPSK
V. 26 bis	2400, (75 opt.)	sync	HDX	—	FDX	DPSK
V. 27 bis	4800, (75 opt.)	sync	—	HDX	FDX	DPSK
V. 27 ter	4800, (75 opt.)	sync	HDX	—	—	DPSK
V. 29	9600	sync	—	—	FDX	Combined AM/PSK
V. 32	9600	sync/async	FDX	FDX	—	Combined AM/PSK
V. 33	14400	sync	—	—	FDX	Combined AM/PSK

Table 10.1 CCITT modem recommendations.

as well. Leased telephone lines are not as subject to noise from switches as are dial-up connections, and hence usually have somewhat lower error rates.

Even error rates seemingly as low as 1 in 10 000 can be significant. For example, to replenish a VDU screen in one operation may require, say, 1000 characters. Assuming each character is 8 bits, the total message is 8000 bits long and there is therefore a significant probability that the message will be received in error.

10.3.2   Error detection and control

One of the simplest methods of detecting errors is to add odd or even parity bits to each character as described in Chapter 2. Any error in data transmission involving a single bit or an odd number of bits alters the parity condition, which is easily detected at the receiving end. Errors involving two or an even number of bits do not alter the parity condition and go undetected, which unfortunately is a real possibility because of the occurrence of error 'bursts'. Thus simple parity checks are not sufficiently powerful for use in data communications.

One powerful technique which is used is called the *cyclic redundancy check* (CRC) method. The CRC is added at the end of a data sequence as a *block check character* (BCC). Here the data block is treated as a continuous sequence of bits and not as a group of characters. Suppose the data bits are interpreted as one large binary number, and this is divided, using long division, by an agreed generator binary number. The quotient is discarded and the remainder is attached to the data as a block check character. At the receiver the remainder is again calculated and compared with that attached by the transmitter. Any errors in transmission are very likely to show up as some difference in the two remainders. For CRC, in practice the long division is carried out using modulo-two arithmetic over the data and BCC together. The rules for modulo-two addition and multiplication are the same as in binary arithmetic except that $1 + 1 = 0$ and not 10. That is, there is no carry bit. The rules for modulo-two subtraction are the same as those for addition. The generator binary number is called a generating polynomial—a name that arises out of the algebraic theoretical background of this method. For example, the generating polynomial $X^2 + 1$ is equal to $(1)X^2 + (0)X^1 + (1)X^0$ and corresponds to the binary generator number 101.

A small example of the calculations of the CRC at the transmitter and the error check at the receiver is shown in Fig. 10.9. In practice the data sequence and the generator number are longer than shown. The polynomial $X^{16} + X^{12} + X^5 + 1$ (CCITT recommendation V41) is often used in practice. This polynomial has been found to allow, in a block size of 260 bits, the detection of every pattern of single and odd numbers of errors, any single error burst up to 16 bits in length, and a large percentage of other error patterns. A feature of CRC techniques is the high protection obtained with relatively few redundant check bits. Other polynomials are also used, such as the so-called CRC 16 which is: $X^{16} + X^{15} + X^2 + 1$.

Automatic repeat request (ARQ) methods are most commonly used for the control of errors. They are based on the straightforward idea that the receiver, on detection of an error, informs the transmitter and the block in error is

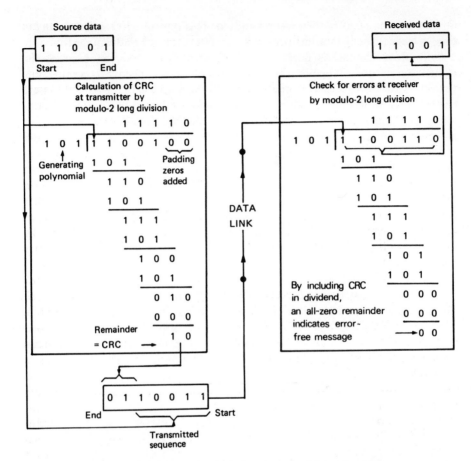

Figure 10.9 Cyclic redundancy check calculations at transmitter and receiver.

retransmitted. Obviously a half or full duplex communications circuit is required to provide the feedback path.

A commonly used method is *stop-and-wait* ARQ, which is also called *idle* ARQ. This is illustrated in Fig. 10.10. The transmitter sends a block and stops and waits for a positive acknowledgement (ACK) from the receiver that this was received without errors being detected. The transmitter then sends the next data block and so on. If a block is received with an error, a negative acknowledgement is returned

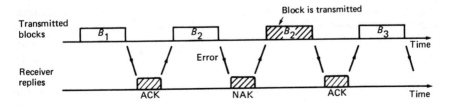

Figure 10.10 Stop-and-wait ARQ.

(NAK) and the block is then re-transmitted. This type of ARQ is simple and is used in basic types of data-link protocols (see later). It has the advantage that only a half-duplex channel is necessary for its operation. However, because the transmitter has to wait before sending the next block, the effective data rate is less than the maximum for the channel. As well as the duration of the ACK or NAK characters the hold-ups include the round-trip time taken to transmit the signals along the channel and also the time taken to switch the modem between transmit and receive modes. Typically this delay could be 300 ms or more, which could correspond to a wastage of several hundred bits of lost transmission time for each block.

Continuous ARQ methods are an improvement on 'stop and wait' ARQ, in that data blocks are transmitted continuously without waiting for an acknowledgement. However, a full duplex channel is now required. Fig. 10.11 shows a go-back-two scheme. Here the return channel replies of ACK or NAK refer to the previously transmitted block. When a NAK is returned the transmitter completes transmission of the present block and then repeats the message sequence starting two blocks back. If there is a large round-trip delay, then go-back-three or go-back-N may be necessary, which requires the system to know the length of the blocks and also the delay time and from these calculate the appropriate N. A more satisfactory approach is to number each transmitted block. The receiver then does not need to return an ACK after each error-free-block, but only transmits a NAK when necessary, to which is attached the number of the block in error. Other techniques are also used.

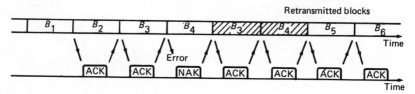

Figure 10.11 Go-back-two ARQ.

While not strictly an ARQ technique, *echoplexing* is mentioned here. This technique is often used with keyboard devices such as teletypewriters and VDUs. Here there is no direct connection in the device from keyboard to printer of display. Instead, characters from the keyboard are echoed back by the computer at the far end of the data link, and then to the printer or display. Erroneous characters are then hopefully seen by the operator. This technique is a useful safeguard, especially in local connections not using a data communications link, where error-detection techniques are not used, or where double errors may be missed by parity checks.

10.3.3 Error correction and forward error control

In this type of error control feedback is not required as in the previously described error detection and ARQ control. Here extra bits called *redundant bits* are included in the message in such a way that the receiver can not only detect that an error has occurred but can correct it. This can be of advantage where return paths do not exist or in long-haul data communication, where the time taken to return ACK and NAK makes ARQ impractical.

A commonly used method is the vertical redundancy check/longitudinal redundancy check (VRC/LRC) method, which is illustrated in Fig. 10.12. The message is assumed to be made up of characters and individual parity bits are attached to each character (these are the VRC bits). The block check character comprises a set of parity bits (these are the LRC bits) each of which is a parity check on the corresponding bits in all characters in the block. If a single bit in the block is received in error, then this will simultaneously cause a corresponding parity bit error in the VRC and LRC to be detected at the receiver, as shown in Fig. 10.13. These two bits thus provide a pair of co-ordinates to locate the error, which is then simply corrected by reversing its binary state.

Other techniques are used such as Hamming codes. Some of these techniques are sufficiently powerful to correct multiple errors.

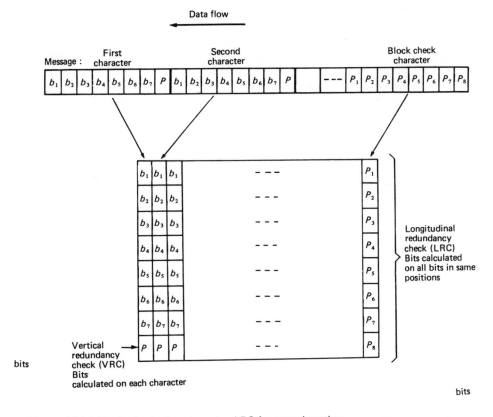

Figure 10.12 Block-check character using LRC for error detection.

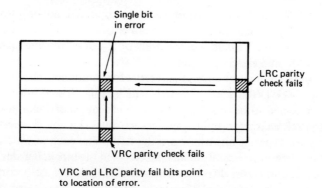

Figure 10.13 Error correction using VRC-LRC.

10.4   Data network configurations

There are various configurations, or *topologies*, of data network in use. Fig. 10.14 shows some of the common ones. The lines in these figures represent physical circuits or *links* which join up geographically separated *nodes*. The nodes can be data terminals, computers, etc.

The *mesh* topology of Fig 10.14(a) has more than the minimum number of links to connect all nodes. As a result there exists more than one path between many, or perhaps all, pairs of nodes. Paths may be direct across one link or may involve several links and other nodes. The advantage is that if one path is out of service, then an alternative is available. If a link is placed between every pair of nodes, then the mesh is *fully* connected, and this maximizes the protection against link

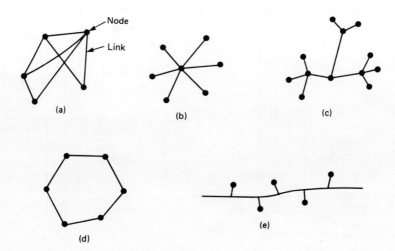

Figure 10.14 Network topologies.

breakdown. Of course, this protection is obtained at the cost of providing the links.

In the *star* configuration, Fig. 10.14(b), the central node performs the switching function. The outer nodes are therefore relieved of this task. This means the network is very dependent on the reliability of the central node. If a single link becomes faulty, then just one outer node is affected.

The *tree* configuration, Fig. 10.14(c) is a generalization of the star network. The central node, which is a switching node, is connected to nodes which are at the centre of a cluster of outer nodes. A node at the centre of a cluster must perform switching operations. The main advantage of the tree topology compared with the star topology is that the number of links to the central node is reduced. In networks with widely dispersed nodes in which clustering can be identified, line costs can be reduced. An example is a branch office containing terminals which is situated in another town from the main office containing the central computer.

The *ring* and *bus* topologies, Fig. 10.14(d) and (e), are popular in local area networks. The advantage of these topologies is that once the link circuitry has been laid new nodes can be connected relatively easily at any point without the need to lay new cables. Care has to be taken with the reliability of rings and busses because any break can disable the whole or a major part of the network.

10.5   Terminal networks

10.5.1   Introduction

Terminal networks were the first type of data communications network to be introduced, and are probably the most widely used type at the present time. The terminals are usually character based and have the appearance of a VDU. Associated with the keyboard and screen is further circuitry to handle the data communication. Alternatively many small desk top computers can function as a data terminal.

The basic form of the network is shown in Fig. 10.15. Because it is a star network the computer is in charge of the communications. The terminals are

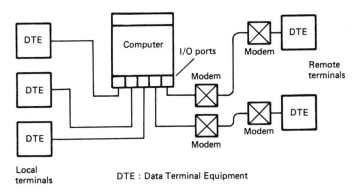

Figure 10.15 Terminal network.

interfaced to the computer via I/O ports using methods described in Chapter 2. Terminals can be local or remote to the computer. Remote terminals normally communicate via telephone lines and hence require modems as shown. Where the telephone link is via the public switched telephone network, dial-up is required. This can be done simply on a conventional telephone. The call is set up manually and a switch on the modem is thrown to disconnect the telephone from the line and to connect in the modem. Alternatively, more expensive auto-dial modems are available which dial the call automatically at the instigation of the computer.

More efficient use of the I/O ports and the data links can be obtained using *multi-drop* or *multi-point* connections, as shown in Fig. 10.16. Modems are inserted if the links are telephone circuits. This arrangement allows several terminals to be connected to one port. Each terminal has a unique address to identify it from the others.

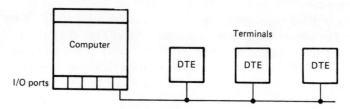

Figure 10.16 Multi-point, multi-drop arrangement.

Terminal networks range in size from the very small with just a few terminals to very large systems with hundreds of terminals, or more, which obtain higher efficiency through the use of special communications equipment.

10.5.2   Data link control

To achieve data communication it is not sufficient to merely set up the links in accordance with the appropriate physical standard such as V.24 coupled with a modem modulation standard (as in Table 10.1). Procedures are required to control the transfer of messages, for the control of errors, to maintain character synchronism and, should it be required, to regulate the flow of data. The procedures are referred to as *Data Link Controls* (DLCs) or *protocols*. Generally their function is to maintain orderly data communications over the links.

Two protocols are in widespread use: Binary Synchronous Control (BSC), and High-level Data Link Control (HDLC). The elements of these are described in the following two sections.

10.5.3   Binary Synchronous Control (BSC)

The ISO standard covering this half-duplex protocol refers to it as *Basic mode*. However, its implementation in IBM equipment is so widespread that it is usually referred to by the name given to it by that company: BSC or *bisync*.

(a) *Message formats*
Data are sent as blocks of characters (ASCII, EBCDIC or 6-bit transcode). The data message format is:

←SYN.SYN.SOH.Header.STX.Text. (ETB or ETX). BCC

The arrow indicates the direction of transmission. At least two SYN characters begin the block to allow the receiver to achieve character synchronization. The start of header character, SOH, indicates a header is to follow. The header is a group of characters that indicates such information as destination, address and message sequence number for error control. Next comes the start of text character, STX, followed by the text of the message itself. The end of the text portion is indicated by ETB, end of transmitted block, or by ETX, end of text character. For message texts which take several blocks to transmit, the first and intermediate blocks use ETB here, and the final block uses ETX. The block check character, BCC, is derived using the LRC method described earlier.

Occasionally it can happen that an ETB or ETX character can appear as part of the text. To avoid the receiver incorrectly interpreting these as true ETB or ETX characters a data link escape character, DLE, is inserted before each occurrence to warn the receiver. Of course, this means now that if DLE occurs naturally in the text an extra DLE must be inserted before that. The receiver then strips off the inserted DLEs before passing on the message text. This achieves what is called *data transparency*.

As well as the data message format there are four short control messages containing respectively, ACK (positive acknowledgement), NAK (negative acknowledgement), ENQ (enquiry), and EOT (end-of-transmission), characters.

(b) *Selection*
The central computer is referred to as the *master station*. The terminals, or cluster controllers (see later) are referred to as *slaves*. The master sends messages to a particular slave using a *selection* procedure. This typically proceeds as follows (for clarity the SYN characters are not shown).

Computer (master)	Terminal (slave)	
Address. Select. ENQ→		Are you ready?
	←ACK	Yes.
BCC.ETX.TEXT.STX. Header. SOH→		
	←ACK	Received correctly.
EOT→		No more.

A character following ENQ indicates selection. Only the addressed slave responds. If the slave is busy then a NAK response is given to ENQ: A NAK is also used if the message is received with errors, and this causes the master to repeat the message.

(c) *Polling*
Polling is the converse of selection and is used by the master to obtain messages from a slave. The master sends a sequence of messages of the form Address. Poll.

ENQ→. As each address is recognized by a slave it reponds as indicated in the following sequence for the case where it has message for the master.

Computer (master)	Terminal (Slave)	
Address. Poll. ENQ→		Any message?
	←SOH.Header. STX. Text. ETX. BCC	Yes, here it is.
ACK→		Received correctly.
	← EOT	End.

The ACK is replaced by a NAK if an error occurs. The message is then repeated.

This sequence is carried out for every terminal. For those terminals with no message for the master, the sequence is:

Computer (Master)	Terminal (slave)	
Address. Poll. ENQ→		Any message?
	←EOT	No.

10.5.4 High-level Data Link Control (HDLC)

Even if the link is full duplex, the essentially half duplex BSC protocol cannot take advantage of it. Full duplex working is provided by HDLC. It is also more flexible and is used widely in terminal networks and computer–computer networks discussed later. HDLC has several modes of operation. One is called *unbalanced normal response* and allocates the ends of the link as *primary* or *secondary* stations. This is similar in concept to master and slave in BSC. Another mode, *asynchronous balanced mode*, gives equal status to the stations and is used typically for computer–computer communication.

HDLC is bit oriented rather than character oriented as is BSC. Like BSC, however, data and control information are conveyed in a block which in HDLC is called a *frame*. The standard frame is partitioned as shown in Fig. 10.17. The flag F at both ends is a unique eight-bit sequence, 01111110, which marks the frame boundaries. Again the problem of data transparency arises if this flag sequence should occur elsewhere in the frame. It is dealt with by simple hardware at the transmitting end which inserts a zero after every sequence of five ones inside the frame. This prevents the formation of six ones, which is part of the flag, from occurring. At the receiver, after every sequence of five ones, a following zero is suppressed. These processes are called *bit stuffing* and *bit stripping*, respectively.

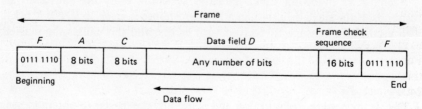

Figure 10.17 HDLC frame format.

The frame is made up of several fields:

1. *Address field A*   This 8 bit word specifies the destination of the frame.
2. *Control field C*   This 8-bit word has three formats corresponding to the use made of the frame. The information format (set by the first bit in C being a 0) is used for normal information messages. The field is used to indicate the transmitter frame sequence number and also that of the last correctly received frame in the other direction. This feature allows full duplex working with the efficient continuous ARQ type of error control. Other formats are the supervisory format (first two bits in C are 10) and the non-sequenced format (first two bits in C are 11) which are used to initiate information transfer, set operating modes, etc.
3. *Data field D*   This contains the message information and can be of any length.
4. *Frame check sequence*   This is a 16-bit cyclic redundancy check sequence which is calculated using the CCITT V41 generating polynomial, on the address, control and data fields, but not the frame flags.

Space does not permit a description of the full set of message sequences in HDLC. In essence, frames are sent independently in both directions in full duplex and the frame sequence number in messages going in one direction allows control of any errors occurring in the other direction. Faulty messages are repeated. If one end of the link has no data to send, error control is maintained by sending short supervisory frames containing the frame sequence number.

10.5.5   Special communications equipment

In computer systems with many peripheral devices, the cost of the data communications links and associated modems etc. can be high. The software burden on the computer itself can also be high. Several types of special communications equipment are used therefore, and some of these items are now discussed.

(a) *Multiplexers*

A multiplexer is a way of combining several low-speed data sources into one higher-speed channel (see Fig. 10.18). This provides a saving in both time and modem costs. A demultiplexer at the far end of the channel separates out the low-speed data streams. In both-way transmission, both of these separate functions are combined in the one unit at each end of the higher-speed channel.

One approach is frequency-division multiplex (FDM) in which at the transmitter end different sinusoidal carrier frequencies are allocated at each low-speed data source. Methods such as frequency-shift modulation etc. are then used to modulate the carrier by the data. In effect this is an upgraded kind of modem. For reliable operation, sufficient spacing between the carriers is necessary, and this limits the number of low-speed channels that caj be multiplexed. Typically, a 2400 baud circuit will handle twelve 110 bits/s data streams.

The second and more usual approach is time-division multiplex. The multiplexer contains a number of registers, one per low-speed channel. Each

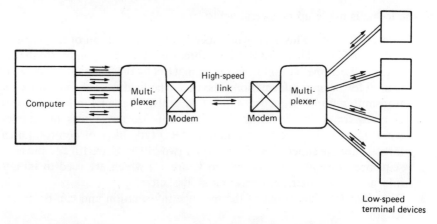

Figure 10.18 Multiplexers connect several low-speed devices on a higher-speed link.

register is capable of storing one character, as it comes in bit by bit from the low-speed source. The multiplexer scans these registers in sequence and empties the contents serially at high speed to form a continuous data stream to the modem. If a register is not yet filled, then a NULL character is sent in the time-slot for that channel. The scanning rate is high, so that a register has always emptied before the next low-speed characters arrives. At the far end, the low-speed channels are separated by a demultiplexer, which works in the reverse way. This method is called character interleaving. An alternative is *bit interleaving*, in which individual bits in the registers are scanned. A multiplexer is transparent in the sense that it appears to the data terminal equipments at both ends as an independent set of separate communications circuits.

At any one time it is unlikely that all multiplexed channels are operating at full speed. A data sequence from a keyboard operator for a 110 bits/s channel reaches this speed only for short periods. The average rate is much less than this maximum. The NULL characters sent when there is no data character to send on a channel time slot constitutes under-usage of the data link. A more efficient multiplexer is the *statistical multiplier* or *stat max*. Here any channel with no character to send is passed over and the time slot is used by the next channel with one to send. Time slots are therefore not wasted. Each character is sent with a short code identifying it to the far end from which channel the character came. This adds to the data transmission burden but overall there is a net saving in data. The avoidance of transmitting NULL characters means that the number of channels can be increased. However, caution is advised. If many channels happen to generate characters at high rates, then the stat max can be overloaded and data lost. In most applications a worthwhile increase in channels over the conventional multiplexer can be achieved while keeping the probability of overload at acceptably low levels. If the link is covered by data link control procedure with error control, then lost data can be recovered.

(b) *Cluster controller*

Cluster controllers are used when several terminals are in local proximity but are remote from the central computer. Figure 10.19 shows the arrangement. The network is now converted from a star topology to a tree.

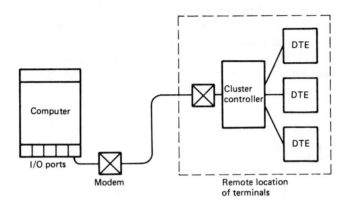

Figure 10.19 Cluster controller.

The cluster controller monitors the terminals for messages to the central computer and distributes messages from the computer to the appropriate terminal. This is done by the cluster controller having its own address. As well as saving on time and modem costs (as do multiplexers) the tasks of the central computer is simplified since it now has to poll or select to a single address rather than several. A further advantage is that the cluster controller can take on the communication work of the terminals. Thus cheaper 'dumb' terminals can be used instead of 'intelligent' terminals. Unlike the multiplexer, the cluster controller is not transparent and has to be chosen to be compatible with the particular communications protocol of the network.

(c) *Front-end processor*

The Front End Processor (FEP), see Fig. 10.20, is a small computer attached to a larger central computer. It relieves the expensive main computer of the burden of

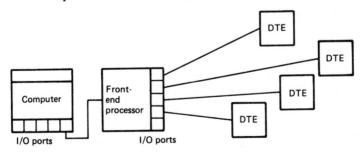

DTE : Data Terminal Equipment

Figure 10.20 Front-end processor.

handling most of the data communications activity. Functions can include code conversion, link and network control and also the collection of data on traffic volume and error occurrences. This data is useful for the management and maintenance of the network.

(d) *Terminal Switching Exchange (TSE)*

This apparatus can be useful in larger installations where the central site contains several computers, and terminal users require access to them. Fig. 10.21 shows a TSE inserted in the network. The user before beginning a session with a computer first keys in the identity of the required computer to the TSE. Assuming an I/O port on that computer is free, the TSE then establishes the connection.

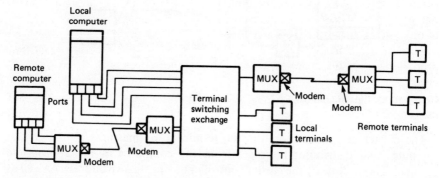

Figure 10.21 Terminal switching exchange.

10.6   Layered model of computer network architectures

Figure 10.22 shows two computers communicating via a data network. The data network can be a public or private network, and in practice many more than two computers can be connected. Computer-to-computer communication is unlike that in terminal networks where a single processing device is linked to subservient terminals. Networked computers communicate more on the basis of equals and have a wider range of requirements. Necessarily, the protocols are more complicated and it is the usual practice to structure these into a hierarchy of

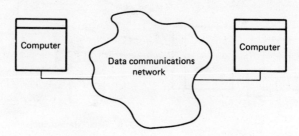

Figure 10.22 Computer-computer data communications network.

layers called a network architecture. Each layer performs its own set of defined functions.

First developments of computer network architectures were proprietary products such as IBM's SNA and DEC's DECNET. These architectures are closed in the sense that only products of the company can take part in the communication activity. An open architecture allows computers of any manufacture to communicate provided they conform to the agreed network protocols. The progress of open architectures has been greatly influenced by the development in the late 1970s and subsequent publication of the ISO Reference Model of Open System Interconnections (OSI). The aim of this is to 'provide a common basis for the co-ordination of standards development for the purpose of system interconnection, while allowing existing standards to be placed into perspective within the overall Reference Model'. Thus the model is not a single real architecture itself but a framework for the development and harmonization of other standard network architectures.

The ISO Reference Model OSI has seven layers as shown in Fig. 10.23. The protocols at any layer, called *peer processes*, are the same. That is, a process at a given level on one host thinks it is communicating with the same process at the corresponding level in the other host. When a process communicates to its peer it uses the services of all processes provided by lower layers. Between any two layers an *interface* defines the services and operations provided by the lower one.

Information that host A wishes to communicate to host B passes down the layers which modify or add to it. The information has a *frame* or *packet* format. In general a layer envelopes the frame with a header and trailer in accordance with the protocol at that level. The next layer does the same so that the structure of the architecture is mirrored in the message with its envelopes. At the bottom layer the frame is physically transported across the network. At host B it passes up through the layers where the envelopes are successively removed and is delivered at the top.

The OSI Reference Model defines the services and functions of each layer. Layers 1–3 relate to protocols of the data communications network, and layers 5–7 allow the operating system in the hosts (which generally are of a different type) to communicate. Layer 4 shields the upper layers from the workings of the network.

The *physical* layer defines the electrical and mechanical interface to the network. It is the only layer with real communication. The protocols at higher layers then have *virtual communication*. The data *link* layer is responsible for reliable communication of each packet across a physical link. Its tasks include establishing and releasing the connection, packet sequencing and error notification. The *network* layer performs the necessary routing functions along possibly a number of physical links, using network addresses. Actual routing strategies are not defined in the model. The *transport* layer has the responsibility to ensure efficient and reliable end-to-end service for messages across the data network. Data networks can take different forms and the transport layer shields the upper layer by offering a network-independent service. The *session* layer provides a service which is analogous to the login and logout procedure in terminal networks. The *presentation* layer is concerned with data representation. For

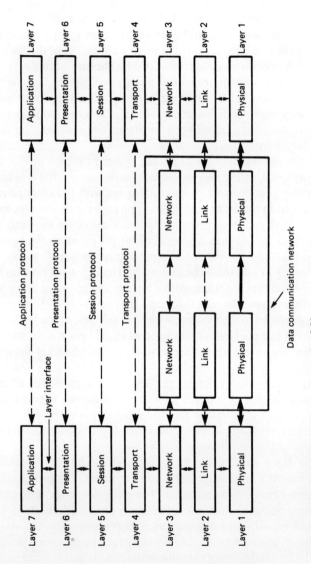

Figure 10.23 The ISO reference model for OSI.

example, if necessary it will convert between ASCII and EBCDIC formats where these are used by the two application processes. The *application* layer is the highest layer in the OSI reference model. It is concerned with providing services which make use of the data communications networks. The range of network services is wide and as yet there are almost no international standards for this layer. Services such as electronic mail, distributed data bases and file transfer are possible.

10.7 Wide area computer networks

10.7.1 Private wide area networks

A wide area network is taken to be one where at least some of its nodes are widely dispersed so that use is made of PTT supplied links.

Some large organizations, such as banks, need wide area networking of computers. The speed and volume of data that is moved is quite high. In such cases the public switched telephone network (PSTN) is not adequate because of the relatively low data rates that can be sustained across it. This requirement arose before the inception of public data networks, and private networks were assembled from private lines leased from the PTT. The communications protocol functions were provided by network architecture software products supplied by computer manufacturers. Prominent among these are IBM's Systems Network Architecture (SNA), DEC's DECNET and the earlier ARPANET. These are layered architectures, but because they predate the ISO reference model for OSI they do not correspond exactly to the latter. the approximate equivalences of SNA and DECNET to the ISO reference model are shown in Fig. 10.24.

Layer	ISO	SNA	DECNET
7	Application	End user	Application
6	Presentation	NAU services	
5	Session	Data flow control	(No layer)
		Transmission control	
4	Transport		Network services
3	Network	Path control	Transport
2	Link	Data link control	Data link control
1	Physical	Physical	Physical

Figure 10.24 Approximate equivalence of SNA and DECNET to ISO reference model.

The original release of SNA in 1974 was for tree networks. It has developed since then and more general topologies could be accommodated in the 1979 release. The nodes in the network are of four types: terminals, controllers of terminals and peripherals, front-end processors, and host processors. Each node has an item of software called a *Network Addressable Unit* (NAU). Each NAU has an address and is used by the communicating process to connect itself to the network. Data are sent in bit-oriented frames and are governed by a data link control protocol called *Synchronous Data Link Control* (SDLC). This protocol was later taken over with small modifications by the standards bodies and called HDLC (see Section 10.5.4). Data are passed down the SNA protocol layers in a similar manner to that described for the ISO reference model. A sequence of headers and tails are attached. The frame then passes across the physical network and up through the protocol layers at the recipient host.

DECNET has similar goals to SNA, that is, to allow the user to set up a private network for distributed processing and networking. The frames or packets in DECNET are not bit oriented but are assembled from characters. Like the SNA frame, DECNET frames can be of any length but in DECNET the length is denoted by a character count in the header rather than by a unique end flag.

10.7.2   Public Data Networks (PDN)

A public data network is one set up and administered by a PTT or equivalent body. Because of the economies of scale and the use of modern purpose-built networking equipment other than leased private lines, a PDN can be expected to provide data networking at lower cost than private networks. A wider base of users can be served who need not convey large high-speed volumes of data. Moreover, users may communicate using equipment from different manufacturers.

After some experimental investigations, the CCITT issued the X-series of recommendations. These are the digital counterparts to the V-series for analogue telephone links, and cover data rates and interfacing. In general the X-series recommendations cover the lower layers of the ISO reference model. Two types of PDN are covered: *Packet-Switched Data Networks* (PSDN) and *Circuit-Switched Data Networks* (CSDN). These are described in the following two subsections.

10.7.3   Packet-switched data network

Data are assembled into packets containing the source and destination addresses and entered to the network where they go to a local Packet Switching Exchange (PSE). The network consists of PSEs nodes connected by data links, as shown in Fig. 10.25. The PSE looks at the addresses and by consulting a routing directory it determines the output link on which to forward the packet. In this way the packet journeys from PSE to PSE. The final PSE passes it to the destination Data Terminal Equipment (DTE).

Any one link contains interspersed packets from several sources going to various destinations. To avoid any very long packet causing undue delays to other packets at a PSE a maximum length for packets is set. Because of this one of

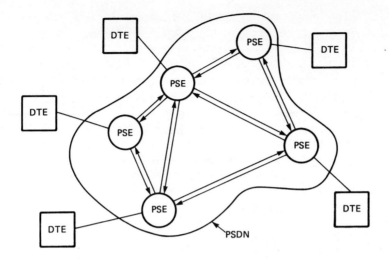

DTE : Data Terminal Equipment
PSE : Packet Switching Exchange

Figure 10.25 Packet switching data network.

the tasks in the ISO reference model transport layer is to split long frame into a number of shorter packets.

Two types of service are offered, called *datagram* and *virtual call* (or *virtual circuit*). In the datagram service each packet is treated as a short self-contained packet and is entered and delivered to the destination without reference to other packets. In the virtual call service a message is made up of a sequence of packets which contain a reference number called the *logical channel number*. This allows the destination DTE to identify from which of several sources the packet was sent. This in effect sets up an end-to-end circuit. Because it is not a physical circuit, but packets moving through possible differing routes through the network, it is called a *virtual circuit*.

The user's DTE is interfaced to the PSDN by *Data Circuit Terminating Equipment* (DCTE) which plays a similar role to the modem in the public switched telephone network (see Fig. 10.26). This interface is covered by the X.25 network access protocol. In fact, it is a set of protocols covering the lower layers of the ISO reference model.

The physical layer is defined in recommendation X.21. Physically the interface comprises five circuits which are as follows: *Transmit* (T) for sending the data, and *Control* (C), *Receive* (R), Indication (I), and *Signal timing* (S). The link layer protocol is based on HDLC and called Link Access Procedure version B (LAPB). The packet layer is also defined and corresponds to the network layer in the ISO reference model.

With X.25 the user DTE needs to be intelligent enough to handle packets. Where the DTE is a computer this need not be a problem. In many cases the user's terminal equipment is a simple character-based device such as a keyboard/VDU. For such cases a special piece of equipment called a Packet

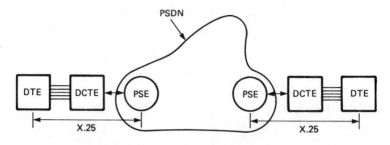

PSE : Packet Switching Exchange
DCTE : Data Circuit Terminating Equipment
DTE : Data Terminal Equipment

Figure 10.26 The X.25 protocol.

Assembler–Disassembler (PAD) can be interposed between the character-based DTE and the PSDN. The operation of the PAD is defined by the X.3, X.25 and X.28 standards.

10.7.4   Circuit-switched data network

The conventional analogue public-switched telephone network is an example of a circuit-switched network. These networks are being replaced by computer controlled digitally switched networks. This, with the conversion to all-digital transmission from the exchange to the subscriber, means that the data can be networked without the need for modems at higher speeds (up to 64 kbits/s). By using several transmission channels simultaneously even higher rates can be provided. This type of network is referred to as an *Integrated Services Digital Network* (ISDN) since it can carry voice and data.

A circuit-switched data network effectively sets up a direct path between the two ends which is permanent for the duration of the call. Unlike packet-switched digital networks, a call once set up must be paid for on a time basis and does not depend on the quantity and rate of data that is conveyed. Unlike packet switching on circuit-switched data networks, no error detection and control is provided, thus the quality of data transmission is not as high. The physical interfacing of the user PTE to the CSDN is covered by X.21, the same as for PSDN. As an interim measure while analogue telephone systems are still in use an alternative, X.21 bis, is provided. The link layer protocol can also be the same as LAPB used in packet switching.

10.8   Local area networks

10.8.1   LAN features

A Local Area Network (LAN) is normally installed at a single site comprising a building or group of buildings such as a factory, hospital, business or university campus. Typically, a LAN is 1 km or less in total length of interconnections. A

LAN does not normally use a data link from the public telephone network and indeed can provide data communications at much higher rates. Devices that are networked include computers, office workstations, computer terminals, printers and plotters and file servers. This allows a wide range of services to be obtained such as electronic mail, sharing of data bases, networked word processing and communal access to high-quality printers and plotters.

The main characteristics of any particular LAN technology concerns its topology, transmission medium, and the access control method to that medium.

LANs have generated much interest and activity among manufacturers and there are now many different architectures. The following subsections describe some of the more important of them.

10.8.2 CSMA/CD local area network

This acronym applies to a media access method called Carrier-Sense-Multiple-Access and Collision Detection. CSMA/CD is most commonly identified with the Ethernet system from the Xerox Corporation. This LAN architecture is a bus architecture based on a 50 ohm co-axial cable as the medium, as shown in Fig. 10.27. The cable length has a maximum of 500 m but this can be extended by using repeaters. A maximum of 1024 Data Terminal Equipments (DTEs), that is computers etc., can be connected to the co-axial cable, thus giving *multiple access*. A non-intrusive tap connects an adjacent transceiver unit (TU) to the cable. The transceiver unit is powered by the DTE and is able to inject signals into, and sense signals on, the co-axial cable. The TU is connected to the host DTE via twisted pairs, and since balanced drivers/differential receivers are used (see Chapter 2), this connection can be up to 50 m long. This gives freedom in siting a DTE computer within an office area, for example.

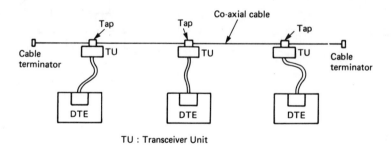

TU : Transceiver Unit
DTE : Data Terminal Equipment

Figure 10.27 The CSMA/CD bus.

A DTE with data to send forms a frame including the data, destination address and a 32-bit cyclic redundancy check sequence. The frame is launched on the cable by the TU. All DTEs check the frame and it is accepted by the one addressed.

With this form of access occasionally more than one DTE will attempt to send frames together and a collision occurs. Each source DTE senses the carrier

(*carrier sense*) and is able to detect the collision (*collision detection*) because the signal on the cable differs from that which the source DTE intended. The source DTEs then inject a jam sequence of random bits to fully corrupt the data on the line so that it is not mistakenly received by any DTE as a good frame. The source DTEs causing the collision then stand off a short random period and try again. Fortunately, collisions are normally quite rare and have negligible effect on effective data rates.

The DTEs contain a Medium Access Control (MAC) unit to implement the CSMA/CD access method and also a separate microprocessor to handle the network functions. These, with the physical arrangement for the co-axial cable and T.U., provide the lower layers of the ISO reference model.

A CSMA/CD LAN architecture is covered by IEEE Standards 802.2 and 802.3.

10.8.3   Token access local area networks

In LANS having this method of access a token is passed among the DTEs in the network. Any DTE with data to send only has permission to do so when it possesses the token. The token consists of a special frame.

Token access can be implemented in a ring topology as shown in Fig. 10.28(a). Data frames and token frames are passed clockwise round the ring. Another topology is the token bus, Fig. 10.28(b). Because of addressing the tokens need not follow the physical sequence of DTEs as is shown.

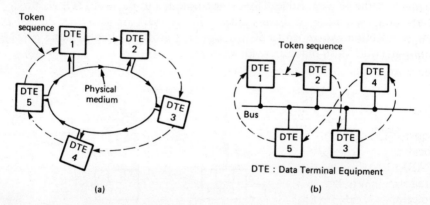

Figure 10.28 Token local area network: (a) ring; (b) bus.

Token access networks allow selective permission to be given to DTEs by attaching priority indicators to the token. Also, where appropriate, DTEs can have their ability to send frames removed, but retain their ability to receive data from other sources.

Examples of token access LANs include the IBM token ring. Both token bus and token ring topologies are covered by IEEE Standards 802.4 and 802.5 respectively, together with IEEE Standard 802.2. The latter standard applies also to CSMA/CD bus networks and provides a common interface of the ISO reference model link layer to the network layer.

The IBM token ring was used as the basis for IEEE 802.4. The 4 Mbits/s ring is formed by sections of co-axial cable or fibre-optic cable which connect together a set of distribution panels. Each distribution panel connects to several DTE stations via ring adaptors. Relays in the distribution panel allow ring adaptors and stations which wish to participate, to be connected into the ring. One of the stations in the ring must be designated as a monitor station which has overall control of the ring and token passing.

Larger networks can be formed from several interconnecting token rings. At the points of interconnection are high-speed data switches called block switches. Data packets therefore have double addresses; one to identify the ring, and the other to identify the station on that ring.

10.8.4   Slotted ring local area network

The Cambridge Ring, common in the UK, is a slotted ring local area network. Bits are circulated round the ring at 10 Mbits/s and the time delay round the ring is adjusted by a special node called a monitor station, so that the total number of bits form a fixed number of slots each able to carry a fixed size frame. The 40-bit frame contains destination node address, source node address, data and control bits. A DTE with information to transmit waits for an empty slot, it marks the slot as full and places its frame on the ring. This frame passes round the ring and is examined by each DTE. The DTEs pass on the frame until it arrives at the recipient DTE. The recipient DTE reads the frame from the slot and marks the frame to indicate that it has done so. Eventually the frame reaches the source DTE which then checks to see if the frame has been read. If so, it marks the slot as empty. The slot is then available for other DTEs. The monitor station also looks after a variety of control and error conditions, such as the source DTE not marking empty a returned frame which would otherwise circulate for ever.

10.8.5   The PABX approach

Most organizations which have local area network requirements also have a local private automatic branch telephone exchange (PABX). In recent years PABXs have been implemented by digital technology, in like manner to the wide area national public switched telephone network. The integration of data and voice in an ISDN PABX provides an alternative data network to the true LANs described above. A PABX network has a star topology with the exchange as the central node and the telephone-instrument/data-access-points as the outer nodes. Although data rates are slower than on LANs the PABX can be attractive for some applications because of the relatively low extra cost of providing the data-networking facilities in addition to the telephone-switching facilities.

References

1.   Scott, P. R. D., *Modems in Data Communications*, NCC Publications, Manchester, 1980.

2. Da Silva, E., *Introduction to Data Communications and LAN Technology*, Collins, London, 1986.

Further Reading

1. Flint, D. C., *The Data Ring Main*, Wiley, Chichester, 1983.
2. Green, P. E., Jr., (ed.), *Computer Network Architectures and Protocols*, Plenum Press, New York, 1982.
3. Halsall, F., *Introduction to Data Communications and Computer Networks*, Addison-Wesley, Wokingham, 1985.
4. Tanenbaum, A. S., *Computer Networks*, Prentice-Hall, London, 1981.
5. Hopper, A., Temple, S., and Williamson, R., *Local Area Network Design*, Addison-Wesley, Wokingham, 1986.

Index